The Nature of MATHEMATICS

The Nature of
MATHEMATICS

FREDERICK H. YOUNG

Oregon State University
Corvallis, Oregon

JOHN WILEY & SONS, INC., New York | London | Sydney

Preface

It is commonly recognized that inadequate communication exists between the mathematician and the general public. An ever-growing number of colleges are attempting to bridge this abyss with courses, primarily terminal in nature, that are designed to acquaint those students who would not ordinarily take mathematics courses with the nature of this fascinating subject. This text has evolved from an attempt by the author to fulfill this design without succumbing to the temptation to titillate the student with tricks, puzzles, and curiosities.

The general purpose of the text is to leave the student with a knowledge of at least some of the aims, techniques, and results of mathematics and with an appreciation of the role of mathematics in the world today. This purpose is subject to three severe restraints. One of these is that the students taking the course have usually had only a minimal secondary preparation, consisting of a year of algebra and a year of geometry in high school. The second constraint is that the great majority of the students, by majoring in those areas most removed from mathematics, are likely to have some antipathy toward the subject. The third constraint is that the time available is always too severely limited.

The text has been developed with these constraints recognized. Thus no apology is offered for the fact that many topics are missing that are considered vital by many mathematicians. As an introduction, the first chapter is a brief survey of the nature and results of mathematics in ancient times, with emphasis on the Babylonians, Egyptians, and Greeks. Because of the author's belief that the concept of number is basic to much of mathematics, the second chapter investigates the properties of number systems from the natural numbers to the reals. The goal is to leave the student with the knowledge that the real numbers are a complete, ordered field, and with an understanding of the meaning of these three words.

The third chapter is designed to illustrate a typical development of mathematics from the concrete to the abstract and back to the concrete, the sequence of observation, induction, and application. For this purpose the chapter begins with the algebra of sets, where pictures can be drawn and relations visualized. This intuitive system of sets is then abstracted to Boolean algebra, where Huntington's postulates are used. Ten theorems are developed, culminating in a theorem of several parts about the partial ordering of the system. These theorems are abstract, and it is not expected of the student that he can develop and prove similar theorems. Instead the student is led to see that the theorems can indeed be proved from the stated postulates and that the theorems obviously have meaning in terms of the preceding algebra of sets. The most that is required of the student is that he be able to prove the dual of a theorem once the proof of one part is given. Once the Boolean algebra has been developed, application is made to switching circuits and to propositional logic. Here, for instance, the student discovers the power of the abstract approach when he discovers that the theorem on partial ordering in a Boolean algebra gives him a considerable amount of knowledge about logical implication.

The fourth chapter explores residue classes and the solutions of congruences. The appropriate comparisons are made between the algebraic structure of modular arithmetic and the more familiar number systems of Chapter 2. Emphasis is laid on the existence of algorithms for the solution of classes of problems. Euclid's division algorithm is shown to be basic.

The fifth chapter is devoted to the cartesian coordinate system. The student is introduced to the line and its algebraic properties corresponding to geometric properties. The various conic sections are defined geometrically and their equations and invariant properties investigated. This is primarily a preparation for later work with functions and relations and for calculus.

Chapter 6 defines functions and relations and develops the "set-builder" notation for them. Inverses of functions, composite functions, and special functions such as the greatest integer function and the absolute value function are examined.

The seventh chapter is an introduction to calculus. Pertinent definitions are carefully given, but the development is principally intuitive. Since no use is made of the trigonometric functions in this work, attention is directed toward polynomials and rational algebraic functions. Applications are made to simple maximum-minimum problems, to freely falling body problems, and to area of regions bounded by the graphs of polynomials.

Chapter 8 introduces the student to matrices and determinants. The arithmetic operations with vectors and matrices are motivated by systems of linear equations. Techniques are derived for obtaining matrix inverses. A system of square matrices is shown to be a ring with unity, which is compared with the field structure of Chapter 2. Determinants are defined recursively, and a number of theorems are given, not all proved, for manipulation of determinants. Some of the common applications of determinants are given.

Chapter 9 is an introduction to the digital computer. Some interesting algorithms are derived for binary arithmetic and binary-decimal conversion. The Boolean algebra of Chapter 3 is used to combine flip-flops, AND-gates, and OR-gates to mechanize binary addition and subtraction, together with some logical control. A minimal set of computer instructions is included with which simple programs can be written. Finally, there is a brief discussion of compiler languages and what they do.

The text is designed in such a way that it can be used for a variety of courses. A minimal course of three quarter-hours can be based on Chapters 2 and 3. This would enable the student to cover the natural numbers, integers, rationals, and real numbers, the algebra of sets, abstract Boolean algebra, switching circuits (briefly), and propositional logic. Since the logic is shown at the outset to form a Boolean algebra, all that is necessary is to interpret the algebraic theorems in the new context. Implication, for instance, appears as the partial ordering relation of the Boolean algebra.

A longer course, but one still possessing a strong unity, consists of Chapters 1, 2, 3, 5, 6, and 7. This will lead the student through an introduction to analytic geometry and functions and relations to limits and calculus.

If the instructor wishes greater stress on algebra than on analysis, he can base a course on Chapter 1, 2, 3, 4, and 8. In this course the student would progress through congruences and an introduction to linear algebra.

Chapter 9 is quite different from anything usually found in a work of this sort. It is the feeling of the author, who is probably prejudiced, that there are four pertinent facts about digital computers: (1) they are here to stay; (2) they are accessible without undue effort to the novice; (3) students find them enormously interesting; (4) their importance in the world of mathematics is not universally realized. Furthermore, the binary number system lends itself to some beautiful algorithms relating to Chapters 1 and 2, and the Boolean algebra of Chapter 3 is precisely the tool needed to discuss the logical organization of a computer. Since, in addition, computers are frequently used for linear inequalities (Chapter 6), simultaneous congruences and greatest common divisor algorithms (Chapter 4), and throughout calculus (Chapter 7), this chapter can easily be associated with any of the possible courses suggested above.

The author wishes to express his gratitude to Professor Franz E. Hohn of the University of Illinois, to Professor Robert Z. Norman of Dartmouth College, and to Professor Z. L. Loflin of the University of Southwestern Louisiana for their meticulous reviews of the manuscript and for their valuable suggestions. In addition the author is deeply grateful for the patient assistance and encouragement supplied by Andrew Ford, John Hoey, and other editors of John Wiley & Sons.

Frederick H. Young

May, 1967

Contents

4

5

6

7

8

9

The Nature of MATHEMATICS

1

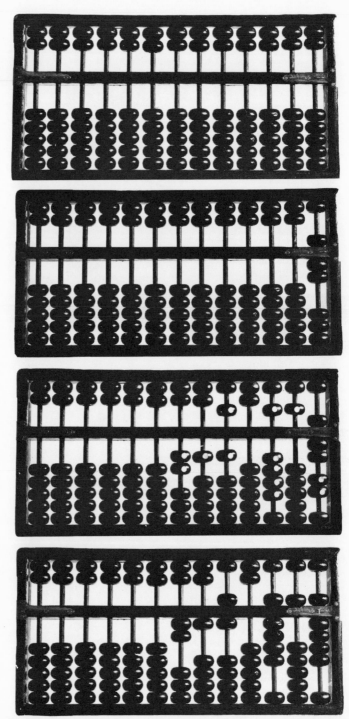

Addition with an abacus; 7 + 2,160,952 = 2,160,959.

1.1 IN THE BEGINNING

The earliest recorded history reveals that man already had a well-developed sense of geometry and arithmetic. Such knowledge certainly antedated writing. Thus we can only conjecture as to the first conscious counting and the first geometric idea. As soon as man had domesticated animals he needed some way to count his flock. Probably the counting was first done by the use of tallies or markers, such as pebbles or sticks, to record a number of animals. This method is still in use. Some sheepherders in this country still count their sheep with the help of notches in a tally stick. The abacus, still used by millions of people in the Orient, is a refinement of the ancient method of recording numbers with pebbles. Our words "calculate" and "calculus" reflect this early use of a pebble as a marker, for "pebble" was the original meaning of "calculus."

When people gave up their nomadic ways and formed fixed communities, the necessity for surveying arose. This was particularly true of the early Egyptians who raised crops along the Nile. Each year the great river flooded, depositing a new layer of rich silt along its banks but also destroying many field markers. This meant that the fields had to be resurveyed each year. Also, some fields were divided between sons or combined to form larger fields. Instruments to measure angles, directions, and lengths were invented.

1.2 ANCIENT GEOMETRY

Since nearly all education was limited to the priesthood, which meant the royalty and aristocracy, it is probable that mathematical knowledge was a jealously guarded secret. It is evident from the great pyramid of Gizeh, which was constructed about 2900 B.C., that considerable accuracy was achieved by these early geometers. It has been calculated that the sides of the square pyramid had a relative error in length of only 1 part in 14,000. The angles differ from right angles by not more than 1 part in 27,000. Such skill in the use of geometric tools very likely resulted from the religious significance of astronomy. The relentless periodicity of the heavenly bodies awed the early shepherds, who surely must have attributed divine control to the sun, moon, stars, and planets. Indeed, in many early civilizations the sun and moon were themselves accepted as deities.

1.3 CALENDARS

We find the earliest surviving evidence of mathematical activity in many primitive societies in their calendars. Aside from the daily cycle, the most noticeable periodicity in the skies is exhibited by the moon. The recurrence of the full moon every 29 or 30 days led to the lunar month that was commonly used, even by the American Indians, to measure intervals of time. However, difficulties arose when an attempt was made to link the lunar month to the solar year. It didn't come out even. The solar year has about 11 more days than 12 lunar months. Some societies allowed for this discrepancy by permitting each third year to have 13 months. The early Greeks, before the fifth century B.C., worked out an eight-year cycle in which five years had 12 lunar months and three years had 13. This led to an error of only about a day and a half in eight years. The Babylonians discovered an even better cycle of 235 months in nineteen years. This nineteen-year cycle, which was adopted about 400 B.C., was so accurate that it introduced an error of less than one day in two centuries. There is evidence that the builders of Stonehenge in England were also aware of this nineteen-year cycle. This method for recording the passage of time spread from Babylonia throughout Alexander's Asiatic empire and even as far as China. The Jewish religious calendar currently used in Israel is a slight modification of the nineteen-year cycle.

The Mayan calendar was even more complex and was based on a civil year of 365 days, a "magic cycle" of 360 days, and a "long count" which permitted the correlation of these two over thousands of years. Along with this complicated calendar, the Mayans were the first to develop a number system that we may call "modern." It used a positional notation, like ours, and had a symbol for zero. Unfortunately this advanced arithmetic knowledge was not fated to spread to the rest of the world. As we shall see later, our number system grew from one used by the Hindus and Chinese and transmitted to Europe by the Arabs. In any event, calendar computation puts strong emphasis on numerical calculation. It is interesting to conjecture which came first, the chicken or the egg. Did the requirements for calendar computation cause arithmetic to develop, or did the development of computational techniques lead to complex calendar construction? It is probable that each affected the other.

1.4 EGYPTIAN PAPYRI

Our knowledge of early mathematics depends largely on written records that have survived. Where writing was done on perishable materials no record is left at all, except in very arid regions. The Egyptians wrote on both papyrus and stone. Papyrus is a form of durable paper made from the papyrus reed that abounds in the Nile valley. The extreme dryness of the region has preserved many manuscripts for us, some dating as far back as 4000 B.C. The early Indians and Chinese apparently used bark and bamboo, and very little of their early writing has survived. The Babylonians wrote on wet clay tablets which were than baked. Large numbers of these tablets have been found, so many that most have not yet been translated. Unfortunately, there are too few people capable of such translation.

Two papyri, the Rhind (circa 1650 B.C.) and the Moscow (circa 1850 B.C.), give us most of the knowledge we have of early Egyptian mathematics. The Rhind papyrus was purchased in Egypt by the British Egyptologist A. Henry Rhind. Later it was acquired by the British museum and was finally published in 1927. It is apparently a mathematics text, copied by the scribe Ahmes from an earlier work. The Moscow papyrus consists of 25 problems and the Rhind contains 85. In all of the problems there is no indication of mathematical methods. Instead, problems are worked out as examples for the student to follow. This "cookbook" approach to pedagogy is not unknown today.

Although most of the problems in the two papyri are arithmetic or algebraic, 26 are geometric, and from them we can obtain some idea of the nature, quality, and achievements of early Egyptian geometry. For instance, the area of a circle is taken to be 8/9 of the square on a diameter. This is rather surprising because 3/4 and 4/5 are much better ratios to use. We know that the area of a circle is given by πr^2 or $\pi d^2/4$, where d is the diameter of the circle. Because π (pi) is an irrational number it cannot be expressed exactly by a ratio of integers or as a finite decimal expansion. To four decimal places its approximation is 3.1416. If the area of a circle is taken as 4/5 the square on a diameter, we would have $\pi d^2/4 = 4d^2/5$, or $\pi = 16/5 = 3.2$, which is a little too large. If the ratio 3/4 is used, $\pi d^2/4 = 3d^2/4$, or $\pi = 3$. There is one reference in the Bible that implies that a value of 3 was used for π in the Old Testament days.

Let us return to what we know about mathematics along the Nile. The volume of a right circular cylinder was calculated as the altitude times the area of the base. The Egyptians probably knew that the area of a triangle was half the product of the base and the altitude. Some familiarity with elementary proportion was shown. The most remarkable problem in the Moscow papyrus is one in which the volume of the frustum of a square pyramid is correctly calculated by the formula

$$V = \frac{h(a^2 + ab + b^2)}{3},$$

where h is the height, a is the side of one base, and b is the side of the other base.

The Pythagorean theorem, in case you are a little rusty, states that the square on the hypotenuse of a right triangle is the sum of the squares on the legs. This original statement is geometric, referring to the areas of the squares that are constructed on the sides of the triangle, but today we usually interpret the theorem numerically. If a and b are the lengths of the legs of a right triangle and c is the length of the hypotenuse, then $a^2 + b^2 = c^2$. Two proofs of this theorem will be given in a later section. It will also be shown that the converse of the Pythagorean theorem is also true: if a triangle has sides of lengths a, b, and c, and $a^2 + b^2 = c^2$, then it is a right triangle. Since $3^2 + 4^2 = 9 + 16 = 25 = 5^2$, a triangle with sides 3, 4, and 5 is a right triangle. Thus, if one ties knots at equally spaced intervals in a rope and then stretches it into a triangle with sides containing 3, 4, and 5 intervals, a right triangle is formed. This method can actually be used in plane geometry to construct a perpendicular to a line at a point. Draw a line. With a compass set at a convenient spacing, mark off five intervals from a starting point.

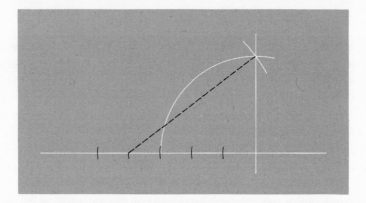

Construct an arc of a circle with a radius of three intervals and its center at the starting point. Finally, intersect this arc with another of a radius of five intervals and its center at the fourth interval.

There is a legend that the Egyptians formed right triangles for use as surveying instruments by tying knots at equal intervals in a rope in order to form triangles with sides of length 3, 4, and 5 intervals. Although this legend is viewed skeptically now, it is true that some writers of ancient Greece referred to the Egyptians as "rope stretchers." We have no evidence that the Egyptians had any idea of formal geometry or of the nature of a proof. Their results may have been entirely derived from experimentation.

A far greater body of material is available concerning the Babylonians, for great quantities of their clay tablets have been collected. However, it was not until the 1930's that the work of François Thureau-Dangin in France and Otto Neugebauer, now in this country, revealed the extensive achievements of the early Babylonians. Their mathematics was more algebraic in nature than was that of the Egyptians. However, tablets dating from 2000 to 1600 B.C. show that the Babylonians knew the area of a rectangle, a triangle, and a trapezoid with one side perpendicular to the base. They used three times the diameter of a circle for its circumference. Their formula, $V = h(a^2 + b^2)/2$, for the volume of the frustum of a square pyramid was incorrect, but they knew that corresponding sides of similar triangles are proportional, that the perpendicular from the vertex of an isosceles triangle bisects the base, that an angle inscribed in a semicircle is a right angle; and they knew the Pythagorean theorem.

So far most of our knowledge of Babylonian geometry is derived from the Yale tablet, which was written about 1600 B.C. As more and more of the tablets are translated our appreciation of the attainments of the mathematicians of ancient Babylonia becomes greater.

1.5 STONEHENGE

The writing media and the climate of the southern Mediterranean have combined to give us copious information about the mathematics of ancient Egypt and Mesopotamia, but similar developments must have been taking place elsewhere. For instance, the remarkable ruins at Stonehenge, on the Salisbury plain of England, have long mystified observers. It is only very recently that investigation has shown the strong probability that Stonehenge was a vast, intricate, and amazingly accurate observatory. Because the English ruins were constructed at about the same time that the Moscow and Rhind papyri were written, the astronomical and geometric accomplishments of whoever built Stonehenge must have been extensive. Unfortunately, we have no written record from these ancient Britons.

1.6 EXERCISES

1. If necessity is the mother of invention, what necessity probably led prehistoric man to invent numbers?
2. What necessity probably led prehistoric man to invent geometry?
3. Why do we know more about the mathematics of ancient Egypt and Babylonia than we do about the mathematics of others of that time?
4. How would you characterize ancient geometry? Was it like that taught in modern high schools? How did it differ?
*5. What was the most remarkable formula known to have been discovered by the Egyptians?
*6. Draw a picture of a frustum of a right pyramid.
*7. If the great pyramid at Gizeh was originally 768 feet on a side, by how much did the sides vary from each other? Give your answer in inches.
*8. If a frustum of a square pyramid is 768 feet on a side at the bottom, and if its top (451 feet up) is 144 square feet in area, find its volume in cubic feet. Use the Egyptian formula.
*9. Repeat Exercise 8, using the incorrect Babylonian formula.
10. If the area of a circle is taken as 8/9 the square on a diameter, what value is being used for π?

1.7 CLASSICAL GEOMETRY

The mathematics, and in particular the geometry, before about 1000 B.C. was empirical in nature. That is, experimentation—trial and error—led to certain sets of rules that seemed to work. We have no evidence that the ancient geometers ever asked the major question, "Why?" Tradition credits Thales of Miletus (640?–546 B.C.), one of the seven wise men of antiquity, with the first demonstrative geometry early in the sixth century B.C. He is credited with the first proofs that a circle is bisected by a diameter, that the base angles of an isosceles triangle are equal; that the vertical angles formed by two intersecting lines are equal; that two triangles are congruent if they have two angles and a side in each respectively equal; and that an angle inscribed in a semicircle is a right angle. Some of these results were known to the Babylonians, but it is thought that the concept of a proof had not yet been born.

* Solutions for exercises preceded by asterisks are found at the back of the book.

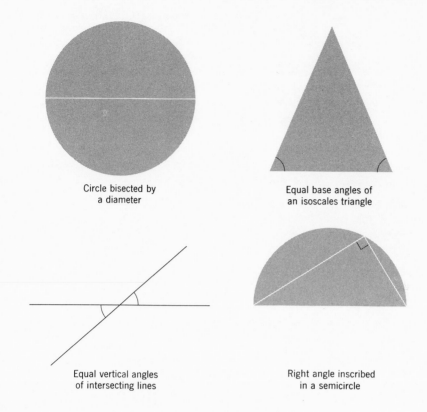

Circle bisected by
a diameter

Equal base angles of
an isoscales triangle

Equal vertical angles
of intersecting lines

Right angle inscribed
in a semicircle

1.8 THE PYTHAGOREAN THEOREM

Another mathematician of the sixth century B.C. was Pythagoras, about fifty years younger than Thales. Pythagoras founded a famous school in Crotona, a Greek settlement in southern Italy. The Pythagoreans mixed genuine mathematics with numerology, philosophy, and mysticism. Our knowledge of the work of Pythagoras is based on reports written several hundred years after his death and is consequently a mixture of fact and legend. It seems probable that all the mathematical work of the school was credited to Pythagoras himself, whether or not he was actually the creator. The most famous result is certainly the theorem that bears the name of Pythagoras, that the square on the hypotenuse of a right triangle equals the sum of the squares on the legs. We don't know the original proof, but it has been conjectured that it was a dissection proof something like the one that follows. A square with side of length $a + b$ can be dissected in two ways, as shown in the figure. Because the areas of the two squares are equal it follows that

$$a^2 + b^2 = c^2.$$

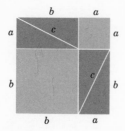 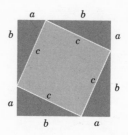

It is left for the student to show that this result is indeed a consequence of the two dissections.

There are nearly 400 known proofs of the Pythagorean theorem. A particularly simple proof is based on ratios of sides in similar triangles, as follows. Let a right triangle be drawn with the hypotenuse as base. Denote the length of the legs by a and b and the hypotenuse by c. A perpendicular dropped from the right angle to the base divides the base into parts we shall label x and $c - x$ and forms two smaller right triangles. Since each of these has an angle in common with the original triangle, all three triangles are similar. Since ratios of corresponding sides in similar triangles are equal, we can write

$$\frac{x}{a} = \frac{a}{c}, \quad \text{or} \quad a^2 = cx,$$

and

$$\frac{c - x}{b} = \frac{b}{c},$$

or

$$b^2 = c^2 - cx.$$

By addition,

$$a^2 + b^2 = c^2.$$

As we shall see in Chapter 2, there is a one-to-one correspondence between real numbers and lengths of line segments. That is, every length corresponds

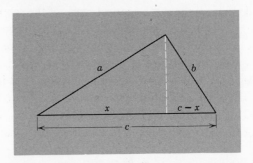

to a real number. The real numbers can be divided into two classes: those numbers that can be represented as ratios of integers, like 2/3 and 15/7, and those that cannot be represented in this way. The first class forms the set we call the *rational* numbers. The second class is called the set of *irrational* numbers. It is not at all obvious that any irrational numbers actually exist. In fact, an awareness of their existence occurred only after the Pythagorean theorem became known. We shall show below how the Pythagorean theorem implies the existence of irrationals. We now know that there are many "more" irrationals than rationals, although there are infinitely many of each. There are more irrationals than rationals in the sense that if a line segment is constructed at random, its length is virtually certain to be irrational. We shall return to this concept later. At this time we shall prove that there is at least one irrational number, $\sqrt{2}$.

1.9   THE IRRATIONALITY OF $\sqrt{2}$

The method of proof is one commonly employed in mathematics. We shall assume that $\sqrt{2}$ is rational and then show that this assumption leads to a contradiction. Since we can construct a line segment of length $\sqrt{2}$, we know that $\sqrt{2}$ is a real number. Since every real number is either rational or irrational, if we can show that $\sqrt{2}$ is not rational, it must be irrational.

The Pythagorean theorem is used only to show that there is a line segment whose length is $\sqrt{2}$. To construct such a line segment, we first construct a square one unit on a side. The diagonal of the square divides it into two right triangles whose legs are of length 1. By the Pythagorean theorem, the square of the length of the hypotenuse is $1^2 + 1^2 = 2$.

Thus the length of the diagonal of the square is a number whose square is 2. We denote such a number by $\sqrt{2}$.

If $\sqrt{2}$ is rational it can be expressed as the ratio of two integers having no factor in common: that is, $\sqrt{2} = a/b$, or $a^2 = 2b^2$. Since a and b have no factor in common, either a or b is odd (or both are odd). Since the squares of even numbers are even and the squares of odd numbers are odd, either

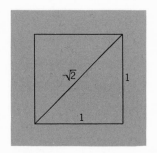

a^2 or b^2 is odd. Since $a^2 = 2b^2$, a^2 is even and b^2 is odd. But if a^2 is an even square, then a is itself even. That is, there is an integer n such that $a = 2n$, or $a^2 = 4n^2$. Hence $4n^2 = 2b^2$, or $b^2 = 2n^2$, so that b is also even. This contradiction of the assumption that a and b are not both even proves that $\sqrt{2}$ cannot be expressed as a ratio of two integers. Since the philosophy of the Pythagoreans was based on properties assigned to the integers, the existence of irrational numbers came to them as a shock. According to legend, one of the Pythagoreans was drowned for revealing the discovery to outsiders.

1.10   THE CONVERSE OF THE PYTHAGOREAN THEOREM

The Pythagorean theorem states that if a triangle with sides a, b, and c is a right triangle, then $a^2 + b^2 = c^2$. The converse of this theorem is also true. That is, if a triangle has sides a, b, and c satisfying the relationship $a^2 + b^2 = c^2$, then it is a right triangle. We shall prove this by a contradiction. Suppose that a triangle has sides a, b, and c, that $a^2 + b^2 = c^2$, but that the angle opposite the side of length c is not a right angle. Then this angle must be either larger or smaller than 90°. If it is larger than 90°, we can drop a perpendicular from one end of the longest side (length c) to the extension of the other side and label the lengths involved. Since the triangle with sides of length $a + x$, y, and c is a right triangle, the Pythagorean theorem tells us that

$$(a + x)^2 + y^2 = c^2, \quad \text{or} \quad a^2 + 2ax + x^2 + y^2 = c^2.$$

Since the triangle with sides x, y, and b is a right triangle, we have $x^2 + y^2 = b^2$. When this result is substituted in the preceding equation, we have $a^2 + 2ax + b^2 = c^2$. By assumption, $a^2 + b^2 = c^2$. When this is subtracted from the preceding, we have $2ax = 0$. Since neither 2 nor a is 0, we conclude that $x = 0$, and that our triangle is indeed a right triangle.

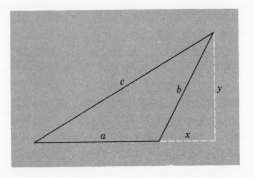

1.11 THE GIANTS: EUCLID, ARCHIMEDES, AND APOLLONIUS

Between 600 B.C. and 300 B.C., or roughly from Thales to Euclid, the idea of geometry as a set of logical deductions from explicitly stated postulates was developed. Much of the geometry taught in high school today was created during this period. Its culmination was Euclid's *Elements*, apparently written about 300 B.C. We don't know just when Euclid was born or when he died, and we have no copy of the *Elements*. The modern versions of Euclid's work are based on a revision by Theon of Alexandria almost 700 years later. It is thought that the greater part of the geometry of the *Elements* was known before Euclid, but to him goes the honor of synthesizing geometry into a coherent, logical unit. Euclid clearly stated certain axioms (general truths) and postulates (geometric truths) from which all his theorems were developed. Today we no longer distinguish between axioms and postulates, and we recognize that there were still some unstated assumptions in the *Elements*, but Euclid's work stood without significant modification for over 2000 years.

The next giant of classical Greek mathematics, Archimedes (287–212 B.C.), was one of the greatest scientists mankind has known. He was born, lived, and died in Syracuse, a Greek city-state in Sicily. His contributions to geometry include the treatises *On the Quadrature of the Parabola*, *On the Sphere and Cylinder*, *On the Dimensions of the Circle*, *On Spirals*, and *On Conoids and Spheroids*. To most of the mathematicians of classical Greek times mathematics was a purely mental discipline. Archimedes, however, went beyond this. His interest encompassed the world about him. He is considered to be the originator of the theories of mechanics and hydrostatics. He discovered that a body immersed in a fluid loses as much weight as the weight of an equal volume of the fluid, and he used this discovery to verify that the crown of King Hiero II was not made of pure gold. His inventions include the compound pulley and the water screw, still in use today.

Archimedes used methods that are essentially those of calculus to find the volume of a sphere, a paraboloid of revolution, and many other geometric solids. Although arithmetic was commonly considered to be of interest only in commerce, Archimedes developed computational techniques that enabled him to compute π to a precision unequaled for many centuries, and he published a fascinating paper in which he showed how to construct numbers exceeding the number of grains of sand required to fill the known universe. In this latter work he came very close to developing the modern concept of the logarithm.

In 212 B.C. the Romans attacked Syracuse. Tradition relates that Archimedes was sitting in the marketplace absorbed in geometric figures he had drawn in the sand when a Roman soldier came by. Archimedes cried out for the soldier not to disturb his circles, but the soldier callously struck him down. Over a century later Cicero found his gravestone, overgrown with bushes, and on it was a sphere enclosed in a cylinder of the same height. It had been Archimedes who had demonstrated that these two solids had volumes in the ratio of three to two.

Apollonius (262–200 B.C.) was a younger contemporary of Archimedes who was called the "Great Geometer." In his work, *Conic Sections*, we find a thorough investigation of the ellipse, parabola, and hyperbola. These curves are discussed in Chapter 5.

1.12   THE PARALLEL POSTULATE

From Euclid's time, mathematicians were troubled by one of his postulates. A common form of this postulate, equivalent to that given by Euclid, is that given a point P on line l in a plane, not more than one line can be drawn through P that does not intersect l. This form is usually called "Playfair's axiom," but it was first stated by Ludlam in 1794. It seemed to many that the parallel postulate was really a theorem that could be deduced from the remaining postulates of Euclid. For two millenia after Euclid mathematicians tried in vain to prove such a "theorem." We know that two early Greek geometers, Proclus and Ptolemy, attempted such proofs or at least discussed such an attempt. Ptolemy remarked that the proof would require much demonstration and many theorems!

An Italian mathematician, Saccheri, struggled for years with the parallel postulate and finally published *Euclid Vindicated from all Defects* in 1733. What Saccheri had actually done was to prove that there existed geometries in which the postulate did not hold, but he was led into such difficulties and had so much doubt that he concluded that Euclid's postulate must be the only valid one. It was nearly a hundred years later that János Bolyai (1802–1860) of Hungary and Nicolai Lobachevsky (1793–1856) of Russia independently proved that consistent geometries could be constructed in which the parallel postulate did not hold. Any such geometry is now called "non-Euclidean," and a variety of non-Euclidean geometries are now known and used. In the geometry of Bolyai and Lobachevsky it is postulated that more than one line can be drawn through a point that do not intersect a given line. A geometry developed later by George Riemann (1826–1866), a German mathematician, postulated that *no* parallel lines existed. Einstein's theory of relativity utilizes a geometry of space that is non-Euclidean.

A basic assumption of two-dimensional geometry is that figures like triangles, circles, and polygons can be moved about without any "stretching." If a triangle is cut from a sheet of paper, it fits flat against a plane and can be slid freely about without distortion. A similar situation holds on a sphere. A small cap that fits a sphere can be moved about on the sphere with no stretching. Thus a geometry can be constructed for the surface of a sphere. The lines in this geometry are "great circles," the intersections of the sphere with planes through its center. On a globe, the equator and all meridians are great circles.

The geometry of the spherical surface is radically different from the geometry of the plane. For instance, since every pair of great circles intersect, there is no line through a point not on a given line that does not intersect the given line. In the plane the sum of the angles of a triangle is always 180°, independent of the size and shape of the triangle. On a sphere, on the other hand, the sum of the angles of a triangle is always greater than 180°, and the sum depends on the size of the triangle. It is very simple to construct a triangle with *three* right angles. Consider the triangle formed by the equator and any two meridians that are 90° apart. All three angles of the equilateral triangle are right angles. If we decrease the lengths of the three sides, keeping them equal, we obtain a smaller equilateral triangle. What about the angles of the smaller triangle? They, too, shrink as the sides shrink. Thus two equilateral triangles of different size on the sphere have different angles. In short, no two triangles are similar unless they are congruent.

It is interesting to examine our shrinking triangle as it gets smaller and smaller. The sum of its angles gets closer and closer to 180°. If we were to consider a race of extremely small people, microscopic in size, inhabiting the surface of the sphere, their land would seem very flat. Further, for all practical purposes, the geometry of Euclid would represent the true state of affairs quite well. It is no wonder that early man thought the earth was flat.

1.13   EXERCISES

1. How did the geometry of the classical Greeks differ from the earlier Egyptian and Babylonian geometry?
*2. Show that the dissection of the two squares given in the text actually proves that $a^2 + b^2 = c^2$.

*3. Consider the dissection of a square shown in the figure. What algebraic formula does it represent?

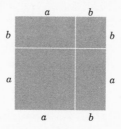

Exercise 3

4. Consider the dissection and reassembly shown in the figure. What algebraic formula does it represent?

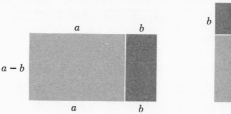

Exercise 4

*5. If the legs of a right triangle are of length 7 and 24, how long is the hypotenuse?
6. If the legs of a right triangle are of length 12 and 35, how long is the hypotenuse?
*7. If the hypotenuse of a right triangle is 17 inches and one leg is 8 inches long, how long is the other leg?
8. If the hypotenuse of a right triangle is 29 inches and one leg is 21 inches long, how long is the other leg?
*9. If a right isosceles triangle has legs of length $\sqrt{2}$, how long is the hypotenuse?
10. If a right isosceles triangle has a hypotenuse 1 unit long, how long are the legs?
11. Find another proof of the Pythagorean theorem. Look in encyclopedias or in geometry texts in the library.
*12. If p and q are positive integers and p is larger than q, show that a triangle with sides a, b, and c is a right triangle if $a = p^2 - q^2$, $b = 2pq$, and $c = p^2 + q^2$.
13. Prove that for every positive integer n a triangle whose sides have length $2n + 1$, $2n(n + 1)$, and $2n(n + 1) + 1$ is a right triangle.

*14. Prove that for every integer n greater than 1, a triangle whose sides have length $2n$, $n^2 - 1$, and $n^2 + 1$ is a right triangle.

15. Try to find four positive integers a, b, c, and d such that $a^2 + b^2 + c^2 = d^2$.

16. In geometry on a sphere the sum of the angles of a triangle always exceeds 180°. Is there an upper bound? What is it?

*17. Prove that every angle inscribed in a semicircle is a right angle. Proceed as follows: choose an arbitrary point on a semicircle of radius 1. Drop the perpendicular to the diameter and let its length be y. The base of the perpendicular divides the diameter into two parts of length $1 + x$ and $1 - x$. Since every point on the semicircle is 1 unit from the center, $x^2 + y^2 = 1$. Now join the point on the semicircle to the endpoints of the diameter and show that the resulting triangle is a right triangle with hypotenuse of length 2.

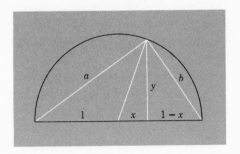

Show $a^2 + b^2 = 2^2$

1.14 ANGLE TRISECTION

Much of geometry does not depend directly on number. In Euclid's *Elements* the emphasis is on construction. The Euclidean tools of straightedge and compass restrict the geometer to figures that can be constructed from circles and straight lines. Individual points can be found on more general curves, but even here there is limited scope. In analytic geometry, on the other hand, many such curves can be represented by equations. For instance, the equation $y = x^2$ corresponds to a particular parabola, which is shown below. The problem of finding a point on the parabola lying on a line segment joining two points in the plane is very difficult when Euclidean methods are used. The same problem is reduced to a simple algebraic problem in analytic geometry. A more extended discussion of analytic geometry is given in Section 1.15 and in Chapter 5. Many other coordinate systems in two or more dimensions have been introduced and put to use since the time of Descartes.

Euclidean geometry is a gentleman's game. One follows the rules. These rules are so restrictive that many apparently simple operations are impossible.

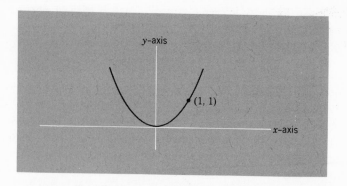

For instance, it is not always possible to trisect an angle with compass and straightedge alone. This fact was not proved, however, until 1837, when P. L. Wantzel's proof appeared in a French mathematical journal. This concluded over 2000 years of vain effort. Despite the fact that this proof is well known, each year mathematicians are pestered by well-meaning but mathematically ignorant people who insist that they have managed to trisect an angle. Many of these fallacious "proofs" are extremely ingenious, always very involved, and sometimes very good approximations to the desired trisection. Of course, it is possible, by quite simple methods, to construct an approximation to the trisection of an angle that has an error less than any preassigned amount, but the exact construction is impossible without ruler and compass.

Yet the trisection problem is a paradox. It is at the same time both impossible and very easy. The apparent contradiction lies in the fact that trisection is truly impossible with compass and unadorned straightedge, but the construction is quite simple if two marks can be made on the straightedge.

Let us trisect an angle *AOB*. Construct a circle with center at *O*. We may

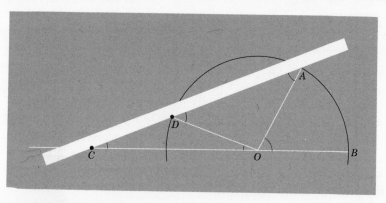

d *B* lie on the circle. Extend the line from *B* through *O*. ... on a straightedge in such a way that the distance between ... the radius of the circle. Then place the straightedge so that one mark is on the extension of *BO* (label this point *C*), the other mark is on the circle (label this point *D*), and the edge of the straightedge passes through *A*. Then construct line *DO*.

Since $CD = DO$, triangle CDO is isosceles and $\angle DCO = \angle DOC$. A theorem of Euclidean geometry states than an external angle of a triangle is the sum of the opposite interior angles. In this case, $\angle ADO$ is an exterior angle of triangle CDO. Hence, it is the sum, $\angle DCO + \angle DOC = 2\angle DCO$. We now observe that triangle ADO is isosceles, having two sides that are radii of the circle. Hence, $\angle DAO = \angle ADO = 2\angle DCO$. Finally, $\angle AOB$ is an exterior angle of triangle AOC, so that

$$\angle AOB = \angle DCO + \angle DAO = \angle DCO + 2\angle DCO = 3\angle DCO.$$

This completes the proof. $\angle DCO$ is one third of $\angle AOB$. The construction is simple, the proof is simple, but the rules of the game have been violated by placing marks on the straightedge. This construction, incidentally, was given by Archimedes. This indicates that the Greeks were well aware of the restrictive nature of their assumptions.

A concept that took a long time to mature was the one-to-one correspondence between points on a line and real numbers. The next step is to realize that every point in a plane can be specified by an ordered pair of numbers. From time to time throughout history various mathematicians made tentative steps in this direction, but the mathematical world was made aware of this relationship by René Descartes (1596–1650) in his *Geometry* published in 1637. A contemporary countryman, Pierre de Fermat (1601–1665), used the same techniques even before the publication of Descartes' *Geometry*.

1.15 COORDINATE GEOMETRY

Let us see how points in a plane can be represented uniquely by ordered pairs of numbers. Construct a horizontal line, which we shall call the *x-axis*. Construct a vertical line, which we shall call the *y-axis*, intersecting the first line at a point which we shall call the *origin*. Establish a unit of length and mark off these units on the two axes. Let *P* be any point in the plane. Draw a line through *P* perpendicular to the *x*-axis. Let *A* be the point where the perpendicular intersects the axis, and let *a* be the distance from the origin to *A*. Similarly, draw a line through *P* perpendicular to the *y*-axis. Let *B* be the point where the perpendicular intersects the axis, and let *b* be the distance

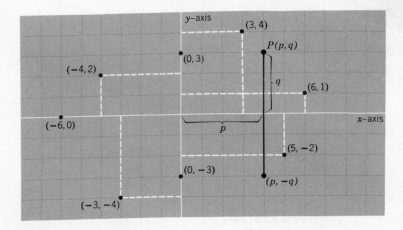

from the origin to B. We shall now construct an ordered pair of numbers (x, y), where $x = a$ if P lies to the right of the y-axis and $x = -a$ if the point lies to the left of the y-axis. The second element of the ordered pair, y, is b if P lies above the x-axis and $-b$ if the point is below the axis. Above is a figure showing a set of axes and the ordered pairs corresponding to some points in the plane.

Any system of associating sets of numbers with points in a plane or higher-dimensional space is called a *coordinate system*, and the one we have discussed is called a *cartesian* coordinate system in honor of Descartes. The members of the ordered pair (x, y) are called the *cartesian coordinates* of the point. The order is important, of course, since $(3, 5)$ and $(5, 3)$ represent different points.

Consider the equation

$$x + y = 4.$$

We can draw a "picture" of this equation by associating the point (x, y) with

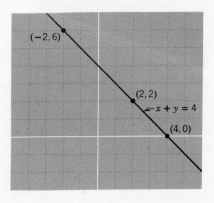

each pair of numbers that satisfy the given equation. Our picture or *graph* contains the points (4, 0), (2, 2), (−2, 6), and every point on the line.

In the same way, much more complicated relationships can be represented by graphs and when this is done algebra and geometry merge. For instance, the geometric problem of finding a point where two lines intersect is now indistinguishable from the algebraic problem of solving a pair of simultaneous equations.

The unification of algebra and geometry works for the benefit of both disciplines. Not only are algebraic methods used to solve geometric problems, but it is also possible to study the algebraic properties of equations by considering their geometric representations, their graphs. An almost immediate consequence of this new freedom was the invention of calculus simultaneously by Isaac Newton (1642–1727) and Gottfried Leibniz (1646–1716). It is customary to give these men credit for the invention of calculus, for our modern development of this subject stems directly from their work; but earlier work by Fermat and others all the way back to Archimedes laid the groundwork for them. Indeed, Newton once said, "If I have seen farther than other men, it is because I stand on the shoulders of giants."

1.16 TOPOLOGY

Imagine geometric figures that are constructed of rubber so that they can be stretched and distorted from one shape or size to another. Such transformations from one form to another are called continuous if the edges and surfaces are not torn in the process. In a loose sense, points that are close together are transformed into points that are close together. A circle, for instance, can be continuously transformed into a triangle or a square, but not into two separate circles. A sphere can be transformed continuously into a cube, but not into a doughnut shape. Certain properties are preserved in continuous transformations. For example, a circle has the property that we can traverse the entire curve by starting at a point and proceeding around the curve until we reach the starting point. The same is true of a triangle or a square. Every circle on the surface of a sphere can be shrunk to a point on the sphere, but this is not true on a doughnut-shaped surface. Properties like these, which are preserved under a transformation, are called *invariant*, and topology is the branch of mathematics that deals with properties that are invariant under continuous transformations.

One topological result is that if one considers the surface of the earth to consist of flat areas, mountain peaks, and passes between peaks, then the number of passes is two less than the sum of the peaks and flat areas. This

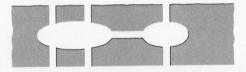

The seven bridges of Königsberg

result was obtained by the Swiss mathematician Leonhard Euler (1707–1783). Another interesting problem was shown by Euler to have no solution. This is the problem of the seven bridges of Königsberg (now Kaliningrad), a city located on both sides of the Pregel River and on two islands. The islands and the river banks are connected by seven bridges. The problem is to find a path that enables one to visit both islands and both sides of the river while traversing each bridge exactly once.

Another problem still remains unsolved today. Consider an ordinary map of a number of countries. What is the minimum number of colors that must be used in order that no two countries sharing a common border shall have the same color? We interpret border to have length, not to consist merely of isolated points. This is called the *four-color problem* and has been attacked by many mathematicians. It can be shown that no more than five colors are required, but no one has ever produced a map needing more than four colors. Oddly enough, the color problem has been solved for the torus, which is the mathematical name for a solid shaped like a doughnut.

Some interesting topological concepts can be demonstrated with a sheet of paper, a pair of scissors, and a little glue or mending tape. Cut a rectangular strip about two inches wide and eighteen inches long (the dimensions are not important). This strip has some obvious properties. For instance, the rectangle has two sides and four edges. But if two opposite edges are brought together in the simplest way and joined with tape, those two edges are no longer present. We may describe the resulting surface as a "tube" or as an endless belt, depending on whether we have joined the long or short edges of the rectangle. Although these may appear to be different, they are topologically the same. The surface has two sides and two edges. We can't get from one side to the other without crossing an edge. But suppose that the strip of paper is given a half twist before the two shorter edges are joined. The resulting surface, called a *Möbius strip*, has some surprising topological properties. It has only *one* side and *one* edge. Some people have to see this to believe it. When we say that a Möbius strip has only one side, we mean that any two points on the surface can be joined by an arc that does not cross an edge. Similarly, if one starts at a point on the edge and progresses along the edge until the starting point is reached, the entire edge will be traversed.

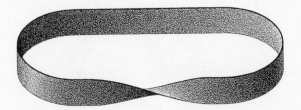

The Möbius strip is actually of practical use. Some belts that are used to drive heavy machinery are given a half twist in order to form Möbius strips. This is frequently done when it is necessary to keep the belts waxed. By pressing a single cake of wax across the belt at one point, the entire surface of the belt is waxed. Also, the entire surface of the belt wears uniformly, not just half of it.

Mathematicians never leave well enough alone. There is a constant striving for generalization. Let us start with the region between two concentric circles in a plane. Let us draw a line across the region, from edge to edge, and draw two arrows pointing in opposite directions on either side of the line. If the region is now cut along the line and a half-twist is made before joining the ends, the arrows point in the same direction in the resulting Möbius strip. This operation of a half-twist cannot be performed entirely in the plane, no matter how flexible the material. A third dimension is required.

Now let us consider a torus (a surface shaped like a doughnut). Let us draw a line around the torus as shown with arrows on either side pointing in opposite directions. If the torus is now cut along the line and the edges rejoined in such a way that the arrows point in the same direction, the resulting configuration is called a *Klein bottle*. In order to perform this operation, however, we find that three dimensions are insufficient, no matter how flexible the material of the torus. Just as a third dimension is required to construct a Möbius strip, a fourth dimension is required to form a Klein bottle. Although a Klein bottle cannot be constructed physically, its mathematical

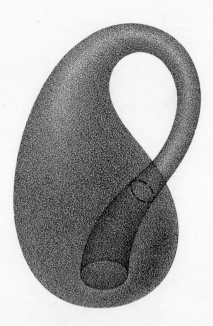

properties can be studied. Both the torus and the Klein bottle are surfaces having no edge. The surface of the torus separates the inside from the outside, but the Klein bottle does not do this. The inside and outside merge into a single side.

Another important result of topology is that if the surface of a sphere is stretched or deformed in any way without tearing or folding and such that the result is still the surface of the same sphere, then at least one point remains unchanged. Such "fixed-point" theorems are of importance in many branches of mathematics. The theorem about the sphere has some unusual interpretations. For instance, if a billiard ball is uniformly covered by hair, it is not possible to comb it flat without having a cowlick. Also, a consequence is that at any given instant there always exists at least one pair of antipodal points on the surface of the earth with precisely the same temperature and barometric pressure.

1.17 FAMOUS PROBLEMS OF ANTIQUITY

It is not surprising that the ancient Greeks occasionally encountered problems they could not solve. Although these problems arose from geometry, their solution, or rather the proof of their unsolvability, had to wait until mathematicians understood more about the nature of numbers. It was shown by the Pythagoreans that there were irrational numbers, like $\sqrt{2}$, but what was yet unknown was that there were two kinds of irrational numbers, those that could be expressed by means of some combination of radical signs, and those that could not. Among the latter are found numbers that are not the roots of any polynomial. These are called *transcendental* numbers. An example is π. Thus the first of the three problems that defied the Greeks and their successors for many centuries involved the number π. The problem was to construct a square whose area was equal to that of a given circle. Suppose the circle has radius 1. Then its area is π. The problem then reduces to finding, or constructing, a number whose square is π. The only numbers that can be constructed by the use of a straightedge and compass are numbers that are expressible by means of a finite number of operations of addition, subtraction, multiplication, division, and the extraction of square roots, starting with positive integers. Because π is not of this sort, neither is $\sqrt{\pi}$, the number needed to square the circle.

The other two problems are apparently quite different from each other. One is to construct a cube that has twice the volume of a given cube, and the other is to trisect an arbitrary angle. In both cases it has been shown that these problems are equivalent to solving a third-degree equation whose roots cannot be constructed with ruler and compass. As a footnote it may be mentioned that some historians now surmise that the problem of duplicating the cube may have arisen originally from religious sources, from the problem of constructing a cubic altar block exactly twice the volume of another.

1.18   EXERCISES

*1. Locate the following points on a cartesian coordinate system: $(0, 0)$, $(3, 4)$, $(3, -4)$, $(-3, 4)$, $(-3, -4)$.

2. Locate the following points on a cartesian coordinate system: $(-3, -7)$, $(-2, -5)$, $(0, -1)$, $(2, 3)$, $(4, 7)$.

*3. Find five ordered pairs representing points on the graph of $y = 2x - 1$.

4. Find five ordered pairs representing points on the graph of $2x + 3y = 10$.

*5. How do we know that $(3, 4)$ and $(-4, 3)$ are points on the graph of $x^2 + y^2 = 25$?

6. (a) Find three points on the graph of $4x + y = 7$ and draw the line.
   (b) Find three points on the graph of $2x - 3y = 7$ and draw the line.
   (c) From the graphs of parts (a) and (b), what is the common solution to the pair of equations $4x + y = 7$ and $2x - 3y = 7$?

*7. Show that the seven bridges of Königsberg exercise can be solved if one bridge is removed.

8. Show that the seven bridges of Königsberg exercise can be solved if one more bridge is built.

*9. Draw a map of four countries that requires four colors.

10. A slit is cut in an innertube. The entire tube is pushed through the slit, which is then closed. What does it look like? This is hard. Remember that you can stretch the tube as much as you please as long as it isn't torn.

11. Construct a Möbius strip from a strip of paper. Then,
    (a) Starting at a point in the center of the strip, draw a line down the middle until you return to the starting point.
    (b) Cut along this line with a pair of scissors.
    (c) Describe the result.
    (d) Cut the resulting strip in the same way.
    (e) Describe the result.

12. Construct a Möbius strip from a strip of paper. Then,
    (a) Starting at a point one third of the way from the edge, draw a line parallel to the edge.
    (b) Cut along this line with a pair of scissors.
    (c) Describe the result.

1.19 THE BEGINNING OF ARITHMETIC, NUMERATION

Until relatively recent times all of mathematics could be divided into two areas that had only a small overlap, arithmetic and geometry. So far we have discussed the development of geometry from observed relationships to abstract mathematical systems. Arithmetic, too, went through a similar development. We are using the word "arithmetic" in a broad sense to encompass counting, numeration, calculation, the number concept, and algebra in general. In this broad sense we must assume that arithmetic had its sources far back in prehistory. In fact a rudimentary counting is done by many animals. There is evidence that crows, for instance, can distinguish among one, two, and three objects but not more than three. Thus the first concept of number was certainly that of assigning a sound, mark, or symbol of some kind to a group of objects to record the number of objects in the group. The counting numbers are what we call the "natural numbers," the positive integers, 1, 2, 3, ... The symbols used form the "numerals." As soon as it became necessary to count very many objects the number of symbols needed created a pressure to group things in some way. For instance, let us suppose that we associate numbers with the fingers of one hand. Then we might count: one finger, two fingers, three fingers, four fingers, one hand, one hand and one finger, and so forth. Let us call five hands a tree. Then the number 38 would be: one tree, two hands, and three fingers. Notice that the order in which we give the groups is immaterial. The next step would be to create a symbolism for our words. If a finger is represented by $\cap$, a hand by ψ, and a tree by $\curlyvee$, then our number 38 could be written as $\curlyvee \psi$ $\psi \cap\cap\cap$, or as $\psi\curlyvee\psi$ $\cap\cap\cap$.

A new symbol is used for each group of five things, so five is said to be the *base* of this number system. In various places and at various times, 2, 3, 5, 10, 12, 20, and 60 have been used as number bases. The Babylonians used 60 as a base, and the Mayan Indians in Central America used 20. At the present time we most frequently use a base of 10, but the words "dozen" and "gross" reflect the use of 12 as a base in England and the United States, and the word "score" reflects the use of 20 as a base. Modern digital computers frequently use two or a power of two as a base for their internal computation.

1	$\mid$	A vertical staff
10	$\cap$	A heel bone
10^2		A scrool
10^3		A lotus flower
10^4		A pointing finger
10^5		A burbot fish
10^6		An astonished man

In our earlier example of a base-5 system, we denoted a number by a grouping of symbols. The order was not particularly important. Most early number systems were of this sort. The ancient Egyptians, for instance, used a base of 10 with separate symbols for each power of 10. The hieroglyphs used were:

$$10235 = 5 + 3(10) + 2(10^2) + 1(10^4) = {}^{\mid}_{\mid}{}^{\mid} \cap\cap\cap ??\, \emptyset\,.$$

The Babylonians generally wrote on damp clay, making wedge-shaped (cuneiform) characters. They combined 10 and 60 as bases, using base 10 for numbers less than 60. Also, they used the symbol $\ulcorner$ to indicate subtraction. This simplified the writing of some numbers. The symbol for 1 is the same as the Egyptian. For 10 they used $<$. Thus $28 = 30 - 2 = \;{<}{<}{<} \ulcorner_{\mid\mid}$.

1.20 ROMAN NUMERALS

As late as Roman times a similar system was used. The basic symbols used in Roman numerals are given below.

1	I
5	V
10	X
50	L
100	C
500	D
1000	M

For larger numbers a bar over a symbol indicates that the number represented by the symbol is to be multiplied by 1000. A double bar indicates that this operation is to be repeated. Thus

$$M = 1,000$$
$$\overline{M} = 1,000,000$$
$$\overline{\overline{M}} = 1,000,000,000.$$

In the Roman numerals the principle of subtraction is used in a way that does not require an additional symbol, as did the Babylonian system. Instead, if a numeral for a smaller number precedes that representing a larger, the smaller is subtracted from the larger. For example, 4 is represented by IV, 40 by XL, and 900 by CM. This subtractive principle, however, is optional and was introduced at a relatively late date. It follows that the representation of a number in Roman numerals is not unique.

A number system such as the Romans used appears clumsy, yet it was used extensively and for a long time. Roman numerals were used almost exclusively throughout Europe until the appearance of the printing press. The press accomplished two things: it standardized the form of the Hindu-Arabic numerals, and it permitted a much larger number of people to become acquainted with the system. The principal trouble with Roman numerals and similar systems is that addition and subtraction are awkward, and multiplication and division are incredibly difficult. The obvious advantages of the Hindu-Arabic system of numeration soon caused the Roman numerals to slip to a position of minor importance. Today the Roman numerals are used chiefly on monuments and title pages. When a motion picture is to be shown on television the date is invariably given in Roman numerals and is shown for a very brief interval. Because most of the viewers are not adept at reading Roman numerals, they are not alerted by the sight of MCMXXXIV for a few seconds on the screen that they are about to be subjected to a 1934 movie.

The Roman Empire was the center of world trade. Vast amounts of goods and money were involved, and accounting procedures were nearly as important as today. This pressing need for arithmetic computation and the awkward character of the Roman numerals combined to bring an early version of the digital computer into everyday use. This was the counting board or abacus. Originally the counting board was simply a board with a line or groove for each of the Roman numerals. Pebbles or beads were used to specify a number, a pebble on a line for each occurrence of the corresponding numeral in the number being represented. Later the number of pebbles on a line was fixed, and the position of a pebble at one end of a groove or the other indicated whether a symbol was "active" or "passive," that is, to be counted in the representation or not to be counted. In an even later modification the grooves became wires and the pebbles became beads strung on the wires. This is essentially the form of the abacus still in use in many Oriental countries. There are two forms of the abacus used at present. The Chinese *suan pan* has each wire divided into two segments with five counters on one side and two on the other. The Japanese *soroban* uses a division of four and two.

The abacus is an essential piece of equipment for each school child in the Orient. The smaller the child is, the larger the abacus. The markers on the large abacus used by the small child are large wooden knobs, easy for his unskilled hands to manipulate. On an abacus used by an accomplished adult, like an Eastern version of a cash register for instance, the markers are delicate ivory beads. An expert operator of an abacus uses the "touch" system, not looking at the beads at all. His fingers fly and his speed is comparable to that achieved on an electric desk calculator. In recent years experiments in this country have been carried out that seem to show that the use of an abacus by children in the primary grades leads them more quickly to an understanding of arithmetic.

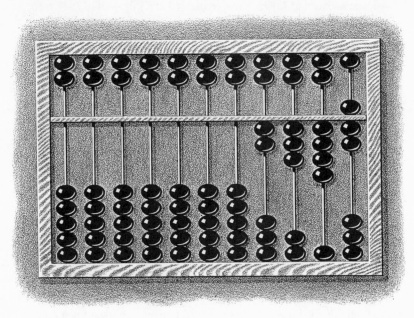

The *suan pan*

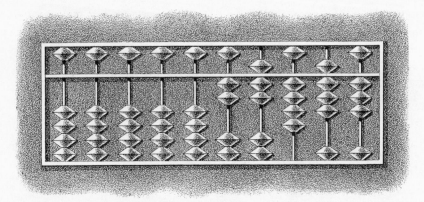

The *soroban*

1.21 MULTIPLICATIVE SYSTEMS

The numeration systems we have mentioned were based on the addition (and sometimes subtraction) of members of a group. The classical Chinese-Japanese systems were based on multiplication as well as addition. For instance, the number 6543 would be written as 6(1000) + 5(100) + 4(10) + 3, written vertically:

尤	6
千	1000
五	5
百	100
四	4
十	10
三	3

So far we have seen systems of numerals that are adequate only for the positive integers. Also, writing larger and larger numbers becomes increasingly difficult or cumbersome. It was one of Archimedes' proudest accomplishments that he was able to write numbers large enough to count the grains of sand on all the beaches of the Mediterranean. Arithmetic using these numeral systems is so difficult that devices had to be used for assistance. Early aids were dust or sand boxes in which marks could be made and smoothed away, boards on which pebbles could be moved, and various forms of the abacus. Still, numbers were thought of as representing or counting objects or portions of them. Thus the ancient arithmetic was extended only far enough to include the positive integers and the positive fractions. Work with fractions was quite difficult. The Egyptians and Babylonians usually expressed any fraction as a sum of *unit fractions*, i.e., reciprocals of integers. For example, we can write $25/32 = 1/2 + 1/4 + 1/32$.

1.22 POSITIONAL NUMBER SYSTEMS

The title of this section is not technically correct. It should read *Positional Numeration Systems*, but the incorrect usage is so common that we have permitted it to appear.

Today we use a positional system for most of our arithmetic. In this system each digit is multiplied by a power of 10 that depends on the position of the digit. For example,

$$237.82 = 2(10^2) + 3(10) + 7 + 8(10^{-1}) + 2(10^{-2}).$$

The enormous advantage of such a system is that there is no limit to the size of the numbers that can be written using only the digits from 0 through 9. Actually, there is also no limit to the size of the numbers that can be expressed in an additive or multiplicative system, but either many new symbols must be introduced or large numbers must be represented by long strings of symbols. Furthermore, addition and multiplication are simple operations that can be completely defined in terms of tables of addition and multiplication of the ten digits. The rather cheap price that we pay is that a "carry" must be considered in the arithmetic operations.

It is possible to use bases other than 10 for a positional system. We pointed out earlier that several other bases have, in fact, been used. Let us consider a positional numeration system with base 5. In this system, $(324)_5$ means $3(5^2) + 2(5) + 4 = 75 + 10 + 4 = 89$ in base 10. *We shall adopt the convention that a numeral to base 10 will be written without parentheses, but a numeral to any other base will be written in parentheses with the base as a subscript.* As an aid to computation we can write out the addition and multiplication tables for base 5. In the base-5 system we use only the digits 0, 1, 2, 3, and 4; $5 = (10)_5$. See Tables 1 and 2. Hence, to form the sum $(324)_5 + (402)_5$,

<table>
<tr><td colspan="6">**Table 1. $(+)$**</td><td colspan="6">**Table 2. $(\cdot)$**</td></tr>
<tr><td></td><td>0</td><td>1</td><td>2</td><td>3</td><td>4</td><td></td><td>0</td><td>1</td><td>2</td><td>3</td><td>4</td></tr>
<tr><td>0</td><td>0</td><td>1</td><td>2</td><td>3</td><td>4</td><td>0</td><td>0</td><td>0</td><td>0</td><td>0</td><td>0</td></tr>
<tr><td>1</td><td>1</td><td>2</td><td>3</td><td>4</td><td>10</td><td>1</td><td>0</td><td>1</td><td>2</td><td>3</td><td>4</td></tr>
<tr><td>2</td><td>2</td><td>3</td><td>4</td><td>10</td><td>11</td><td>2</td><td>0</td><td>2</td><td>4</td><td>11</td><td>13</td></tr>
<tr><td>3</td><td>3</td><td>4</td><td>10</td><td>11</td><td>12</td><td>3</td><td>0</td><td>3</td><td>11</td><td>14</td><td>22</td></tr>
<tr><td>4</td><td>4</td><td>10</td><td>11</td><td>12</td><td>13</td><td>4</td><td>0</td><td>4</td><td>13</td><td>22</td><td>31</td></tr>
</table>

we write one below the other and obtain the sum and carry from the addition table.

$$\overset{1}{3}24$$
$$402$$
$$\overline{}$$

1231, or $(324)_5 + (402)_5 = (1231)_5$.

We can check our work by changing each of the three numerals to base 10.

$$(324)_5 = 89, \qquad (402)_5 = 102, \qquad (1231)_5 = 191.$$

Since $89 + 102 = 191$, our addition is correct.

Fewer distinct digits are needed for a smaller base, but numerals in general become longer when a small base is used. For example, in base 2, the only symbols that are used are 0 and 1, but

$$93 = 64 + 16 + 8 + 4 + 1$$
$$= 1(2^6) + 0(2^5) + 1(2^4) + 1(2^3) + 1(2^2) + 0(2) + 1 = (1011101)_2.$$

There is an active group in this country that wishes us to convert to a *duodecimal* system, using a base of 12. Because such a base requires twelve symbols, two new ones must be introduced, x for 10 and e for 11 having been suggested. In this system 10 represents a dozen and 100 a gross. The advantage claimed for this system lies in the fact that 12 has so many divisors. If a dollar had 144 cents, or $(100)_{12}$, it would be possible to have coins representing 1/2, 1/3, 1/4, 1/6, 1/8, 1/9, 1/12, 1/16, 1/18, 1/24, 1/36, 1/48, 1/72, and 1/144 of a dollar. Because all multiples of these fractions have terminating decimal representations in base 12, some simplification of arithmetic is possible. There is probably more justification for using a base of 8. This is called the *octal* system. Since $(100)_8 = 64$, each octal dollar would consist of two halves of 32 cents, each half would consist of two quarters of 16 cents, each quarter would consist of two eighths of 8 cents, and each eighth would consist of two sixteenths of 4 cents. Making change would be easier. Also, because fewer symbols are used, addition and multiplication are easier to learn. Moreover, it is simple to convert from octal to *binary* (base 2), the number system used internally by most digital computers. Since $8 = 2^3$, each octal digit can be converted directly to three binary digits. For example, $(5)_8 = (101)_2$, $(7)_8 = (111)_2$, and $(3)_8 = (11)_2$. Thus $(573)_8 = (101, 111, 011)_2$. This simplicity of conversion also works in reverse. For example, $(10, 110)_2 = (26)_8$. At least one manufacturer in this country makes octal desk calculators for use in computer centers.

A symbol for zero is obviously a great convenience in our positional numeral system. There is no general agreement about when or where it first appeared. The Greeks occasionally used a symbol something like the letter omicron to denote an empty position. The Hindus apparently first used symbols like our digits from 1 to 9, but they did not use 0 until about 600 A.D. The symbols of the Hindus were modified by the Arabs and transmitted to the western world later. By the year 800 A.D. the Hindu-Arabic numeration scheme was essentially that of modern usage. The use of a positional system with ten as a base was also found in China as early as 1000 B.C., but no symbol for zero was employed. Instead, a blank space was sometimes used. There is still argument about whether the Hindu number system was influenced more by the Greeks or by the Chinese.

The introduction and acceptance of negative numbers occurred much later than the appearance of zero. Even Descartes referred to negative solutions of quadratic equations as "imaginary." The modern concept of number and number systems is a product of the last hundred years.

1.23 EXERCISES

  *1. Write the numbers from 1 to 20 in the binary number system.
   2. Write the numbers from 1 to 10 in base 3.
  *3. Write the numbers from 10 to 20 in base 5.
   4. Write the numbers from 10 to 20 in base 8.
  *5. Write the number 1432 in hieroglyphs.
   6. Write the number 37 in cuneiform characters.
  *7. Form addition and multiplication tables for base 2.
   8. Form addition and multiplication tables for base 8.
  *9. What rational number is expressed in base 2 as 10.101?
  10. Write 119/16 in base 2.
 *11. Add $(237)_8$ and $(564)_8$ and express the sum in base 8 and in base 10.
  12. Add $(237)_{12}$ and $(564)_{12}$ and express the sum in base 12 and in base 10.
 *13. Add $(101101)_2$ and $(110110)_2$ and express the sum in base 2 and in base 10.
  14. Add $(10111)_2$ and $(1001)_2$ and express the sum in base 2 and in base 10.
 *15. Multiply $(1101)_2$ and $(101)_2$ and express the product in base 2 and in base 10.
  16. Carry out the indicated operations in Roman numerals:
       *(a) XVII + LXVI
        (b) XLVII + LXXXIV
       *(c) LXXXIV − XLVI
        (d) CCLXVI − CXLIV
  17. Carry out the indicated operations in Roman numerals:
       *(a) IV·XV
        (b) L·L
       *(c) XVII·LXVI
        (d) CXI·LV

1.24 COMPUTATION, FALSE POSITION

In the last sections we have seen something of how the ancients wrote numerals. How did they use them? To what extent could they carry out arithmetic and algebraic processes? From the Rhind papyrus we find evidence that the Egyptians used some rather complicated techniques. For instance, they frequently solved equations by a method called "false position." As an example of this, suppose that we wish to solve the equation $x + x/7 = 24$. Remember that with the Egyptian notation the treatment of fractions involved unit fractions, and the given problem is equivalent to $x(1 + 1/7) = 24$. Using the method of false position, we shall first guess, then correct our guess to obtain the correct solution. Let us try 7. This will eliminate the fraction in the equation, and we find that $x + x/7 = 7 + 1 = 8$. Now, if 8 were multiplied by 3, we would get 24, the desired amount on the right side of the equation. Hence we multiply our first guess by 3 and guess now that $x = 21$ is the solution. Since this number satisfies the equation, it is the solution.

As another example, let us try to find an x such that $x/3 - x/4 = 5$. Let us try 72. This yields $72/3 - 72/4 = 24 - 18 = 6$. Then, by proportion, the ratio of x to 72 is the ratio of 5 to 6. Since five sixths of 72 is 60, 60 is the desired result.

1.25 EGYPTIAN MULTIPLICATION

The Egyptians performed their multiplication by a simple scheme that involved only addition and multiplication by 2. Any positive integer can be expressed as a sum of powers of 2. For instance, $26 = 16 + 8 + 2$. Let us multiply 26 by 35, using the Egyptian method of doubling and then adding the appropriate multiples of 35.

$$
\begin{array}{rl}
1 & 35 \\
2 * & 70 \\
4 & 140 \\
8 * & 280 \\
16 * & 560 \\
\hline
& 910
\end{array}
$$

We have added the numbers corresponding to 2, 8, and 16 times 35. Explicitly, the process is equivalent to writing

$$(26)(35) = (2 + 8 + 16)(35) = 2(35) + 8(35) + 16(35)$$
$$= 70 + 280 + 560 = 910.$$

We have expressed 26 as $16 + 8 + 2$. In the binary system we have $26 = (11010)_2$. The method of Egyptian multiplication, then, is actually equivalent to finding the sum of the numbers obtained by multiplying a number by the powers of 2 corresponding to 1's in the binary representation of the multiplier.

1.26   SQUARE ROOT

In primary school we learned a method of extracting square roots of numbers that is methodical but rather tedious, and most of us soon forgot it. We find that the Babylonians used several methods for extracting square roots. One very interesting approximation is

$$\sqrt{2} \doteq 1 + \frac{24}{60} + \frac{51}{60^2} + \frac{10}{60^3} \doteq 1.414213,$$

where the error is of the order of 1 in the last digit. (The symbol $\doteq$ means "approximately equal.") The result above is surprisingly accurate, but we don't know if they had a general method of this type for finding the square root of any positive number. Another method, much cruder, used the formula $\sqrt{a^2 + h} \doteq a + h/2a$. This is quite good if the quantity under the radical sign is near a perfect square and h is small relative to a. For example, $\sqrt{10} = \sqrt{3^2 + 1} \doteq 3 + 1/6 = 3.166. \ldots$ The correct value to six decimal places is 3.162278.

There is reason to believe that the Babylonians also knew the method of iteration in common use today. To find $\sqrt{a}$, make an initial guess, say x_1. If x_1 is exact, $x_1^2 = a$, or $x_1 = a/x_1$. If x_1 is too large, however, then a/x_1 is smaller than $\sqrt{a}$, which must lie between the two. A similar situation holds if x_1 is too small. Thus, let x_2, our next approximation, be the average of x_1 and a/x_1, or $x_2 = (x_1 + a/x_1)/2$. In general, we repeat the process to obtain a sequence of approximations that get closer and closer to $\sqrt{a}$. At any step, $x_{n+1} = (x_n + a/x_n)/2$. This method converges rapidly and is frequently programmed on modern digital computers. Let us try to approximate $\sqrt{10}$ by this method, using $x_1 = 3$.

$$x_2 = \frac{3 + 10/3}{2} = \frac{19}{6} = 3.1666\cdots$$

$$x_3 = \frac{19/6 + 60/19}{2} = \frac{721}{228} = 3.16228\cdots$$

As we have seen earlier, the correct value to six decimal places is 3.162278.

1.27 TABLES

The Babylonians made frequent use of numerical tables. One tablet gives the squares and cubes of the integers from 1 to 30 and also the combination $n^3 + n^2$ for n in this range. Many cubic equations can be reduced to the form $x^3 + x^2 = c$, which can then be solved by the use of the table.

The most remarkable table that has been found is on a tablet called *Plimpton 322*, number 322 in the G. A. Plimpton collection of Babylonian tablets at Columbia University. It was written sometime between 1900 and 1600 B.C. and consists of all or parts of four columns of figures. The first three are primitive Pythagorean triplets, sets of integers a, b, and c with no factor in common and such that $a^2 + b^2 = c^2$. That is, each triplet could be taken as the lengths of sides of a right triangle. Furthermore, if we denote by B the angle opposite side b, then the entries in the fourth column, which are $(c/a)^2$, are the squares of the secant of B, in our modern trigonometric terminology. What is more remarkable, the triangles given form a sequence in which the secant of B decreases almost exactly by $1/60$ as we go down the table from one entry to the next, and as angle B decreases from very nearly 45° to 31°. It has been surmised that there were other tables similar to Plimpton 322 for the ranges from 30° to 16° and from 15° to 0°. How were these triangles discovered? Euclid's *Elements* is the earliest work in which we find a method for generating all primitive Pythagorean triplets. At any event, the Babylonians apparently knew the Pythagorean theorem more than a thousand years before Pythagoras lived.

1.28 EXERCISES

*1. Solve $x + 3x/5 = 40$ by false position.

2. Solve $2x - 4x/5 = -18$ by false position.

*3. Solve $2x/3 - 5x/4 = 14$ by false position. (Try $x = 12$.)

4. Solve $7x/3 - 5x/7 = 17$ by false position. (Try $x = 21$.)

*5. Use the Egyptian multiplication method to find the following products:
   (a) (37)(33),   (b) (29)(32),   (c) (16)(43),   (d) (88)(71).

6. Prove that $\sqrt{3}$ is irrational.

*7. Define an infinite set of irrational numbers.

8. 11/5 is an approximation to $\sqrt{5}$. Use the method of iteration to find a better approximation. Express your answer in decimals and compare it with a value of $\sqrt{5}$ from a book of tables.

*9. Approximate $\sqrt{102}$ by the "cruder" method of the Babylonians and compare your answer with the value of $\sqrt{102}$ from a book of tables.

10. The ancient Greeks believed that the most beautifully proportioned rectangle was one that when reduced by a square on the shorter side left a rectangle similar to the original. Suppose the original rectangle had shorter side 1 and longer side x. Find x. (Draw a picture, label the parts, and set up the appropriate ratio of sides. Then solve the resulting quadratic equation.)

*11. Consider the spiral of right triangles in the figure.

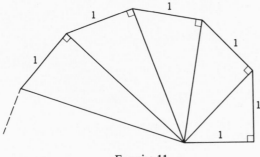

Exercise 11

What sequence of numbers is represented by the lengths of the hypotenuses of the successive triangles?

1.29 PLAYING WITH NUMBERS, NUMBER THEORY

The Babylonians and Egyptians have left us only fragments of their mathematics. We are impressed with what they accomplished, but we have no hint as to whether they ever formed a mathematical theory. From the fragmentary evidence we have we can tell only that they used many geometric and numerical results and relationships to help them build tombs, to survey land, to handle commercial transactions, to take inventories, to construct calendars, and to keep track of the astronomical bodies. The approach of the Pythagoreans was different. Their philosophy was based on the creed "All things are number." Much of what the Pythagoreans developed would be called numerology today, for it attributed mystic characteristics to the integers. However, this mysticism led them to do what had perhaps never been done before —to examine the integers for their own sake, rather than as tools for counting and measuring. Thus the Pythagoreans were the first known students of "number theory."

1.30 PERFECT, IMPERFECT, AND FRIENDLY NUMBERS

We know that any integer greater than 1 is *prime* if it cannot be factored into the product of two distinct positive integers other than itself and 1. If it is not prime it is composite, and its *proper divisors* are those positive integers less than the number that are factors of it. The Pythagoreans classified all numbers as *perfect*, *deficient*, or *abundant*. If the sum of the proper divisors of an integer n is equal to n, then n is perfect. If the sum is less than n, n is deficient, and if the sum is greater than n, n is abundant. Since 6 has proper divisors 1, 2, and 3, and $1 + 2 + 3 = 6$, 6 is perfect. Since 8 has proper divisors 1, 2, and 4, and $1 + 2 + 4 = 7 < 8$, 8 is deficient. Since 12 has proper divisors 1, 2, 3, 4, and 6, and $1 + 2 + 3 + 4 + 6 = 16 > 12$, 12 is abundant. A belief in numerology persisted for a long time and, in fact, still exists among the superstitious. Medieval theologians considered that because God created the earth in six days, the creation was perfect. On the other hand, the second creation was the new start made by the descendants of the eight passengers of Noah's ark. Because 8 is a deficient number the second creation was imperfect.

The first few abundant numbers are 12, 18, 20, 24, 30, 36, and 40. These are all even, and as we examine larger and larger integers, we still find that the abundant numbers are even. A reasonable conjecture seems to be that *all* abundant numbers are even, but the conjecture is false. There exist odd abundant numbers, but the smallest is 945, whose proper factors are 1, 3, 5, 7, 9, 15, 21, 27, 35, 45, 63, 105, 135, 189, and 315. The sum of the divisors is 975.

Two numbers are said to be *amicable*, or *friendly*, if each is the sum of the proper divisors of the other. Pythagoras is credited with the discovery that 284 and 220 are amicable. These numbers were used as friendship charms and were used in astrology and sorcery. It was over 2000 years until Pierre de Fermat announced in 1636 that 17,296 and 18,416 were amicable. The Swiss mathematician Leonhard Euler (1707–1783) gave more than 60 pairs. Over 400 pairs are now known.

Perfect numbers are rarer. Until recently only 12 had been found. Euclid proved about 300 B.C. that if $2^n - 1$ is a prime number, then $2^{n-1}(2^n - 1)$ is perfect. All perfect numbers known are even, and it is an unsolved problem whether or not there exist any odd perfect numbers.

1.31 DIOPHANTOS

Diophantos of Alexandria probably lived in the first century of our era. He wrote three works, *Arithmetica*, *On Polygonal Numbers*, and *Prisms*, of which parts of the first two are known. He was one of the most important figures in developing algebraic number theory. To have some idea of the sort of problem with which Diophantos worked, consider the following problems from *Arithmetica*. By "number" he means "positive rational number."

> *Problem 29, Book II.*
> Find two square numbers such that when one forms their product and adds either of the numbers to it, the result is a square number.
>
> *Problem 7, Book III.*
> Find three numbers such that their sum is a square number and the sum of any two of them is a square number.
>
> *Problem 9, Book III.*
> Find three numbers in arithmetic progression such that the sum of any two of them is a square number.
>
> *Problem 15, Book III.*
> Find three numbers such that the product of any two of them minus the third is a square number.
>
> *Problem 11, Book IV.*
> Find two numbers such that their sum is equal to the sum of their cubes.
>
> *Problem 22, Book IV.*
> Find three numbers in geometric progression such that the difference between any two of them is a square number.
>
> *Problem 18, Book VI.*
> Find a Pythagorean triangle in which the length of the bisector of one of the acute angles is rational.

Problems of this sort are called *Diophantine* problems, although the term is usually used today to refer to problems in which solutions in positive integers are sought. The study of Diophantine equations is a standard part of present-day courses in number theory.

1.32 FERMAT

Let us return to that remarkable seventeenth-century genius Pierre de Fermat (1601?–1665). He was a lawyer and judge at Toulouse, and his recreation was mathematics. He ventured into many fields but he is best known for his work in number theory. Although he published nothing, his work has been preserved in letters he wrote to other mathematicians and in notes found after his death. Many of these notes were statements, without proof, of results he had obtained. Nearly all of Fermat's statements have since been proved, but one has resisted all proof or disproof for 300 years, although attempted by many eminent mathematicians: the equation $x^n + y^n = z^n$ has no solution in positive integers for *any* n greater than 2. Fermat remarked in the margin of a translation of Diophantos by Bachet that he had found an admirable proof of this result but that the margin was too narrow to contain it. It is probably the most famous unsolved problem in all of mathematics.

1.33 EXERCISES

*1. Classify the integers from 2 to 20 as perfect, deficient, or abundant.

2. There is a perfect number between 20 and 30. Find it.

*3. Prove that 945 is an abundant number. (This is the smallest odd abundant number.)

4. For what integers from 2 to 9 is $2^n - 1$ a prime number?

*5. For each of the primes of Problem 4 find the corresponding Euclidean perfect number.

6. Find at least two solutions in integers (positive or negative) of the diophantine equation $5x + 13y = 1$.

*7. Find at least two solutions in integers to the diophantine equation $7x + 6y = 3$.

8. Express 29 as a sum of two squares of positive integers.

*9. Express 29 as a sum of three squares of positive integers.

10. Express 29 as a difference of squares of positive integers. (Hint: If $29 = a^2 - b^2$, then $29 = (a + b)(a - b)$. What are the factors of 29?)

1.34 RECOMMENDED READING

Allman, G. J., *Greek Geometry from Thales to Euclid*, Dublin, University Press, 1889.

Boyer, C. B., "Myth, the Muse, and Mathesis," *Math. Teach.*, vol. 57, no. 4, April, 1964, pp. 242–253.

Coolidge, J. L., *A History of Geometrical Methods*, New York, Oxford University Press, 1940.

Dantzig, T., *Number, the Language of Science*, 3d ed., New York, Macmillan, 1939.

Eves, H., *An Introduction to the History of Mathematics*, New York, Rinehart, 1953.

Hawkins, G. S., "The Secret of Stonehenge," *Harpers*, vol. 238, no. 1369, June, 1964, pp. 96–99.

Newman, J. R., *The World of Mathematics*, Vol. 1, Simon and Schuster, 1956.

Ore, O., *Number Theory and Its History*, McGraw-Hill, 1948.

van der Waerden, B. L., *Science Awakening*, translated by A. Dresden, Groningen, Holland, P. Noordhoff, Ltd., 1954.

Scientific American, vol. 211, no. 3, Sept., 1964, entire issue.

2

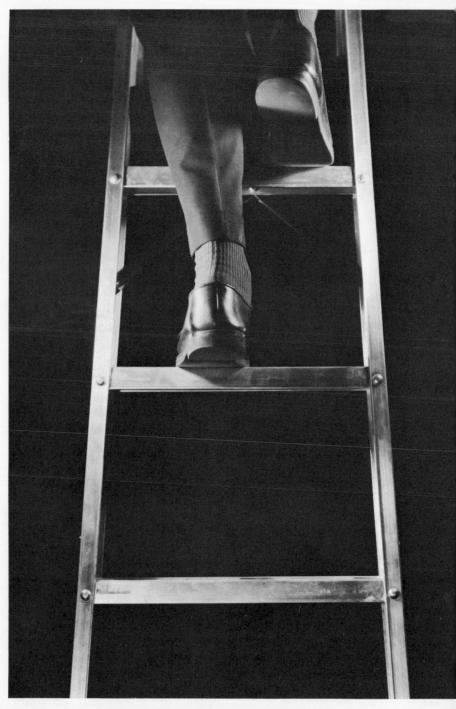

Step by step toward the infinite; the principle of mathematical induction.

2.1 THE NATURAL NUMBERS

The earliest form of arithmetic activity must have been counting. It is easy to imagine some of the problems encountered by ancient peoples in their attempt to formulate a numeration system that was both adequate for their needs and simple to use. We have the advantage of thousands of years of experience in our present positional system. We learn to count when we are very young, and throughout our primary and secondary education we utilize numbers as a part of our language. When do numbers cease being merely a part of language and become a part of mathematics? In order to answer this question we must somehow define the word "mathematics." This is a word whose meaning has varied widely from time to time and from person to person. Even today there is no general agreement on precisely what mathematics is. For our purposes we shall define mathematics to be *the study of the formulation, properties, and consequences of logical systems.* With this definition we would classify as mathematical the work of the Greek geometers who examined the world about them, formulated a system of abstract axioms and postulates about a pair of essentially undefined things called "point" and "line," and then proceeded to examine the logical consequences of this system in the form of theorems. The final step is to apply these theorems to the outside world, from which the whole process started.

A similar process for the concept of numbers was developed only in the last century. Let us try to develop a mathematical theory for the system of positive integers, 1, 2, 3, . . . , which we shall call the *natural numbers*. We have all our experience with the use of numbers to draw on. For a first approach, let us consider the set of all natural numbers. What can we say about them? What properties do they have? Let us start a list.

1. We can always add any two natural numbers and get a natural number.
2. We can always multiply any two natural numbers and get a natural number.

3. It doesn't matter in which order we add or multiply two numbers. That is, if a and b are natural numbers, $a + b = b + a$ and $ab = ba$.

4. The natural numbers are arranged in a sort of "natural" order. That is, if a and b are any two natural numbers, then either $a = b$, a is smaller than b, or a is greater than b.

5. There is a smallest natural number, 1.

6. There is no largest natural number. That is, if n is any natural number, we can add 1 and get a larger number.

7. We can reach *any* natural number by starting with 1 and adding enough 1's.

There are other properties that may occur to us, but this is at least a start. Of these properties, the seventh is particularly important, as we shall see in the next section.

2.2 PEANO'S POSTULATES

Early in the twentieth century Guiseppe Peano (1858–1932) based one of the first sets of postulates for the natural numbers on the last property of the preceding section. This set is quite abstract, and it is a long and difficult task to obtain the properties of natural numbers from these postulates. The importance of Peano's postulates for us is that it is *possible* to give a simple basis from which can be derived all the properties of natural numbers that we use in arithmetic and algebra.

Basically, the set he gave was the following:

1. 1 is a natural number.
2. Every natural number x has a successor, x'.
3. 1 is not the successor of any natural number.
4. If the successors of any natural numbers x and y are equal, then $x = y$.
5. If M is any set of natural numbers such that

      1. 1 belongs to M, and
      2. if x belongs to M, then x' belongs to M,

then M contains all natural numbers.

In this set, "1" and "successor" are really undefined, but we shall think of x' as being $x + 1$. In this way, $2 = 1'$, $3 = 2'$, $4 = 3'$, and so forth. "Natural number" is defined implicitly by the set of postulates. The postulates, in effect, say that if n is *any* natural number, we can count from 1 to n. Postulate 4 asserts that the natural numbers form a simple sequence in which there is no branching. Each natural number, other than 1, follows a single predecessor in this sequence. Postulate 5 is of particular importance, and it will be examined in greater detail in Section 2.5. It is usually called the "induction postulate." Let us restate it.

2.3   THE INDUCTION POSTULATE

If *M* is a set of natural numbers that

1. contains 1, and
2. contains $k + 1$ whenever it contains k,

then *M* contains *all* natural numbers.

2.4   EXERCISES

1. Give one possible definition of "mathematics."
2. The word "set" has been used several times. What does it mean?
*3. What similarity is there between the natural numbers and plane geometry?
4. Make a list of all the properties that you can think of that hold for all natural numbers.
*5. What arithmetic operations are *not* always possible in the natural numbers?
6. A natural number is *prime* if it is greater than 1 and has no factors other than itself and 1. List the first ten primes.
*7. Find five consecutive natural numbers that are *not* prime.
8. Express 165 as a product of prime numbers.
*9. Find the prime numbers that are factors of both 70 and 84.
10. Find the smallest natural number that is divisible by both 70 and 84.
*11. Dots can be arranged to form a sequence of triangles as shown below:

$$\cdot, \quad \cdot \ \cdot, \quad \cdot \ \cdot \ \cdot, \quad \cdot \ \cdot \ \cdot \ \cdot, \quad \text{etc.}$$

(a) Try to find a formula for the number of dots forming the perimeter of the *n*th triangle for *n* greater than 1.
(b) Try to find a formula for the number of dots forming the *n*th triangle for each natural number *n*.

12. Dots can be arranged to form a sequence of squares as shown below:

$$\cdot, \quad \cdot \ \cdot, \quad \cdot \ \cdot \ \cdot, \quad \cdot \ \cdot \ \cdot \ \cdot, \quad \text{etc.}$$

(a) Try to find a formula for the number of dots in the perimeter of the nth square for each natural number n greater than 1.

(b) Try to find a formula for the number of dots forming the nth square for each natural number n.

(c) How many dots must be added to the nth square to form the next?

(d) From parts (b) and (c), show that the sum of the first n odd natural numbers is n^2.

2.5 MATHEMATICAL INDUCTION

Let us return to the induction postulate and see how it can be used to prove a theorem. We observe that

$$
\begin{aligned}
1 &= 1 \\
1 + 3 &= 4 \\
1 + 3 + 5 &= 9 \\
1 + 3 + 5 + 7 &= 16.
\end{aligned}
$$

There is apparently a pattern emerging. We may conjecture that the sum of the first n odd integers is n^2. Is this always true? What would constitute a *proof* that it is true? We could try some more cases, but even if we tried hundreds of cases and never found the conjecture to fail, this would not be a proof that it was true for every n. Perhaps we were just lucky. The induction postulate, however, opens the way to a mathematical proof.

Let M be the set of all natural numbers n such that the sum of the first n odd integers is n^2.

1. If $n = 1$, then the conjecture asserts that $1 = 1^2$. Since this is true, 1 belongs to M.

2. If k belongs to M, then the conjecture is true for $n = k$, and

$$1 + 3 + \cdots + (2k - 1) = k^2.$$

Further, if this is a true equation, we can add the same thing to both sides of the equation without disturbing the equality. Let us add $2k + 1$, the next odd number. Then

$$1 + 3 + \cdots + (2k - 1) + (2k + 1) = k^2 + 2k + 1 = (k + 1)^2.$$

But this last equation states that the sum of the first $k + 1$ odd integers is $(k + 1)^2$. This shows that the conjecture is true for $k + 1$. Thus, if k belongs to M, then $k + 1$ also belongs to M. By the induction postulate, then, M contains *all* natural numbers; or our conjecture is true for every positive integer. This method of proof, called "mathematical induction," is one of the most powerful in all of mathematics.

2.6   N-FACTORIAL

The induction postulate also plays a role in definitions. For example, let us define *n-factorial*, written $n!$, by the following pair of equations: $0! = 1$, and $n! = n(n-1)!$ for all natural numbers n. We can now show by mathematical induction that we have actually defined $n!$ for every natural number. First, if $n = 1$,

$$1! = 1(0!) = 1(1) = 1.$$

Thus $1!$ is defined. Second, if $k!$ is defined,

$$(k+1)! = (k+1)(k!),$$

so that $(k+1)!$ is defined. Hence, by the induction postulate, $n!$ is defined for every natural number. We can work our way up to $n!$ for any n by starting with $0!$ and using the defining relation over and over. For example, to find $5!$ we proceed as follows:

$$
\begin{aligned}
0! &= 1 \\
1! &= 1(0!) = 1(1) = 1 \\
2! &= 2(1!) = 2(1) = 2 \\
3! &= 3(2!) = 3(2) = 6 \\
4! &= 4(3!) = 4(6) = 24 \\
5! &= 5(4!) = 5(24) = 120.
\end{aligned}
$$

It is like climbing a ladder. If we can get a foot on the first rung, and if we can always climb one rung higher from wherever we are, we can climb as high as we please. There is no rung that we cannot reach.

2.7   EXPONENTS

Let x be any real number. Let us make the following pair of definitions:

$$x^1 = x \quad \text{and} \quad x^{n+1} = x^n \cdot x^1$$

for every natural number n. It should be clear that precisely the same argument can be used here that was used with the factorial function to show that x^n has actually been defined for all natural numbers.

The definition that has been given for x^n can be used with mathematical induction to prove that $x^m \cdot x^n = x^{m+n}$ for every pair of natural numbers m and n.

Let m be any given natural number. Let M be the set of all natural numbers for which $x^m \cdot x^n = x^{m+n}$.

1. If $n = 1$, $x^m \cdot x^1 = x^{m+1}$ by definition. Thus 1 belongs to M.
2. If k belongs to M, $x^m \cdot x^k = x^{m+k}$. Then, since $x^{k+1} = x^k \cdot x^1$,

$$x^m \cdot x^{k+1} = x^m(x^k \cdot x^1) = (x^m \cdot x^k)x^1 = x^{m+k} \cdot x^1 = x^{m+k+1}.$$

Since this is the statement of our proposition for $n = k + 1$, $k + 1$ belongs to M. We have shown that whenever k belongs to M, then $k + 1$ belongs to M. By the induction postulate, then, M contains all natural numbers. That is,

$$x^m \cdot x^n = x^{m+n}$$

for any m and for every natural number n.

2.8 AN INEQUALITY

An inequality that is frequently used in mathematics is

$$(1 + h)^n \geq 1 + nh$$

($\geq$ means "greater than or equal to") for all natural numbers n whenever h is positive. Equality holds for $n = 1$, but there is strict inequality for $n > 1$. It is not necessary that h be an integer; it is merely assumed to be a positive number.

Let M be the set of natural numbers for which $(1 + h)^n \geq 1 + nh$.

1. Since $(1 + h)^1 = (1 + h) = 1 + 1 \cdot h$, the proposition is true for $n = 1$, so that 1 belongs to M.
2. If k belongs to M, then $(1 + h)^k \geq 1 + kh$. If this is true, the inequality is preserved if we multiply both sides by the positive quantity $(1 + h)$. Then

$$(1 + h)(1 + h)^k = (1 + h)^{k+1} \geq (1 + h)(1 + kh) = 1 + (k + 1)h + kh^2.$$

Since kh^2 is positive, $(1 + h)^{k+1} > 1 + (k + 1)h$. Since this is the statement of our proposition for $n = k + 1$, $k + 1$ belongs to M whenever k does. Thus, by the induction postulate, our proposition is true for all natural numbers.

2.9 GEOMETRIC PROGRESSIONS

A sequence of numbers such that every pair of successive numbers is in the same ratio is called a *geometric progression*. For example, the sequences below are geometric progressions:

(3, 6, 12, 24, 48)   Each term is twice its predecessor.
(2, 1, 1/2, 1/4, 1/8)   Each term is half its precedessor.
(4, −12, 36, −108)   The ratio of any term to its predecessor is −3.

In general, if a is the first term and r is the constant ratio, a geometric progression of n terms has the form

$$(a, ar, ar^2, ar^3, \ldots, ar^{n-1}).$$

What is the sum of the terms of a geometric progression? Let us prove that

$$a + ar + ar^2 + ar^3 + \cdots + ar^{n-1} = \frac{a - ar^n}{1 - r},$$

provided r is not 1. Our proof is by mathematical induction. Let M be the set of natural numbers for which the statement is true.

1. If $n = 1$, there is but one term in the progression, and the sum is therefore just a. Also,

$$\frac{a - ar^1}{1 - r} = \frac{a(1 - r)}{1 - r} = a.$$

Thus 1 belongs to M.

2. If k belongs to M, then

$$a + ar + ar^2 + \cdots + ar^{k-1} = \frac{a - ar^k}{1 - r}.$$

If this is a true equation, it will remain valid if we add the same thing, ar^k, to both sides. Then we have

$$a + ar + ar^2 + \cdots + ar^{k-1} + ar^k = \frac{a - ar^k}{1 - r} + ar^k = \frac{a - ar^k}{1 - r} + \frac{ar^k(1 - r)}{1 - r}$$

$$= \frac{a - ar^k + ar^k - ar^{k+1}}{1 - r} = \frac{a - ar^{k+1}}{1 - r}.$$

But this is precisely our proposition for $n = k + 1$. Hence, if any natural number k belongs to M, then $k + 1$ also belongs to M. By the induction postulate, then, M contains all natural numbers, or our proposition is valid for every natural number.

Example 1. Evaluate

$$3 + 6 + 12 + 24 + 48 + 96 + 192.$$

This is a geometric progression in which $a = 3$, $r = 2$, and $n = 7$. Thus its sum is

$$\frac{a(1 - r^n)}{1 - r} = \frac{3(1 - 2^7)}{1 - 2} = \frac{3(1 - 128)}{-1} = 3(127) = 381.$$

Example 2. Evaluate

$$2 - 2^2 + 2^3 - 2^4 + 2^5 - 2^6.$$

This is a geometric progression in which $a = 2$, $r = -2$, and $n = 6$. Thus its sum is

$$\frac{2[1 - (-2)^6]}{1 - (-2)} = \frac{2(1 - 64)}{1 + 2} = \frac{2(-63)}{3} = -42.$$

2.10 EXERCISES

*1. Prove that $1 + 2 + 3 + \cdots + n = n(n + 1)/2$ for every natural number n.

2. Find the sum of the first 100 natural numbers. (Use the formula of Problem 1.)

*3. Prove that $1 + 2 + 2^2 + \cdots + 2^{n-1} = 2^n - 1$.

*4. The Fibonacci sequence $\{u_1, u_2, \ldots, u_n, \ldots\}$ is defined by the following three statements: $u_1 = 1$, $u_2 = 1$, $u_{n+2} = u_n + u_{n+1}$ for all natural numbers n.
   (a) Write the first ten numbers in the sequence.
   (b) Why has every number in the sequence been defined?

*5. Let l be the last term of a geometric progression of n terms, so that $l = ar^{n-1}$. Then S, the sum of the first n terms of the progression, is given by $S = (a - rl)/(1 - r)$. If a geometric progression has first term 2, last term 54, and sum 80, find r and the number of terms.

6. Evaluate $-1 + 2 - 4 + 8 - 16 + 32$ as a sum of a geometric progression.

7. Evaluate each of the following sums of geometric progressions:
   (a) $1 + \frac{1}{2}$
   (b) $1 + \frac{1}{2} + \frac{1}{4}$
   (c) $1 + \frac{1}{2} + \frac{1}{4} + \frac{1}{8}$
   (d) $1 + \frac{1}{2} + \frac{1}{4} + \frac{1}{8} + \frac{1}{16}$
   (e) $1 + \frac{1}{2} + \frac{1}{4} + \frac{1}{8} + \frac{1}{16} + \frac{1}{32}$
   (f) $1 + \frac{1}{2} + \frac{1}{4} + \frac{1}{8} + \frac{1}{16} + \frac{1}{32} + \frac{1}{64}$

8. In Exercise 7, as the number of terms increases, does the sum appear to get closer to some fixed number? What number?

*9. A frog is two yards from a pool. His first jump takes him half way to the pool, and each successive jump takes him half the remaining distance to the pool (see Exercise 7).

    (a) How far is the frog from the pool after 3 jumps? After 6 jumps? After n jumps?

    (b) How many jumps must the frog make to get within one inch of the pool?

10. A frog is three yards from a pool. His first jump takes him two thirds of the way to the pool, and each successive jump takes him two thirds of the remaining distance.

    (a) How far is the frog from the pool after 3 jumps? After 6 jumps? After n jumps?

    (b) How many jumps must the frog make to get within one inch of the pool?

*11. List the values of $n!$ for $n = 1$ to $n = 10$.

12. How many numbers can be written using all the digits 1, 3, 5, 7, 9 without repetition? (Hint: How many choices are there for the first digit? Having chosen one digit to be first, how many choices are there for the second digit?)

*13. Suppose that a state wishes to have license plates consisting of three letters followed by three digits.

    (a) How many distinct license plates can be made if repetitions are permitted? (That is, ABA-000 is acceptable.)

    (b) How many can be made if numbers can be repeated but not letters?

    (c) How many can be made if neither numbers nor letters can be repeated?

2.11 ALGEBRAIC PROPERTIES

In the proofs given so far we performed many arithmetic operations whose validity is not immediately obvious from Peano's postulates. The algebraic laws obeyed by the operations of addition and multiplication are consequences derivable from, but well hidden in, the set of postulates. Let us state such a set of laws that explicitly give the properties of the arithmetic operations.

As a prelude to these laws, let us state the properties of equality that we shall use in our work. The unqualified word "number" is used because the properties hold in the natural numbers, the integers, the rational numbers, and the real numbers.

    E1. For every number a, $a = a$. (Equality is reflexive.)

    E2. If $a = b$, then $b = a$. (Equality is symmetric.)

    E3. If $a = b$ and $b = c$, then $a = c$. (Equality is transitive.)

    E4. If $a = b$, then a may be replaced by b in any algebraic expression. (Replacement property.)

E5. If $a = b$, then for every number d,

$$a + d = b + d \quad \text{and} \quad ad = bd.$$

(When equal numbers are added to or multiplied by equal numbers, the results are equal.

We now observe that the set of natural numbers possesses the following properties:

A1. Closure Law for Addition. The set is *closed under addition*. This means that if a and b are members of the set, then there is a unique member c such that
$$a + b = c.$$

A2. Commutative Law for Addition. The operation of addition is *commutative*. That is, if a and b are any two members of the set,

$$a + b = b + a.$$

A3. Associative Law for Addition. The operation of addition is *associative*. That is, if a, b, and c are any three members of the set,

$$a + (b + c) = (a + b) + c.$$

C1. Cancellation Law for Addition. If a, b, and c are any members of the set for which $a + b = a + c$, then

$$b = c.$$

M1. Closure Law for Multiplication. The set is *closed under multiplication*. That is, if a and b are any two members of the set, then there is a unique member c such that

$$ab = c.$$

M2. Commutative Law for Multiplication. The operation of multiplication is *commutative*. That is, if a and b are any two members of the set, then
$$ab = ba.$$

M3. Associative Law for Multiplication. The operation of multiplication is *associative*. That is, if a, b, and c are any three members of the set,
$$a(bc) = (ab)c.$$

M4. Identity for Multiplication. There is a unique member 1 such that for every member a of the set,

$$1(a) = a(1) = a.$$

The number 1 is called the *identity of multiplication.*

C2. Cancellation Law for Multiplication. If a, b, and c are any members of the set for which $ab = ac$, then

$$b = c.$$

D. Distributive Law. Multiplication *distributes* over addition. That is, if a, b, and c are any three members of the set, then

$$a(b + c) = ab + ac.$$

In this list we shall consider C1 and C2 to be "temporary" laws. That is, they are valid for the natural numbers, but in more comprehensive number systems they will follow as rather trivial consequences of other properties of the systems. To be precise, C1 is easily proved in the set of integers, and C2 is proved with similar ease in the set of rational numbers.

The familiar arithmetic "number facts" are subsumed under A1 and M1. That is, if we wish to express 13 as $10 + 3$, the appropriate justification is A1.

The following example shows how the preceding properties can be used in the solution of a simple algebraic problem.

Example. Find a natural number x, if one exists, such that

$$2x + 3 = 13.$$

Solution: Suppose $2x + 3 = 13$ for some natural number x. Then,

$13 = 10 + 3$	A1
$2x + 3 = 10 + 3$	E4
$2x = 10$	C1
$10 = 2(5)$	M1
$2x = 2(5)$	E4
$x = 5$	C2

Thus, if any natural number is a solution, it must be 5. Since $2 \cdot 5 + 3 = 13$, the equation is satisfied, and 5 *is* the desired solution.

2.12 ORDER

It is clear that the natural numbers are ordered. That is, in the process of counting, we find each natural number falling into a certain place. Each number precedes another, and, with the exception of 1, each number follows another. In general we can compare any two natural numbers and tell which precedes the other in the natural order. If a and b are natural numbers and a precedes b, we shall write $a < b$. The mathematical definition of $<$ is given below.

> **Definition of $<$.** If a and b are natural numbers, then $a < b$ (read "a is less than b") if and only if there is some natural number c such that $a + c = b$.

We shall find that a similar relation holds in the integers, rational numbers, and real numbers, but in those systems a slight change will be necessary in the definition of $<$. We shall require that the number c be positive. So far we have had no occasion to refer to "positive" numbers. They will be encountered first when we get to the integers. In the natural numbers, however, any value of c is acceptable. For example, $3 < 10$ because 7 is a natural number and $3 + 7 = 10$.

The order in the natural numbers is said to be linear. That is, we can arrange them along a straight line in such a way that if $m < n$, then m precedes n in the arrangement.

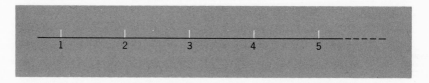

An important property of the "less than" relation is that if $a < b$ and $b < c$, then $a < c$. This property, called the *transitive law*, is fundamental in any ordering of a set of elements. Its proof is quite simple if we keep in mind the definition of $<$.

Since $a < b$, there is a natural number m such that $a + m = b$.
Since $b < c$, there is a natural number n such that $b + n = c$.
Then

$$a + m + n = b + n = c.$$

Since $m + n$ is a natural number that, when added to a, yields c, $a < c$. The student should show how the associative law for addition, A3, and the replacement property, E4, have been used in the proof.

A consequence of our definition of the ordering of the natural numbers is that any two of them can be compared. If a and b are any two natural numbers, either they are equal or one of them is less than the other. This important property is expressed in the following law.

T. **Trichotomy Law.**   If a and b are members of the set of natural numbers, exactly one of the following holds:

$$a = b, \quad a < b, \quad \text{or} \quad b < a.$$

The laws above justify the operations that we perform in arithmetic and algebraic manipulation involving natural numbers. In the natural number system we are severely restricted in our applications to algebra because many simple equations have no solutions. The equation $x + a = b$ does not, in general, have a solution in the set of natural numbers. For instance, there is no natural number satisfying the equation $x + 5 = 3$. Despite this algebraic deficiency, the set of natural numbers provides a basis for a wealth of interesting problems concerned with prime numbers, factorization of integers, and problems involving counting. Many of these problems will be discussed in Chapter 4. In this chapter we shall extend the system of natural numbers to the integers, then to the rational numbers, and finally to the real numbers. At each stage we shall state explicitly what laws are obeyed by the system so that the solution of an algebraic problem becomes a theorem whose proof is derivable from the stated laws.

2.13 EXERCISES

1. In each of the following, give the law that justifies the statement.
   *(a) $3 + 5 = 5 + 3$
   (b) $x(x + y) = x^2 + xy$
   *(c) If $2x = 6$, then $x = 3$.
   (d) $5 \cdot 6 = 10 \cdot 3$
   *(e) $7 \cdot 1 = 7$
   (f) If $3 + y = 3 + 7$, then $y = 7$.
   *(g) $99 \cdot 576$ is a natural number.
   (h) $99 + 576$ is a natural number.
   *(i) $5 + 6 = 7 + 4$
   (j) $17 \cdot 13 = 13 \cdot 17$

   *(k) If $x \neq y$ and x is not less than y, then $y < x$. ($\neq$ means "is not equal to.")
   (l) If $x = 3$, then $x + 5 = 8$.
   *(m) If $x = 3$, then $5x = 15$.
   (n) If $2x = y$, then $y = 2x$.
   *(o) If $x = y$ and $2x + 3 = 7$, then $2y + 3 = 7$.

*2. Solve the following equation for x, giving a reason for each step: $3x + 4 = 19$.
3. What operation can always be performed in the set of integers that cannot always be performed in the set of natural numbers?
4. Solve the following equation for x, giving a reason for each step: $4x + 5 = 17$.
*5. (a) Show that for every integer x, $(x - 2)(x - 3) = x^2 - 5x + 6$.
   (b) Show that $x = 2$ and $x = 3$ are solutions of $x^2 - 5x + 6 = 0$
6. If x is any natural number, show that $3x < 4x$.
*7. (a) Find a natural number x for which $2x^2 < x + 2$. Are there more?
   (b) Find a natural number x for which $x + x < x^2$. Are there more?

8. If x and y are natural numbers with $x < y$, show the following:
   (a) $ax < ay$ for every natural number a.
   (b) $x^2 < xy$
   (c) $xy < y^2$
   (d) The product of two distinct natural numbers always lies between the squares of the numbers.
   (e) If $x < y$, then $x^2 < y^2$.
*9. Why is there no natural number x such that $x + 5 = 3$? (Hint: Use T.)
10. Show that $x^2 < x^3$ for every natural number x except 1.

2.14 THE INTEGERS

In the last section we saw that the simple equation $x + 5 = 3$ has no solution in the set of natural numbers. To remedy this situation we shall make our first extension of the system of natural numbers by adjoining some more numbers of a different kind. The first number we adjoin is denoted by 0 and has the property that for every natural number a,

$$a + 0 = 0 + a = a.$$

Since no natural number has this property, we have added something new. Our next step is to adjoin a set of new numbers, one for each natural number. These new numbers will be the *negative integers*. The natural numbers, when imbedded in this larger set, will be called the *positive integers*. For each natural number a we define $-a$ to be a number such that

$$a + (-a) = -a + a = 0.$$

We call $-a$ the additive inverse of a. The set consisting of the natural numbers, 0, and the negative integers is called the set of *integers*. A mathematician can show, with some effort, that the integers can be defined in such a way that they satisfy all the laws for the natural numbers and two additional ones as well.

A4. **Identity for Addition.** There is a unique member of the set, 0 such that

$$a + 0 = 0 + a = a$$

for every a in the set.

A5. **Additive Inverse.** For every a in the set there is a unique member $-a$ such that

$$a + (-a) = -a + a = 0.$$

Note the word "unique" in A4 and A5. This means that there is one and only one number in the set that behaves like 0, and every number has one and only one additive inverse.

In order for T to hold in our system of integers we must modify our definition of $<$ so that $a < b$ means that there is a *positive integer* c such that $a + c = b$. In general, an equivalent condition is that $b + (-a)$ is a positive number.

By A4, $0 + a = a$ for every integer a. In particular, when a is positive, it follows that $0 < a$. On the other hand, if b is negative, then it is the additive inverse of a positive integer $-b$. By A5, $b + (-b) = 0$. Hence, for every negative integer b, $b < 0$. We shall frequently use the briefer statements "$0 < a$" or "$b < 0$" in place of the longer "a is positive" or "b is negative." We define $a > b$ to mean that $b < a$. Similarly, $a \geq b$ means that a is greater than b or possibly equal to it, and $a \leq b$ means that a is less than or equal to b.

The order of the integers clearly preserves the order of the natural numbers, and we can extend the "number line" to the left. The set of all integers can be arranged along a line in such a way that $m < n$ if and only if m lies to the left of n on the line.

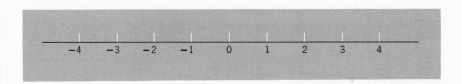

For example, since $-3 + 1 = -2$, we have $-3 < -2$, and -3 lies to the left of -2.

In the system of integers, it is no longer necessary to assume C1, as the following proof shows:

$$
\begin{array}{ll}
a + b = a + c & \text{Given} \\
-a + (a + b) = -a + (a + c) & \text{E5} \\
(-a + a) + b = (-a + a) + c & \text{A3} \\
0 + b = 0 + c & \text{A5} \\
b = c & \text{A4}
\end{array}
$$

Notice that C1 is still valid; it is merely unnecessary to assume it as a postulate. C1 can still be used to shorten proofs whenever it is convenient.

In algebraic proofs there is a strong temptation to take several steps at once. However, since a reason is required for each step, the temptation should be resisted.

The number 0 has an important property expressed in the following theorem.

Theorem 1. *In any number system satisfying the algebraic laws of the integers, $a(0) = 0$.*

Proof:

$$a(0) + a = a(0) + a(1) \qquad \text{M4}$$
$$a(0) + a = a(0 + 1) \qquad \text{D}$$
$$a(0) + a = a(1) \qquad \text{A4}$$
$$a(0) + a = a \qquad \text{M4}$$
$$a(0) + a = 0 + a \qquad \text{A4}$$
$$a(0) = 0 \qquad \text{C1}$$

One of the mysterious rules of signed numbers is that the product of two negatives is positive. Frequently this is justified by analogy, which may be convincing, but it is certainly not a mathematical proof. Does it follow as a logical consequence of our laws?

Theorem 2. *In any number system satisfying the algebraic laws of the integers, for any a and b, $(-a)(-b) = ab$.*

Proof:

$$(-a)(-b) = 0 + (-a)(-b) \qquad \text{A4}$$
$$= a(0) + (-a)(-b) \qquad \text{Th. 1}$$
$$= a[b + (-b)] + (-a)(-b) \qquad \text{A5}$$
$$= [ab + a(-b)] + (-a)(-b) \qquad \text{D}$$
$$= ab + [a(-b) + (-a)(-b)] \qquad \text{A3}$$
$$= ab + [a + (-a)](-b) \qquad \text{D and M2}$$
$$= ab + 0(-b) \qquad \text{A5}$$
$$= ab + 0 \qquad \text{Th. 1}$$
$$= ab \qquad \text{A4}$$

2.15 SUBTRACTION

The operation of subtraction can now be added for convenience. We define $a - b$ to mean $a + (-b)$. Clearly, it is not necessary to consider subtraction separately from addition.

We can now demonstrate the application of our laws to the solution of a simple algebraic problem, giving an explicit reason for each step.

Example 1. Find an integer x, if one exists, such that

$$x + 7 = 3.$$

Solution: Suppose there is an integer x such that $x + 7 = 3$. Then

$$(x + 7) + (-7) = 3 + (-7) \qquad \text{E5}$$
$$-7 = -3 + (-4) \qquad \text{A1}$$

Thus $\qquad (x + 7) + (-7) = 3 + [(-3) + (-4)] \qquad \text{E4}$
$$x + [7 + (-7)] = [3 + (-3)] + (-4) \qquad \text{A3}$$
$$x + 0 = 0 + (-4) \qquad \text{A5}$$
$$x = -4 \qquad \text{A4}$$

Since -4 satisfies the given equation, it is the desired solution.

E4 is used so commonly that we shall no longer list it as a reason for a step in a proof.

Example 2. Find an integer x, if one exists, such that

$$3x - 5 = 13.$$

Solution: Suppose there is an integer x such that $3x - 5 = 13$. Then

$$(3x - 5) + 5 = 13 + 5 \qquad \text{E5}$$
$$3x + (-5 + 5) = 18 \qquad \text{A3 and A1 and definition of subtraction}$$
$$3x + 0 = 18 \qquad \text{A5}$$
$$3x = 3(6) \qquad \text{A4 and M1}$$
$$x = 6 \qquad \text{C2}$$

Since 6 satisfies the given equation, it is the desired solution.

2.16 EXERCISES

*1. Solve the equation $x + 6 = 2$, giving a reason for each step.
 2. Solve the equation $x - 2 = -6$, giving a reason for each step.
*3. Solve the equation $3x - 4 = 2$, giving a reason for each step.
 4. Solve the equation $2x + 5 = -7$, giving a reason for each step.
*5. Which of the properties of the integers are not satisfied by the set of odd integers?
*6. Which of the properties of the integers are not satisfied by the set of even integers?
 7. Give an example of an equation that can be solved in the set of integers but not in the set of natural numbers.
 8. Give an example of an equation that cannot be solved in the set of integers.
*9. Prove by mathematical induction that every set of one or more natural numbers contains a smallest natural number. Start by letting S be a set of one or more natural numbers with no smallest element. Let M be the set of all natural numbers less than every number in S. Then show that M contains *all* natural numbers, contradicting the assumption that S contains at least one element.

10. Is the property given in Problem 9 also true of the integers? That is, does every set of one or more integers have a smallest element? Prove it or give a counter-example.

*11. Prove that 0 is unique in the integers. That is, show that if x is an integer such that $a + x = x + a = a$ for every integer a, then $x = 0$.

12. Prove that the additive inverse of each integer is unique. That is, if x is an integer such that $a + x = x + a = 0$, then $x = -a$.

*13. By the closure law of multiplication for natural numbers, the square of every natural number is a natural number. From this it follows that if a is any positive integer, its square is a positive integer. Prove that the square of every nonzero integer is positive.

14. If x and y are natural numbers with $x^2 < y^2$, prove that $x < y$.

*15. Show why $x^2 + 4 = 0$ cannot have a solution in the set of integers. Give reasons.

2.17 THE RATIONAL NUMBERS

The integers form a rich, meaningful system of numbers, and there are many problems of great interest, some yet unsolved, involving only integers. However, this number system is still inadequate for all but the very simplest algebra. For instance, we cannot yet solve the equation $2x = 3$. It is time to adjoin some more numbers, to extend our system by including the fractions. To do this, for every integer c different from 0, we introduce a new number, c^{-1}, with the property that

$$c(c^{-1}) = (c^{-1})c = 1.$$

We call c^{-1} the *multiplicative inverse* of c. We can also write c^{-1} in the form $1/c$. Then every fraction, or ratio of two integers, p/q, with $q \neq 0$, can be considered as the product $p(q^{-1})$. It is clear that 0 cannot have a multiplicative inverse. If it did, $1/0$ would be a number such that $0(1/0) = 1$. Since the rational numbers obey all the algebraic laws of the integers, Theorem 1 holds in the rationals. Thus $a \cdot 0 = 0$ for every rational number a. Hence there is no number a such that $a \cdot 0 = 1$: 0 has no multiplicative inverse. It follows that division by 0 has no meaning in the rationals.

It is possible to extend the system of integers to the system of all ratios of integers, p/q, with $q \neq 0$, in such a way that the extended system satisfies all the laws for the integers and the following one.

> **M5. Multiplicative Inverse.** For every a in the set, except 0, there is a unique member a^{-1} such that
>
> $$a \cdot a^{-1} = a^{-1} \cdot a = 1.$$

The resulting number system is called the *rational number system*. The integers are represented in the rationals by the fractions whose denominators are 1. The positive numbers in the system of rationals consist of all numbers of the form p/q where p and q have the same sign. Now that the positive rationals have been specified, we can extend our order to this system. For rational numbers r_1 and r_2, $r_1 < r_2$ if and only if there is a positive rational number c such that $r_1 + c = r_2$. Since the integers correspond to the rational numbers whose denominators are 1, this ordering of the rational numbers preserves the ordering of the integers.

In the rationals, we find that a fraction may have many different representations. Let us find a condition that will permit us to identify two rational numbers that have different form.

So far, we have used parentheses rather liberally. Let us agree that the superscript -1 will apply only to the symbol immediately preceding it unless parentheses are used. Thus the inverse of ab must be written $(ab)^{-1}$, but ab^{-1} will mean $a(b^{-1})$. Now we are ready for our theorem.

Theorem 3.   *If $b \neq 0$, and $q \neq 0$, then $a/b = p/q$ if and only if $aq = bp$.*

Proof: Let us use the superscript notation.

$$
\begin{array}{ll}
ab^{-1} = pq^{-1} & \text{Given} \\
(ab^{-1})(bq) = (pq^{-1})(bq) & \text{E5} \\
(aq)(b^{-1}b) = (bp)(q^{-1}q) & \text{M2 and M3} \\
(aq)(1) = (bp)(1) & \text{M5} \\
aq = bp & \text{M4}
\end{array}
$$

To say that $a/b = p/q$ *if and only if* $aq = bp$ means that we must prove two things, that if $a/b = p/q$, then $aq = bp$, and if $aq = bp$, then $a/b = p/q$. We have proved only the first, but the steps are reversible. That is, if we assume $aq = bp$ as given, with neither b nor q zero, then we can write the steps in reverse order with a reason for each step.

$$
\begin{array}{ll}
aq = bp & \text{Given} \\
(aq)(1) = (bp)(1) & \text{M4} \\
(aq)(b^{-1}b) = (bp)(q^{-1}q) & \text{M5} \\
(ab^{-1})(bq) = (pq^{-1})(bq) & \text{M2 and M3} \\
ab^{-1} = pq^{-1} & \text{C2}
\end{array}
$$

There are three more simple theorems that we need in order to manipulate rational numbers easily.

Theorem 4.   *For any integers a and b that are different from zero,*

$$
\frac{1}{a}\frac{1}{b} = \frac{1}{ab}.
$$

Proof: We must show that $a^{-1}b^{-1} = (ab)^{-1}$.

$$\begin{aligned} (ab)(a^{-1}b^{-1}) &= (aa^{-1})(bb^{-1}) && \text{M2 and M3} \\ &= 1 \cdot 1 && \text{M5} \\ &= 1 && \text{M4} \end{aligned}$$

Thus $(a^{-1}b^{-1})$ is a multiplicative inverse of ab. By M5, such inverses are unique. Hence,

$$a^{-1}b^{-1} = (ab)^{-1}.$$

Theorem 5. *If b and d are integers different from zero,*

$$\frac{a}{b}\frac{c}{d} = \frac{ac}{bd}.$$

Proof: We must show that $(ab^{-1})(cd^{-1}) = (ac)(bd)^{-1}$.

$$\begin{aligned} (ab^{-1})(cd^{-1}) &= (ac)(b^{-1}d^{-1}) && \text{M2 and M3} \\ &= (ac)(bd)^{-1} && \text{Th. 4} \end{aligned}$$

We have shown that the product of two fractions is formed by multiplying the numerators and the denominators, respectively.

The addition of fractions is a more complicated process. The following theorem establishes and justifies the method for such an operation.

Theorem 6. *If b and d are integers different from zero,*

$$\frac{a}{b} + \frac{c}{d} = \frac{ad + bc}{bd}.$$

Proof: By M5, if n is any nonzero integer, $n/n = 1$. Since the rationals satisfy M4, no rational number is altered if multiplied by 1. Hence

$$\begin{aligned} \frac{a}{b} + \frac{c}{d} &= \left(\frac{a}{b}\right)\left(\frac{d}{d}\right) + \left(\frac{c}{d}\right)\left(\frac{b}{b}\right) && \text{M4} \\ &= \frac{ad}{bd} + \frac{bc}{bd} && \text{Th. 5 and M2} \\ &= ad\left(\frac{1}{bd}\right) + bc\left(\frac{1}{bd}\right) && \text{Definition} \\ &= (ad + bc)\left(\frac{1}{bd}\right) && \text{D} \\ &= \frac{ad + bc}{bd} && \text{Definition} \end{aligned}$$

2.18 ALGEBRAIC MANIPULATION

Much of the algebraic manipulation that we do is based on the fact that a quantity remains unchanged if zero is added to it or if it is multiplied by one. These are properties A4 and M4. Another highly useful operation is factoring out a common factor from a sum. This is property D, of course, and it is much used in work with fractions. In the following example a complex fraction is first simplified by being multiplied by 1 in the form 12/12, where 12 is the least common multiple of the individual denominators appearing in the complex fraction.

Example 1. Simplify

$$\frac{2/3 + 3/4}{5/3 - 1/2} + \frac{3}{14}.$$

$$\frac{2/3 + 3/4}{5/3 - 1/2} + \frac{3}{14} = \left(\frac{12}{12}\right)\frac{2/3 + 3/4}{5/3 - 1/2} + \frac{3}{14} \qquad \text{M4}\left(\frac{12}{12} = 1\right)$$

$$= \frac{12(2/3) + 12(3/4)}{12(5/3) - 12(1/2)} + \frac{3}{14} \qquad \text{D and Th. 5}$$

$$= \frac{8 + 9}{20 - 6} + \frac{3}{14} \qquad \text{M1}$$

$$= \frac{17}{14} + \frac{3}{14} = 17\left(\frac{1}{14}\right) + 3\left(\frac{1}{14}\right) \qquad \text{A1 and M1}$$

$$= (17 + 3)\left(\frac{1}{14}\right) \qquad \text{D}$$

$$= \frac{20}{14} = \frac{2 \cdot 10}{2 \cdot 7} \qquad \text{A1 and M1}$$

$$= \frac{2}{2}\frac{10}{7} = 1\left(\frac{10}{7}\right) = \frac{10}{7} \qquad \text{Th. 2 and M5}$$

We usually do problems of this sort in a much briefer manner by combining several steps in one, but the displayed steps of the example demonstrate that our laws are sufficient to justify every operation performed.

Example 2. Simplify the complex fraction.

$$1 + \cfrac{1}{1 + \cfrac{1}{1 + \cfrac{1}{3}}}$$

Work up from the bottom of it.

$$1 + \cfrac{1}{1 + \cfrac{1}{1 + \frac{1}{3}}} = 1 + \cfrac{1}{1 + \left(\cfrac{1}{1 + \frac{1}{3}}\right)\left(\frac{3}{3}\right)} \qquad \text{M4 } (3/3 = 1)$$

$$= 1 + \cfrac{1}{1 + \cfrac{3}{3 + 1}} \qquad \text{Th. 5 and D}$$

$$= 1 + \cfrac{1}{1 + \frac{3}{4}} \qquad \text{A1}$$

$$= 1 + \left(\cfrac{1}{1 + \frac{3}{4}}\right)\left(\frac{4}{4}\right) \qquad \text{M4 } (4/4 = 1)$$

$$= 1 + \frac{4}{4 + 3} \qquad \text{Th. 5 and D}$$

$$= 1 + \frac{4}{7} \qquad \text{A1}$$

$$= \frac{7}{7} + \frac{4}{7} \qquad \text{M5}$$

$$= \frac{11}{7} \qquad \text{D}$$

2.19 EXERCISES

*1. Solve $2x - 3 = 7$, giving a reason for each step.

2. Solve $3x + 2 = x - 5$, giving a reason for each step.

*3. What property permits factoring a common factor from a sum?

*4. Prove that the product of two nonzero rational numbers cannot be zero.

5. How is the property of Exercise 4 used in solving quadratic equations?

*6. Justify the identity, $x^2 - y^2 = (x + y)(x - y)$, using properties of rational numbers.

7. Simplify $\dfrac{1/2 - 1/3}{1/2 + 1/3}$.

8. Simplify $(x^{-1} + y^{-1})/(x^{-1} - y^{-1})$.

*9. Simplify $1/2 + 1/3 + 1/4 + 1/6$.

10. Simplify $1/2 - 1/3 + 1/4 - 1/6 + 1/24$.

*11. Prove that the rational numbers satisfy C2. Use only A1 to A5, M1 to M5, and D.

12. The positive rationals have been defined as the set of all nonzero rationals p/q where p and q have the same sign. Show that the product of any two positive rational numbers is positive.

*13. (a) Show that if r, s, and t are rational numbers with $r < s$ and $t > 0$, then $rt < st$.

(b) Show that if $r < s$ and $t < 0$, then $rt > st$.

(c) Show that if $0 < r < s$, then $0 < s^{-1} < r^{-1}$.

14. Find rational numbers satisfying each of the following:

(a) $(2x + 1)(3x - 2) = 0$

(b) $(3x - 5)(2x + 7) = 0$

*15. Find rational numbers satisfying each of the following:

(a) $2x^2 + 3x - 2 = 0$

(b) $2x^2 + x - 3 = 0$

2.20 FIELD

There are so many systems of mathematical objects that satisfy laws A1 through A5, M1 through M5, and D, that a special name is given to any such system. It is called a *field*. Since the rational numbers satisfy all of these laws and also T, which says there is an order relationship present, we say that the rational numbers form an *ordered field*. The natural numbers and the integers are ordered sets of numbers, but neither is a field because neither satisfies M5, which asserts the existence of a multiplicative inverse.

There are fields, however, that are not ordered. For instance, all integers can be divided into three classes, those that are divisible by 3, those that leave a remainder of 1 when divided by 3, and those that leave a remainder of 2 when divided by 3. Let us represent the first class by 0, the second by 1, and the third by 2. We can construct an arithmetic on these classes by giving their addition and multiplication tables. See Tables 1 and 2. The meaning

Table 1. (+)					Table 2. (·)		
	0	1	2			0	1	2

	0	1	2
0	0	1	2
1	1	2	0
2	2	0	1

	0	1	2
0	0	0	0
1	0	1	2
2	0	2	1

of these tables will now be made clear. Remember that the symbols 0, 1, and 2 are the names of classes of integers. We say that $2 + 2 = 1$ because if any two numbers of the form $3m + 2$ and $3n + 2$ are added, their sum is $3m + 3n + 4 = 3(m + n + 1) + 1$, which is a number in the class 1. The remainder is 1 when it is divided by 3. Similarly, since

$$(3m + 2)(3n + 2) = 9mn + 6m + 6n + 4 = 3(3mn + 2m + 2n + 1) + 1,$$

we find that $(2)(2) = 1$ in our arithmetic of classes. It is easy to show that the system represented by the three symbols 0, 1, and 2, with addition and multiplication as given in the tables, is a field. You will be asked to perform this demonstration in the next problem set.

Although our set of three elements forms a field, it is not ordered. To show this, let us suppose that 1 is positive, or $0 < 1$. Then, since $1 + 1 = 2$, it follows that $1 < 2$, so that 2 is also positive. However, since $1 + 2 = 0$, we have $1 < 0$, which contradicts our assumption that $0 < 1$. It turns out that no matter how we try to define an order relation in this system, the trichotomy law is violated.

2.21 ZERO AS A PRODUCT

An important property of a field is that the converse of Theorem 1 is true. That is, whenever a product of two field elements is zero, then at least one of the elements must be zero.

Theorem 7. . *In any field, if $ax = 0$ and $a \neq 0$, then $x = 0$.*

Proof:	$ax = 0$	Given
	$(a^{-1})ax = (a^{-1})0$	E5 (a^{-1} exists because $a \neq 0$.)
But	$(a^{-1})ax = (a^{-1}a)x = 1(x) = x$	M3, M5, and M4
and	$(a^{-1})0 = 0.$	Th. 1
Thus	$x = 0$	E4

2.22 CHECKING FIELD PROPERTIES

In the examples of the preceding sections we have been faced with the task of checking whether the field properties hold for a certain set of mathematical objects. In each case we were able to do this by examining whether a certain relationship holds in some set of numbers. For instance, where 0, 1, and 2 represent classes of integers leaving the corresponding remainders when divided by 3, we check the commutativity of multiplication by investigating whether $(3m + a)(3n + b) = (3n + b)(3m + a)$, where a and b are 0, 1, or 2. Since this last equation is a statement about integers, and we know that multiplication of any two integers is commutative, it follows that multiplication is commutative in our new system. We say in a case of this sort that the commutative property of multiplication is *inherited*. This holds true for commutativity and associativity of addition and multiplication and for the distributive property. On the other hand, it is necessary to check any property which states that an element of some kind exists or is in the system. Thus it is necessary to check for closure, identities, and inverses.

2.23 ALMOST A FIELD

Let us try again. This time let us put each integer into one of four classes, called 0, 1, 2, and 3, depending upon the remainder left after the integer is divided by 4. That is, every integer in class 0 is a multiple of 4, those in class 1 have the form $4n + 1$, those in class 2 have the form $4n + 2$, and those in class 3 have the form $4n + 3$. As before, we form the addition and multiplication tables for these classes. See Tables 3 and 4.

Table 3. (+)

	0	1	2	3
0	0	1	2	3
1	1	2	3	0
2	2	3	0	1
3	3	0	1	2

Table 4. (·)

	0	1	2	3
0	0	0	0	0
1	0	1	2	3
2	0	2	0	2
3	0	3	2	1

Since every entry in each table is one and only one of the symbols 0, 1, 2, or 3, this new system of four elements is closed under both addition and multiplication. Since both tables are symmetric with respect to the diagonal from upper left to lower right, both operations are commutative. (Why does this insure that the operations are commutative?) The associative and distributive laws can be verified by trying all possible cases or by showing that the property is inherited from the integers. Clearly, 0 is the identity for addition, and 1 is the identity for multiplication. Since there is a 0 in each row of the addition table, each element has an additive inverse. For instance, $1 + 3 = 0$ means that 3 is the additive inverse of 1, or $-1 = 3$. Similarly, $-3 = 1$. Since $2 + 2 = 0$, 2 is its own additive inverse, or $2 = -2$. From the multiplication table we find that

$$(1)(1) = 1 \quad \text{and} \quad (3)(3) = 1.$$

Thus each is its own multiplicative inverse. However, there is no element that can be multiplied by 2 to give 1. That is, 2 has no multiplicative inverse. We do not have a field, but we came close. Observe that even though this system is quite similar to a field, Theorem 7 does not hold for it. In this system 2 is not equal to zero, but $2 \cdot 2 = 0$.

We have seen that the system of three elements yields a field, but the system of four elements does not. In the problems you will be asked to ponder this strange situation. The mathematician worries about such things. What property does the number 3 have that makes it differ from 4 in this respect?

The mathematical importance of the field is that it is precisely the field properties that are used in basic algebraic manipulation.

Although we shall not discuss complex numbers in this course, they provide another example of a field that is not ordered.

2.24 EXERCISES

*1. Verify that the set of three elements given in the text $\{0, 1, 2\}$, satisfies all the properties of a field.

2. Divide all integers into two classes. Let 0 represent all even integers, and let 1 represent all odd integers.
    (a) Construct addition and multiplication tables for the set $\{0, 1\}$, just as was done for the set $\{0, 1, 2\}$ in the text.
    (b) Verify that this simple system is actually a field.

3. Place all integers in classes denoted by 0, 1, 2, 3, or 4, depending on the remainder left after division by 5.
    (a) Construct addition and multiplication tables for the set.
    (b) Is the resulting system a field? Give your reasons.

*4. Place all integers in classes denoted by 0, 1, 2, 3, 4, or 5, depending on the remainder left after division by 6.
    (a) Construct addition and multiplication tables for the set.
    (b) Is the resulting system a field? Give your reasons.

*5. Try to suggest a reason for the fact that systems of two, three, or five elements give fields but systems of four or six elements do not.

6. Consider the set of all rational numbers whose denominators are powers of 2. Do they form a field? Notice that the set contains all integers because $n = n/1 = n/(2^0)$.

*7. In the set of classes of Exercise 3, find
    (a) the additive inverses of 1, 2, 3, and 4;
    (b) the multiplicative inverses of 2, 3, and 4.

8. In the set of classes of Exercise 4, find
    (a) the additive inverses of 1, 2, 3, 4, and 5;
    (b) the multiplicative inverses of those classes possessing such inverses.

9. Let us extend the rational numbers by appending a new number i. Consider the set of all numbers of the form $a + bi$ for rational a and b where addition and multiplication are defined below for arbitrary rational numbers a, b, c, and d:

$$(a + bi) + (c + di) = a + c + (b + d)i$$
$$(a + bi)(c + di) = ac - bd + (ad + bc)i$$

Also, $0 + 0i = 0,\ a + 0i = a,$ and $1i = i$

Prove that the set is a field.

*10. In the set of Exercise 9, find
  (a) the additive inverses of $2 + 3i$ and $4 - 5i$;
  (b) the multiplicative inverses of $2 + 3i$ and $4 - 5i$.

2.25 THE REAL NUMBERS

In this chapter we have seen that there is a fairly straight path leading from the simple garden of the natural numbers through the integers to the broad field of the rational numbers. In this nicely ordered field we carry out most of our elementary algebra. We can solve simultaneous equations. We are complete masters of the linear equation (first-degree). We have the number system used for all measurements in the physical world. Is there any point in going on? The answer is certainly in the affirmative. We have seen that it is highly desirable to be able to study geometry from an algebraic standpoint. For this we must have a one-to-one correspondence between numbers and points on a line, and the rational numbers are not adequate for the job. Suppose that we set up a coordinate system with points represented by ordered pairs of rational numbers. We can construct a circle with center at the origin that passes through the point $(1, 1)$. The equation of this circle is $x^2 + y^2 = 2$. Where does the circle intersect the x-axis? At the point of intersection, $y = 0$, so that $x^2 = 2$. But there is *no* rational number whose square is 2. Hence, in this coordinate system the circle does not intersect the x-axis. This deplorable situation comes about because our rational number system does not contain enough numbers. Even putting in all numbers expressible by radical signs is not enough, for we still would be unable to assign a number to the exact circumference of a circle of radius 1.

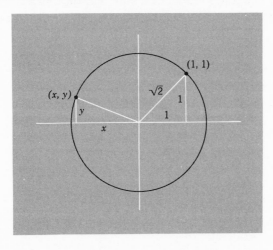

It is no longer as simple to extend our number system as it was before. Our goal is to have a number system such that every length corresponds to a number. In other words, we must be able to establish a one-to-one correspondence between the points on a line and numbers of the system. The system that makes this possible is called the *real number system*.

There are several ways to accomplish this goal. The one that we shall use approaches the real numbers through the concept of upper bounds.

2.26 UPPER BOUNDS AND LEAST UPPER BOUNDS

A set of numbers is said to be *bounded above* if there exists some number b that is not exceeded by any member of the set. That is, if x is any number in the set, then $x \leq b$. We call b an *upper bound* to the set. For example, let S be the set $\{1, 2, 3, 4, 5\}$. Acceptable upper bounds to S are 10, 123, 15, 7, 5, 1000, 5.237, and 2π. Clearly, *any* number that is not smaller than 5 is an upper bound. But 4 is not an upper bound because we can find an element of the set, 5, which exceeds 4. Of all upper bounds, the smallest is 5.

We shall call a number a *least upper bound* of a set if

1. it is an upper bound, and
2. no other upper bound is smaller.

It is possible that a set has no upper bound. For instance, let S be the set of all even integers. Then S is not bounded above.

If a set of numbers has only finitely many elements, the least upper bound is easily found. All that need be done is to compare each element with the others until the largest is found. In a finite set, then, the least upper bound must be a member of the set. On the other hand, if a set has infinitely many members, it is possible that no member of the set is an upper bound. For example, consider a set consisting of infinitely many rational numbers, the set of all numbers of the form $n/(n + 1)$ where n assumes the value of every natural number. The set then contains $1/2, 2/3, 3/4, 4/5, \ldots, 87/88$, and so forth. If we divide n by $n + 1$, we find that

$$\frac{n}{n + 1} = 1 - \frac{1}{n + 1}.$$

Since $1/(n + 1)$ is positive, this says that every member of the set is less than 1, or 1 is an upper bound. Now let us show that no number less than 1 can be an upper bound. If r is any positive number less than 1, then $1 - r$ is a positive number, as is $r/(1 - r)$. Since there are integers larger than any given positive number, let n be an integer such that

$$n > \frac{r}{1-r}.$$

Then

$$n - nr > r, \quad \text{or} \quad n > nr + r, \quad \text{or} \quad n > r(n+1), \quad \text{or} \quad \frac{n}{n+1} > r.$$

That is, if r is any number smaller than 1, there is an integer n such that $n/(n+1)$ is larger than r. Thus r is *not* an upper bound of the set. We have shown two things:

1. 1 is an upper bound of the set, and
2. no number less than 1 is an upper bound of the set.

From these two statements we can conclude that 1 is the least upper bound of our set. We should observe that in this example the least upper bound of the set is not actually a member of the set. Hence the least upper bound of a given set may or may not belong to the set.

Because of its importance and its elegance, let us recall the proof that $\sqrt{2}$ is not a rational number. We note the following facts:

1. Every integer is either odd or even.
2. If an integer is even, it is of the form $2n$. Then its square is $4n^2$. That is, the square of an even integer is a multiple of 4.
3. If an integer is odd, it is of the form $2n + 1$. Then its square is of the form $4n^2 + 4n + 1$, which is odd. That is, the square of an odd integer is odd.
4. By (2) and (3), if a square is even it is the square of an even integer, and if a square is odd, it is the square of an odd integer.
5. Every rational number can be expressed as a ratio of two integers with no common factor greater than one. In such a ratio, either the numerator or the denominator (or both) must be odd.

Now let us assume that $\sqrt{2}$ is a rational number. We shall show that this assumption leads to a contradiction. If $\sqrt{2}$ is rational, we can write it as p/q in simplest form where, by (5), either p or q is odd. But if $\sqrt{2} = p/q$, then $q\sqrt{2} = p$. If two numbers are equal, their squares are equal, or $2q^2 = p^2$. Thus p^2 is even. By (4), it follows that p is even, so that there is an integer n such that $p = 2n$, or $p^2 = 4n^2$. It then follows that $2q^2 = 4n^2$, or $q^2 = 2n^2$. By (4), again, we find that q is even, which contradicts our assumption that p or q is odd. Hence $\sqrt{2}$ cannot be expressed as a ratio of integers. We say that $\sqrt{2}$ is irrational.

Let S be the set of all rational numbers whose squares are not greater than 2. This set includes 0, 1, and 1.4, but it does not include 1.5, whose square is 2.25. Thus S is bounded above by 1.5. We can find a smaller upper bound by arithmetic trial. We find that $1.41^2 = 1.9881$, so 1.41 is not an upper bound, but, since $1.42^2 = 2.0164$, 1.42 is an upper bound. By more arithmetic effort we can find that there is an upper bound somewhere between 1.414 and 1.415. Does S have a least upper bound? What is it? It can be shown that no rational number can possibly be a least upper bound of S. In fact, we have a method, presented in a later section, that will permit us to use *any* rational upper bound to the set to find another rational upper bound that is smaller. We conclude, then, that if S has a least upper bound it cannot be a rational number.

We are now ready to extend our rational number system to a larger system in which there are no "missing points" on the number line.

2.27 COMPLETENESS AND THE REAL NUMBERS

A set of numbers is said to be *complete* if every nonempty subset that is bounded above has a least upper bound in the set.

We now define the *real numbers* to be a *complete, ordered field*. It is possible to define the real numbers in this way because there is only one ordered field that is complete, a fact we shall not prove here. What we have done, effectively, is to take the ordered field of rational numbers and adjoin all least upper bounds of subsets that are bounded above. In this way the set of rational numbers whose squares are less than 2 now has a least upper bound, $\sqrt{2}$, in the real numbers, even though it has no least upper bound in the rationals. The latter fact demonstrates that the rational numbers are *not* complete.

For another example, consider the circle of diameter 1. The circumference of this circle is denoted by the symbol π. Let us inscribe a square in the circle and circumscribe another square about the circle. The circumference of the circle is a number lying between the perimeter of the inscribed square and that of the circumscribed square. The circumscribed square clearly has a perimeter of 4, and it can be shown that the inscribed square has a perimiter of $2\sqrt{2}$. Thus, since π is the length of the circle,

$$2\sqrt{2} < \pi < 4.$$

The vertices of the inscribed square divide the circle into four arcs. If each of these is bisected we obtain eight points that form the vertices of a regular

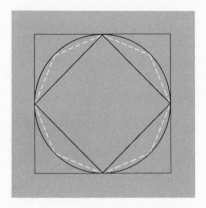

octagon. The perimeter of this octagon is greater than that of the inscribed square but less than the length of the circle. If the eight arcs are again bisected, a regular polygon of sixteen sides can be formed whose perimeter is greater than that of the octagon but still less than the circle. In this way we get a sequence of numbers that are increasing but certainly bounded above by 4, the perimeter of the circumscribed square. The least upper bound of this set is the circumference of the circle, or π, and the process given here was used by Archimedes in the second century B.C. to obtain an approximation to π that was remarkably good.

Finally, let us consider a line on which there is a reference point, labeled 0. If the line is horizontal, select a point a convenient distance to the right of the reference point and label it 1. We shall call the line segment from 0 to 1 the "unit interval." By an elementary geometric construction we can construct a line segment whose length is any rational multiple of the length of the unit interval. If r is any rational number, construct a line segment whose length is r times the length of the unit interval and lay it off along the line from 0 to the right if r is positive, to the left if r is negative. Label the point r. In this way we have assigned a point on the line to each rational number, and if r_1 and r_2 are rational numbers with $r_1 < r_2$, then the point labeled r_1 lies to the left of the point labeled r_2. There are points on the line that remain unlabeled. One such point is obtained by constructing the diagonal of a square whose sides are formed by copies of the unit interval. We have proved earlier that the length of this diagonal is $\sqrt{2}$ times the length of the unit interval and that $\sqrt{2}$ is not a rational number. Hence, if the diagonal of the square is laid off from 0, the resulting point on the line is not represented by one of our rational numbers. Now let p be any point on the line. Let r be any rational number corresponding to a point to the right of p. Let S be the set of all rational numbers that are labels of points to the left of p. Then

r is an upper bound to the set S, and S is not empty. By the completeness property, S has a least upper bound, which is a real number. If this real number is denoted by p, we have demonstrated that there is a one-to-one correspondence between the set of all real numbers and the set of all points on a line. That is, the real numbers can be used to assign a length to every line segment. Thus our goal has been reached in a satisfactory manner. The field properties permit us to do our ordinary algebra, and the completeness and order properties permit us to apply real numbers in the study of geometry.

2.28 EXERCISES

1. Prove that $\sqrt{2}$ is irrational without referring to the text.
2. Prove that $\sqrt{3}$ is irrational.
*3. Using the fact that $\sqrt{2}$ is irrational, prove that $3 + \sqrt{2}$ is irrational.
4. Using the fact that $\sqrt{3}$ is irrational, prove that $a + b\sqrt{3}$ is irrational, where a and b are rational numbers with $b \neq 0$.
*5. Consider the set of rational numbers corresponding to lengths along the diagonal of a square three units on a side. What is the least upper bound of this set?
6. Consider the set of rational numbers corresponding to lengths along a diagonal of a cube, one unit on a side. What is the least upper bound of this set?
*7. Consider the set of numbers representing the area of regular polygons inscribed in a circle of radius 4. What is the least upper bound of this set?
8. What is the least upper bound of the set $1/3, 2/5, 3/7, \ldots, n/(2n + 1), \ldots$?
*9. What is the least upper bound of the set $1/5, 2/8, 3/11, \ldots, n/(3n + 2), \ldots$?
10. What is the least upper bound of the set of all rational numbers whose cubes are less than 4?
*11. (a) Prove that the set of all numbers of the form $a + b\sqrt{2}$ with a and b rational form a field.
    (b) In this field, what is the reciprocal of $5 + 3\sqrt{2}$? Express your answer in the form $a + b\sqrt{2}$.
12. What goes wrong if we attempt to use the procedure of the text to prove that $\sqrt{4}$ is irrational?
*13. If a nonempty set S of real numbers is bounded above, prove that the set of negatives of the elements of S is bounded below.
14. Prove that every nonempty set of real numbers that is bounded below has a greatest lower bound (a lower bound that is larger than any other lower bound).
*15. Find the greatest lower bound of the set $\{3, -1, 2, 5, -3, 7\}$.
16. Find the least upper bound and greatest lower bound of the set of all reciprocals of natural numbers.

*17. Find the least upper bound and greatest lower bound of the set of numbers of the form $(2n + 1)/(3n - 2)$ where n is a natural number.

2.29 DENSENESS

In the system of natural numbers and in the system of integers it is possible for two numbers to be "next" to each other. For example, 3 and 4 are successive integers. By that we mean that there is no integer between them. As rational numbers, however, $7/2$ is a rational number such that $3 < 7/2 < 4$. Moreover, the average of 3 and $7/2$ is $13/4$, and $3 < 13/4 < 7/2 < 4$. Since for any distinct rational numbers a and b, their average, $(a + b)/2$, lies between a and b, we can continue our process to find as many rational numbers as we please between 3 and 4. In fact, we can find as many rational numbers as we please between *any* two rationals, no matter how little they differ from each other. If any set of numbers has this property, we say that the set is *dense in itself*. If we consider the rationals as points on a number line, then between any two distinct points on the line there are infinitely many rational points. Since the points on the line correspond exactly to the real numbers, we say that the rationals are *dense in the reals*. The importance of this is that if x is any real number and d is any number, real or rational, no matter how small, there is a rational number r such that

$$x - d < r < x + d.$$

That is, there is a rational r that differs from x by less than d, no matter how small d is. This is what we mean when we say that any real number can be "approximated" by rationals. This is also the reason that any length can be represented by a rational number, not exactly but as accurately as the occasion demands.

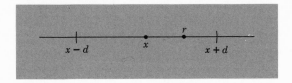

2.30 RATIONAL APPROXIMATIONS

The decimal expansion of every rational number displays a repetitive pattern from some point on. For instance, $1/4$ can be written as $.250\cdots$

with 0's forever after, or as .249··· with 9's continued without end. The number 2/3 can be written as .666··· with the 6's continued forever. We find that every rational number, when written as a decimal, repeats some pattern of digits from some point on. Conversely, every decimal pattern of this sort represents a rational number. What does that leave for the irrationals? They must be precisely the numbers which, when expressed as decimals, do not repeat any pattern. How do we use such numbers in computation? For instance, suppose that I have been hired to paint a circular disk 6 feet in diameter. We have a formula that asserts that the area is πr^2. Thus the area is 9π. How much is that? If I am to be paid one dollar per square foot for painting the circle, how much should I be paid? Obviously, we must make some rational approximation to π. The earliest known approximation, one that appears in the Bible, incidentally, is 3. Many of us learned the approximation 22/7. Later we may have learned 3.1416. If we go to a standard book of tables we find π given as 3.14159265358979323846. Each of these is a better approximation than the preceding. Also, we know about how much error we are making if we choose any one of them. For instance, 3.1416 is within .00005 of the correct value of π. The error involved in using the 20-place approximation is less than 5 preceded by 20 zeros. For the purpose of paying the painter, we need an approximation good enough so that the pay can be computed to the nearest cent.

There are algorithms, procedures of computation, for approximating any irrational number to as many places as we please. In Chapter 1 it was mentioned that one such algorithm was probably used by the Babylonians to approximate square roots. If k is a positive number, then its square root satisfies the equation $x^2 = k$, or $x = k/x$. Suppose that x_1 is a guess. If x_1 is larger than $\sqrt{k}$, then k/x_1 is smaller than $\sqrt{k}$, and vice versa. A better approximation is given by the average of x_1 and k/x_1. Let us call the new approximation x_2. Then

$$x_2 = \frac{x_1 + k/x_1}{2}.$$

This process can now be repeated. Each succeeding approximation will be correct to about twice as many decimal places as its predecessor. Such methods of approximation are called *recursive*. Recursive methods are used in a wide area of computation.

Example 1. A recursive formula for computing the cube root of a number k is given by

$$x_{n+1} = \frac{1}{3}\left(2x_n + \frac{k}{x_n^2}\right).$$

Let us use this to approximate $\sqrt[3]{7}$. Let $x_1 = 2$. Then,

$$x_2 = \frac{4 + 7/4}{3} = \frac{23}{12} = 1.9166\cdots$$

$$x_3 = \frac{\dfrac{23}{6} + \dfrac{7}{529/144}}{3} = \frac{18,215}{9,522} = 1.912938\cdots$$

Tables give the value of $\sqrt[3]{7}$ to six decimal places as 1.912931.

What is worthy of note is that the rational numbers serve to approximate irrational numbers *as closely as we please*. Our processes produce a string of numbers, all rationals, getting closer and closer to the unattainable true value, unattainable in finite decimal expansion form. Consider the sequence of rational approximations 1, 1.4, 1.41, 1.414, 1.4142, 1.41421, ... This sequence can be continued to get us as close as we like to $\sqrt{2}$. Thus we may observe that here is another possible approach to the definition of the real numbers. We could define the real numbers as the set of numbers that can be expressed as infinite decimals. For example, $\sqrt{2}$ is the number obtained if we suppose that one of the algorithms for extracting square roots is applied to 2 endlessly. The rational number $1/3$ can be expressed as $.333\cdots$, where the 3's continue without end. In this form the rational numbers are characterized by the presence of a pattern of digits that repeats forever, whereas the irrational numbers have no such pattern. As we have seen earlier, the infinite decimal representation is not unique for some rational numbers. Numbers that can be expressed as terminating decimals can also be expressed in a form that repeats the digit 9. In order to explore the decimal representation of numbers more thoroughly we would need to know more about infinite sequences, infinite series, and limits than falls within the scope of this text.

2.31 EXERCISES

*1. If it costs $1 per square foot to paint a circle 6 feet in diameter, what approximation to π must be used to determine the cost to the nearest cent?

2. If it costs $1 per square foot to paint a circle 100 feet in diameter, what approximation to π must be used to determine the cost to the nearest cent?

*3. A gold chain, costing $2 per inch, is to join two opposite vertices of a square 3 feet on a side. How much will it cost, to the nearest cent, and what approximation to $\sqrt{2}$ is required to compute the cost?

4. A silver chain, costing $1.50 per inch, is to join two opposite vertices of a cube

10 feet on a side. How much will it cost, to the nearest cent, and what approximation to $\sqrt{3}$ is required to compute the cost?

5. Consider the set of numbers: 3, 3.1, 3.14, 3.141, . . . , in the expansion of π. Give an upper bound to this set. What is the least upper bound?

*6. Show that the least upper bound to the sequence 0.9, 0.99, 0.999, . . . is 1.

*7. What is the smallest real number greater than zero?

8. If a set of real numbers is bounded below, must it have a greatest lower bound? Prove it.

*9. A frog jumps 1 yard in his first jump, 1/2 yard in his second jump, and half the length of the preceding jump in each jump thereafter. Is the total distance he covers bounded? If so, what is the least upper bound?

10. Approximate $\sqrt{2}$ by making two applications of the recursive method using $x_1 = 7/5$.

*11. Approximate $\sqrt{3}$ by making two applications of the recursive method using $x_1 = 9/5$.

2.32 RECOMMENDED READING

Birkhoff, G., and MacLane, S., *A Survey of Modern Algebra*, New York, Macmillan, 1949.

Fine, N. J., *Introduction to Modern Mathematics*, Skokie, Ill., Rand McNally, 1965.

Fujii, J. N., *An Introduction to the Elements of Mathematics*, New York, Wiley, 1961.

Hafstrom, J. E., *Basic Concepts in Modern Mathematics*, Reading, Mass., Addison-Wesley, 1961.

Landau, E., *Foundations of Analysis*, New York, Chelsea Publishing Co., 1951.

McCoy, N. H., *Introduction to Modern Algebra*, Boston, Allyn and Bacon, 1960.

Peterson, J. A., and Hashisaki, J., *Theory of Arithmetic*, 2nd ed., New York, Wiley, 1967.

Rose, I. H., *A Modern Introduction to College Mathematics*, New York, Wiley, 1959.

Whitesitt, J. E., *Principles of Modern Algebra*, Reading, Addison-Wesley, 1964.

3

Chess, a game of logic.

3.1 FROM THE CONCRETE TO THE ABSTRACT AND BACK AGAIN

A certain pattern is apparent in nearly all significant mathematics. First, observation shows certain relationships holding among the members of a set of objects in the physical world. These relationships are examined and formalized. Next, the mathematician sets up an abstract system based on postulates and undefined terms, an abstract system that is a model of the physical system previously investigated. In this abstraction symbols are introduced and theorems proved. Then, if the mathematics is indeed significant, the theorems shed light on the original physical system and show how it is related to other systems that had been apparently quite dissimilar. In most such developments the second, or abstract, step involves extensive mathematical training. However, there is one typical development that is easily accessible to anyone with a minimum of mathematical preparation. In this we start with the observed relationships among sets. These sets can be arbitrary collections of any sort—people, continents, points, numbers, sentences, lines—anything we please. We shall discuss only sets that are clearly defined, those in which it is always possible to determine whether a given object does or does not belong to the set. From the relationships among sets we shall proceed to develop an abstract system called Boolean algebra. We shall discover a number of simple theorems and techniques of computation in this algebra. Finally, we shall show that Boolean algebra gives us information about investigating the truth or falsity of logical statements and, surprisingly, about designing electronic or mechanical switching circuits.

3.2 SETS

Let us begin by considering certain sets of points in a plane. The reason for this is that we can draw pictures to represent our sets, and this may help

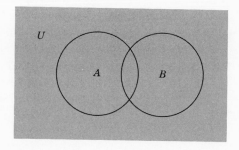

our intuition. We shall denote our sets by capital letters. For the most part we shall limit our attention to the subsets of some given set, which we shall call the *universal set*, denoted by U. U may be the entire plane or merely some part of it. U may even consist of only a finite number of points. If every element of a set P is also an element of a set Q, we shall say that P is a *subset* of Q and write $P \subset Q$.

In general, if A and B are subsets of U, we may have a picture like the one shown. The sets A and B may or may not overlap. Our procedure is to search out relationships, to find sets that are determined in some way by other sets, and to establish a notation for these relationships.

3.3 EQUALITY OF SETS

We shall write $A = B$ if A is a subset of B and B is a subset of A. That is, every element of A is an element of B, and every element of B is an element of A.

3.4 UNION

Given A and B, what other sets can we build from them? One obvious set is that of all points belonging to A or B or both. Let us denote this new set by $A + B$ and call it the *union* of A and B.

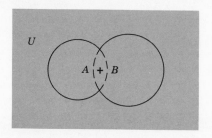

Let us digress for a moment. If a class of students is the universal set, let A be the set of all students with black hair, and let B be the set of students wearing white shoes. From these sets we obtain another set, $A + B$, the set of students who have black hair or are wearing white shoes (or both).

We now have an operation on sets, denoted by $+$. Given any two sets, their union is also an acceptable set contained in the universe. The $+$ of union is certainly not the plus of arithmetic, and we shouldn't expect it to behave in the same way. For instance, what set is defined by $A + A$? This is the set of all points in A or in A. That is, $A + A = A$, itself. If an operation defined on a set of elements has the property that every element in the set when combined with itself yields the element itself, the operation is said to be *idempotent*. Thus union is an idempotent operation on sets. Also, no matter what set A is, we always have $A + U = U$.

Despite the differences between the set operation of union and arithmetic addition, there are certain similarities. For example, for every pair of subsets A and B of a universe U, $A + B$ is a subset of U. That is, the subsets of U are *closed* under union. Obviously, $A + B$ and $B + A$ denote the same set. Hence, union is *commutative*. If A, B, and C are any three subsets of U, then $A + (B + C)$ and $(A + B) + C$ denote precisely the same set, the set of all points in at least one of A, B, and C. Consequently, the operation of union is *associative*. Is there an identity for union? That is, is there a set whose union with A, no matter what set A is, yields A as a result? In other words, is there a set, which we shall denote by $\varnothing$, such that $A + \varnothing = A$ for every A? It is clear that $\varnothing$ must be contained in A. Since A is arbitrary, $\varnothing$ must be contained in every set. But for a given set A, the set of points not in A, called the *complement* of A, is also a perfectly good set. What set is contained in A and also in the complement of A? No set that has any elements in it satisfies such a condition. However, suppose we define a certain set of boys, all those in the United States who are over ten feet tall and have purple hair. Then, given any boy in the United States, we can tell immediately whether he belongs to our set. Consequently, we have a perfectly good set. It just happens not to have any members. In our universe U there is a perfectly good subset, which we shall denote by $\varnothing$, that has no points in it. We shall call $\varnothing$ the *null set* or the *empty set*. Since $A + \varnothing = A$ for every A in U, the null set is the *identity* for the set operation of union.

3.5 EXERCISES

*1. Under what conditions is a set clearly defined?

2. If A is the set of distinct letters found in the word WESTERN,

B is the set of distinct letters found in the word WASHINGTON,

C is the set of distinct letters found in the word STATE, and

D is the set of distinct letters found in the word COLLEGE,

list the elements in the following sets:

*(a) $A + B$ (b) $A + C$ *(c) $A + D$ (d) $B + C$

*(e) $B + D$ (f) $C + D$ *(g) $A + A$ (h) $(A + B) + (C + D)$

3. With A, B, C, and D as in Exercise 2, find $A + (B + C)$ and $(A + B) + C$ and verify that they are the same.

*4. List all subsets of C of Exercise 2.

5. (a) How many subsets does a set of 1 element have?

(b) How many subsets does a set of 2 elements have?

(c) How many subsets does a set of 3 elements have?

(d) How many subsets does a set of 4 elements have?

*6. From Exercise 5, make a conjecture about the number of subsets of a set of n elements and prove your conjecture by mathematical induction.

7. List the algebraic properties of the set operation of union over all subsets of some universe U. (Closure, commutativity, etc.)

8. Shade in the indicated sets.

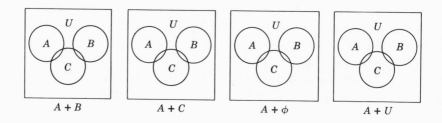

$A + B$ $A + C$ $A + \phi$ $A + U$

Problem 8

*9. What set is a subset of every set?

10. Every set is a subset of what set?

*11. If $A + B = A + C$, is it necessarily true that $B = C$? If so, prove it. If not, produce a counterexample.

3.6 INTERSECTION

Let us return to our two subsets A and B. Other than $A + B$, is there any other set that is determined by A and B? One such set is the collection of all elements that are contained in both A and B, their overlap. This set will be denoted by multiplication, AB, and will be called the *intersection* of A and B. Of course, if A and B are disjoint (don't overlap), then $AB = \varnothing$.

Example 1. If *A* is the set of natural numbers and *B* is the set of all real numbers less than 8, then *AB* is the set of natural numbers less than 8.

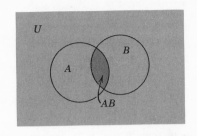

Example 2. If *A* is the set of points in one plane and *B* is the set of points in another plane, then *AB* is the set of all points in the line of intersection of the planes. If $AB = \varnothing$, the planes are parallel.

Let us parallel our previous treatment of set union, but, instead of carrying out a complete argument, let us merely list our results. The student should examine the following statements carefully to convince himself of the validity of each.

1. $AA = A$ for every set *A*, or intersection is *idempotent*.
2. For every *A* and *B* in *U*, *AB* is a well-defined set. Thus, the subsets of *U* are *closed* under intersection.
3. Since $AB = BA$, intersection is *commutative*.
4. Since $A(BC) = (AB)C$, intersection is *associative*.
5. Since $AU = A$ for every *A*, *U* is the *identity* for intersection.

3.7 DISTRIBUTIVE LAWS

Is there anything like a distributive law in our algebra of sets? Let us consider $A(B + C)$. The set so represented must contain those elements that are in *A* and in either *B* or *C* or both. That is, the elements must be in *AB* (both *A* and *B*) or in *AC* (both *A* and *C*). In other words,

$$A(B + C) = AB + AC,$$

and it is true that intersection distributes over union in the algebra of sets.

But let us continue. What can you say about the points in $A + BC$? By $A + BC$ we mean the union of *A* with the intersection of *B* and *C*. This is the set of all elements that are either in *A* or in both *B* and *C*. Let us draw a picture. The shaded area represents $A + BC$. Notice that this region is contained in $A + B$ and also in $A + C$. In fact it is the intersection of $A + B$ and

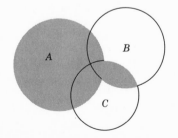

$A + C$. That is,

$$A + BC = (A + B)(A + C).$$

Compare this statement with the previous distributive property,

$$A(B + C) = AB + AC.$$

It is exactly the same except that every occurrence of union or intersection has been replaced by the opposite operation. In the algebra of sets, not only does intersection distribute over union, it is also true that union distributes over intersection.

> **Example 1.** If A is the set of all Australians, B is the set of all Belgians, and C is the set of all people called Charles, then $(A + B)(A + C)$ is the set of all people who are either Australians or Belgians and who are either Australians or are named Charles. This set consists of all Australians and all those who, if they are not Australians, must be Belgians named Charles. That is, we have verified in this case that $(A + B)(A + C) = A + BC$.

3.8 EXERCISES

1. If A is the set of distinct letters in the word WESTERN,
    B is the set of distinct letters in the word WASHINGTON,
    C is the set of distinct letters in the word STATE, and
    D is the set of distinct letters in the word COLLEGE,
   list the elements in the following sets:

   *(a) AB (b) AC *(c) AD (d) BC
   *(e) BD (f) CD *(g) AA (h) $(AB)C$
   *(i) $A(BC)$ (j) $(BC)D$ *(k) $ABCD$ (l) $(A + B)(C + D)$

2. For the sets of Exercise 1, verify that

   (a) $A(B + C) = AB + AC$ (b) $AD + CD = (A + C)D$
   (c) $A + AB = A$ (d) $C + AC = C$
   (e) $B + CD = (B + C)(B + D)$ (f) $B(C + D) = BC + BD$

3. List the algebraic properties of set intersection over all subsets of some universe U.

*4. Prove that A is a subset of B if and only if $AB = A$.

5. Shade in the indicated sets.

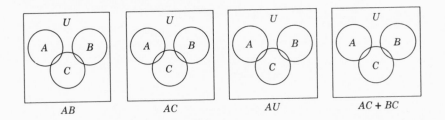

Exercise 5

*6. If $AB = AC$, is it necessarily true that $B = C$? If so, prove it. If not, produce a counterexample.

*7. Let X be the set of all points on a line. Let Y be the set of all points on another line. Describe the intersection of the lines as a set in terms of X and Y.

8. Let C be the set of students taking this course, A the set of students who are on an athletic team, and D the set of students living in dormitories. Describe in words the following sets:

   (a) $C(A + D)$ (b) $A(C + D)$ (c) $C(AD)$ (d) $C + AD$.

*9. If $AB + CD = \varnothing$, what do you know about sets A, B, C, and D?

10. If $(A + B)(C + D) = U$, what do you know about sets A, B, C, and D?

3.9   COMPLEMENT

The complement of any set A was briefly defined as the set of all elements of U that are not in A. Since the complement plays an important role in sets and in the Boolean algebra we shall develop shortly, let us examine it more closely. Let us denote the complement of A by A'. Then $A + A' = U$ and $AA' = \varnothing$, for every point of U is either in A or not in A, and no point is in both A and the complement of A. Since the complement of any set is a well-defined set, we can consider complementation to be an operation on single sets.

What would the complement of A' be? $(A')'$ is the set of all elements that are not outside A, hence are the elements of A itself. Thus

$$(A')' = A.$$

Next, what set is $(A + B)'$? The members of this set are those that are neither in A nor in B. That is, they belong to A' and to B', hence to $A'B'$, or

$$(A + B)' \subset A'B'.$$

Similarly, any element of $A'B'$ is outside A and outside B, hence outside $A + B$, and thus inside $(A + B)'$. That is,

$$A'B' \subset (A + B)'.$$

Since $(A + B)'$ and $A'B'$ are each contained in the other, they are equal.

Our use of parentheses is similar to that in Chapter 2. That is, the complement of AB must be written with parentheses, $(AB)'$. AB' means the intersection of A with the complement of B.

Finally, what set is $(AB)'$? The members of this set are precisely those elements that are not common to both A and B. That is, they comprise the set of elements that are outside A or outside B. Briefly,

$$(AB)' = A' + B'.$$

Example 1. Let U be the set of natural numbers, and let A be the set of even natural numbers. Then A' is the set of odd natural numbers.

Example 2. As before, let U be the set of natural numbers, and let A be the set of even natural numbers. Let B be the set of natural numbers that are multiples of 3, so that B' is the set of all natural numbers not divisible by 3. Then AB is the set of natural numbers that are both even and multiples of 3. That is, AB is the set of all multiples of 6, and $(AB)'$ is the set of all natural numbers that are not divisible by 6. In fact the members of $(AB)'$ are either odd (in A') or not divisible by 3 (in B') or both. Hence $(AB)' = A' + B'$.

3.10 SET INCLUSION

If $A \subset B$, then every element of A is an element of B, so that $A + B = B$. Conversely, if $A + B = B$, then A can have no element that is not already in B. Hence $A \subset B$. We have shown that $A \subset B$ if and only if $A + B = B$. By precisely the same sort of argument we can show that $A \subset B$ if and only if $AB = A$. What other properties hold for set inclusion? Let us list some of the more obvious ones.

1. $A \subset A$. Every set is contained in itself.
2. If $A \subset B$ and $B \subset A$, then $A = B$.

3. If $A \subset B$ and $B \subset C$, then $A \subset C$.
4. If $A \subset B$ and $A \subset C$, then $A \subset BC$ and $A \subset B + C$.
5. If $A \subset B$ and $C \subset D$, then $A + C \subset B + D$ and $AC \subset BD$.
6. The following statements are all equivalent:

$$A \subset B, \quad A + B = B, \quad AB = A, \quad B' \subset A', \quad AB' = \varnothing, \quad A' + B = U.$$

All of these properties follow very simply from the definitions of the symbols involved.

> **Example.** Let U be the set of natural numbers from 1 to 10. Let
> $A = \{2, 4\}, \quad B = \{2, 4, 6, 8\}, \quad C = \{2, 3, 4, 8, 10\}, \quad$ and
> $$D = \{1, 2, 3, 4\}.$$

1. $A \subset B$ since every number in A is also in B. Similarly,

$$A \subset C.$$

2. Since $BC = \{2, 4, 8\}$ and $B + C = \{2, 3, 4, 6, 8, 10\}$,

$$A \subset BC \quad \text{and} \quad A \subset B + C.$$

3. Obviously $D \subset D$. Also, $AD = \{2, 4\}$ and $CD = \{2, 3, 4\}$. Thus,

$$AD \subset CD.$$

4. We have seen that $A \subset B$. We observe that

$$A + B = \{2, 4, 6, 8\} = B.$$

Also,
$$AB = \{2, 4\} = A.$$

5. We find that

$$B' = \{1, 3, 5, 7, 9, 10\} \quad \text{and} \quad A' = \{1, 3, 5, 6, 7, 8, 9, 10\}.$$

Hence,
$$B' \subset A'.$$

6. A and B' have no numbers in common. Thus

$$AB' = \varnothing.$$

7. Finally,

$$A' + B = \{1, 2, 3, 4, 5, 6, 7, 8, 9, 10\} = U.$$

3.11 EXERCISES

*1. What is a simpler way of designating the set $A + AB$?
 2. What is a simpler way of designating the set $A + A'B$?
*3. A universe consists of two sets, A and B, and all possible sets that can be constructed from A and B using union, intersection, and complement. List all possible distinct subsets of U.

In Exercises 4–12 simplify the expressions as much as possible.

 4. $(A + B)(A' + B)$　　　　　　　*5. $AC + ABC + AC'$
 6. $AB + AB' + A'B + A'B'$　　　　*7. $ABC + A' + B' + C'$
 8. $(A + AB + ABC)(A + B + C)$　*9. $(AB' + A'B)'(AB + A'B')'$
10. $(AB + AB' + A'B')'$　　　　　*11. $A'C + B'C + ABCD'$
12. $(A + B' + C)(AB + A'C')'$

*13. Prove that $A = B$ if and only if $AB' + A'B = \emptyset$.
14. A, B, and C are certain subsets of a set with 200 elements. There are 70 in A, 120 in B, 90 in C, 50 in AB, 30 in AC, 40 in BC, and 20 in ABC. Find the number in each of the following: $A + B$, $A + B + C$, $A'BC$, $AB'C'$, $A'B'C'$. (Hint: Draw a picture and fill in the appropriate numbers.)
*15. Is the following report consistent? A survey of 100 students shows that 45 read French, 25 read German, 27 read Spanish, 19 read French and German, 8 read French and Spanish, 10 read Spanish and German, and 3 read all three languages.
*16. How many subsets are there of a set consisting of n elements?
17. Give a verbal argument justifying each of the properties listed for set inclusion.

3.12 DUALITY

Let us summarize what we have found about the algebra of sets in a table. As we do so we shall find that for every valid symbolic statement that we can write there is another that also holds. It is obtained by interchanging the operations of union and intersection and interchanging U and $\emptyset$ when they appear. Each statement is called the "dual" of the other. Thus the work involved in proving that any general statement about sets is valid automatically proves the dual valid.

$$A + A = A \qquad\qquad AA = A$$
$$A + B = B + A \qquad\qquad AB = BA$$

$$A + (B + C) = (A + B) + C \qquad A(BC) = (AB)C$$
$$A(B + C) = AB + AC \qquad A + BC = (A + B)(A + C)$$
$$A + A' = U \qquad AA' = \varnothing$$
$$A + U = U \qquad A\varnothing = \varnothing$$
$$A + \varnothing = A \qquad AU = A$$
$$(A + B)' = A'B' \qquad (AB)' = A' + B'$$

$A \subset B$ if and only if $A' + B = U$ $\qquad$ $A \subset B$ if and only if $AB' = \varnothing$

$A \subset B$ if and only if $A + B = B$ $\qquad$ $A \subset B$ if and only if $AB = A$

$A \subset B$ if and only if $B' \subset A'$

The last three lines above do not express strict duality, but they show that there are five other statements equivalent to $A \subset B$. The implications of this will be seen later in this chapter.

3.13 EXERCISES

*1. What is AB if

   (a) $A \subset B$?   (b) $B \subset A$?

   (c) A and B are disjoint?   (d) $B = \varnothing$?

2. What is $A + B$ if

   (a) $A \subset B$?   (b) $B \subset A$?

   (c) $B = \varnothing$?   (d) $A = U$?

*3. (a) Is $\varnothing$ a member of the empty set?

   (b) Is $\varnothing$ contained in the empty set?

   (c) What is the complement of the universal set?

   (d) What is the complement of the empty set?

4. In each of the figures shade in the appropriate set.

$AC + B$ $\qquad\qquad$ $A(C + B)$ $\qquad\qquad$ ABC' $\qquad\qquad$ $AB'C'$

Exercise 4

*5. In each of the figures shade in the appropriate set.

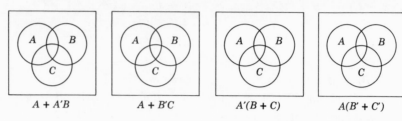

$A + A'B$ ⠀⠀⠀⠀ $A + B'C$ ⠀⠀⠀⠀ $A'(B + C)$ ⠀⠀⠀⠀ $A(B' + C')$

Exercise 5

6. In each of the diagrams label the set indicated by the shaded region. *A* denotes the circle, *B* the triangle, and *C* the square.

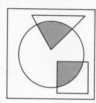

Exercise 6

*7. Nineteen boys turn out for baseball. Of these, 11 are wearing baseball shirts and 14 are wearing baseball pants. There are no boys without one or the other. How many are wearing full uniforms?

8. What, precisely, is meant by the statement that for sets *A* and *B*, $A = B$?

*9. In the diagrams, shade in the appropriate sets.

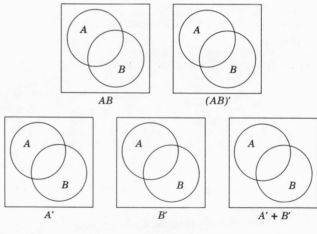

AB ⠀⠀⠀⠀⠀⠀⠀ $(AB)'$

A' ⠀⠀⠀⠀⠀ B' ⠀⠀⠀⠀⠀ $A' + B'$

Exercise 9

*10. Which two sets in Exercise 9 are equal?

11. In the diagrams, shade in the appropriate sets.

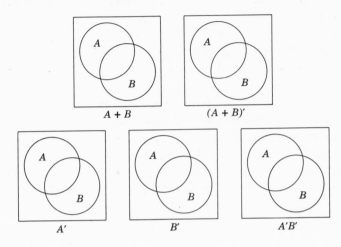

$A + B$ $(A + B)'$

A' B' $A'B'$

Exercise 11

12. Which two sets in Exercise 11 are equal?

3.14 THE ABSTRACTION

The mathematician wishes to study the structure of a mathematical system. This means that he is interested in the relationships and operations that exist in a system, but he is not at all interested in what the symbols represent. We abstract from the system all "meaning," leaving only symbols to be manipulated according to some set of rules. When this is done, the system that results can be studied without reference to content. In such an abstract system the concept of "truth" has no connection with the physical world. A statement is "true" if it can be derived logically from a set of postulates. It is in this sense that Bertrand Russell said, "Thus mathematics may be defined as the subject in which we never know what we are talking about, nor whether what we are saying is true."

Our present goal is to present a set of postulates from which to derive all of the relationships that held in the algebra of sets. In mathematics, as in housekeeping, neatness is a virtue. Our postulational set should be large enough, but not too large. The postulates should be adequate for the derivation of our theorems, but no postulate should be derivable from the remaining ones. That is, there should be no redundancy in the postulates. Having redundancy is not necessarily wrong, but it isn't very satisfactory esthetically.

It could mean that we were not clear about just what assumptions are necessary to obtain our mathematical system, but it might merely mean that we were willing to accept the resulting redundancy in order to save time. This is frequently done, as in high-school geometry. On the other hand, the set of postulates used is not necessarily unique. That is, it is frequently possible to give other sets of postulates that will work just as well. We shall give a set of postulates for Boolean algebra that were first given by E. V. Huntington in 1904.

A word of explanation is necessary. The development given in this chapter from the concrete to the abstract and back again is merely illustrative. It is not implied that the development given here is in any way historical. Boolean algebra actually is named after the Englishman George Boole (1815–1864), who taught for many years at Queens College, Cork. In his work *An Investigation of the Laws of Thought on Which Are Founded the Mathematical Theories of Logic and Probabilities*, 1854, Boole first constructed the mathematical system of this section. As is apparent from the title, the impetus for his work did not come from sets but rather from logic. It is our hope, however, that the course chosen in this text is easier for the student to follow.

3.15 DEFINITIONS

We must define certain operational words before stating our postulates. These definitions are nothing new, but they are given here with reference to a set, called M, of objects, denoted by letters, a, b, c, . . . , to which no concrete meaning is attached.

1. A *binary operation* $*$ on a set M is a rule that assigns to each ordered pair (a, b) of elements of M a unique element

$$c = a * b$$

in M.

2. A binary operation $*$ on a set M is *commutative* if and only if for every a and b in M,

$$a * b = b * a.$$

3. A binary operation $*$ on a set M is *associative* if and only if for every a, b, and c in M,

$$a * (b * c) = (a * b) * c.$$

Whenever an operation is associative, we may write either $a * (b * c)$ or $(a * b) * c$ as $a * b * c$. The equality of $a * (b * c)$ and $(a * b) * c$ removes the ambiguity from $a * b * c$.

4. If $*$ and $\circ$ are two binary operations on M, $*$ is *distributive* over $\circ$ if and only if for every a, b, and c in M,

$$a * (b \circ c) = (a * b) \circ (a * c).$$

5. An element e in M is an *identity* for the binary operation $*$ if and only if

$$a * e = e * a = a$$

for every element a in M.

These definitions attach names to the way binary operations in a system of elements may behave. We have encountered a number of binary operations in our work so far.

In the set of real numbers we have found that addition, subtraction, and multiplication are binary operations. Division is a binary operation on the nonzero real numbers. We have already examined the properties of addition and multiplication rather extensively, but we have slighted the other two.

> **Example 1.** Since $a - (b - c) = a - b + c$, whereas $(a - b) - c = a - b - c$, it is not always true that $a - (b - c) = (a - b) - c$. Hence subtraction is not associative. Similarly, since $a - b \neq b - a$, subtraction is not commutative. Since $a(b - c) = ab - ac$, multiplication distributes over subtraction, but the converse is not true.

> **Example 2.** Since $a/(b/c) = ac/b$, whereas $(a/b)/c = a/bc$, we find that division is not associative. Also, since $a/b \neq b/a$, division is not commutative. Since $a/(b + c) \neq a/b + a/c$ in general, division does not distribute over addition. However,

> $$\frac{a + b}{c} = \frac{a}{c} + \frac{b}{c}.$$

> That is, we may say that division distributes over addition from the right but not from the left.

In the set of all subsets of some universe U, we have examined the binary operations of union and intersection and found that both are commutative and associative and that each distributes over the other.

In the set of all even integers there is an identity for addition but not for multiplication. In the natural numbers there is an identity for multiplication but not for addition.

3.16 BOOLEAN ALGEBRA: HUNTINGTON'S POSTULATES

The four postulates below define the mathematical system that we shall call Boolean algebra. A Boolean algebra B is a set of elements together with two binary operations $(+)$ and $(\cdot)$ (where $a \cdot b$ will be written ab) for which the following properties hold:

P1. The operations $(+)$ and $(\cdot)$ are commutative operations on B.

P2. There exist in B distinct identity elements 0 and 1 relative to the operations $(+)$ and $(\cdot)$ respectively.

P3. Each operation distributes over the other.

P4. For every a in B there exists an element a' in B such that

$$a + a' = 1 \quad \text{and} \quad aa' = 0.$$

At first glance it seems that our postulates are not adequate to represent the algebra of sets. For instance, the associative property is not asserted for either operation, nor is it assumed that $a + a = a$ or $aa = a$. Also, P2 does not assert that the identity elements, 0 and 1, are unique, nor does P4 assert that for some a there might not be more than one element that behaves like a'. All these, then, are theorems to be proved. We shall go through a number of such proofs, not to make the student wholly skilled in Boolean algebra, but rather to give him a taste of theorem proving in an abstract system. Remember, the *only* tools with which we have to work are postulates P1 to P4. Note that there is complete symmetry in the postulates with respect to the two operations and their identities. This means that every proof is automatically associated with the proof of another theorem in which the operations and identities are interchanged. In the first theorem we shall parallel the two proofs. Thereafter the student can supply the dual.

Theorem 1. *For every a in B,*

$$a + a = a \quad \text{and} \quad aa = a.$$

Proof:		
$a = a + 0$	$a = a(1)$	P2
$= a + aa'$	$= a(a + a')$	P4
$= (a + a)(a + a')$	$= aa + aa'$	P3
$= (a + a)1$	$= aa + 0$	P4
$= a + a$	$= aa$	P2

3.17   EXERCISES

1. How many binary operations on sets of elements occur to you?
*2. State which parts, if any, of Huntington's postulates are *not* satisfied by:

    (a) Addition and multiplication over the set of natural numbers.
    (b) Addition and multiplication over the set of integers.
    (c) Addition and multiplication over the set of even integers.
    (d) Union and intersection over the set of all subsets of some universe.

*3. Define a binary operation $*$ on the integers as $a * b = a + b - ab$. Prove that $*$ is commutative and associative.
4. Define a binary operation $*$ on the real numbers as $a * b = a^2 + b$. Prove that $*$ is neither commutative nor associative.
*5. Define a binary operation $*$ on the subsets of a universe U as $A * B = AB' + A'B$. Prove that $*$ is commutative and associative.
6. State Huntington's postulates without referring to the text.
*7. Can the steps in the proof of Theorem 1 be reversed?
8. If $*$ is the binary operation of Exercise 5, shade in $A * B * C$ in the figure.

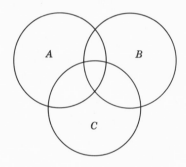

Exercise 8

3.18   MORE THEOREMS

In this section a proof is given for only half of each theorem. The proof of the dual is left as an exercise for the student.

    Theorem 2.   *For every a in B,*

$$a + 1 = 1 \quad and \quad a0 = 0.$$

Proof:

$$
\begin{aligned}
1 &= a + a' & &\text{P4} \\
&= a + a'(1) & &\text{P2} \\
&= (a + a')(a + 1) & &\text{P3} \\
&= 1(a + 1) & &\text{P4} \\
&= a + 1 & &\text{P2}
\end{aligned}
$$

Theorem 3. *For each pair of elements a and b in B,*

$$a + ab = a \quad and \quad a(a + b) = a.$$

Proof:

$$
\begin{aligned}
a &= a(1) & &\text{P2} \\
&= a(1 + b) & &\text{Th. 2 and P1} \\
&= a(1) + ab & &\text{P3} \\
&= a + ab & &\text{P2}
\end{aligned}
$$

Theorem 4. *For each pair of elements a and b in B,*

$$a + a'b = a + b \quad and \quad a' + ab = a' + b.$$

The duals are that

$$a(a' + b) = ab \quad and \quad a'(a + b) = a'b.$$

Proof:

$$
\begin{aligned}
a + a'b &= (a + a')(a + b) & &\text{P3} \\
&= 1(a + b) & &\text{P4} \\
&= a + b & &\text{P2}
\end{aligned}
$$

For the second part, merely interchange a and a'.

The proof of the next theorem is the longest and most complex. It is frequently true that associativity is a difficult property to treat in any system.

Theorem 5. *In every Boolean algebra B, both $(+)$ and $(\cdot)$ are associative.*

Proof: We must show that

$$a + (b + c) = (a + b) + c \quad and \quad a(bc) = (ab)c.$$

We shall show the second. First, we shall show that $a + a(bc) = a + (ab)c$ and that $a' + a(bc) = a' + (ab)c$. Then, by multiplying the corresponding sides of these two equations we shall be able to obtain the desired result.

$$
\begin{aligned}
a + a(bc) &= a & &\text{Th. 3} \\
&= a(a + c) & &\text{Th. 3} \\
&= (a + ab)(a + c) & &\text{Th. 3} \\
&= a + (ab)c & &\text{P3.} \\
a' + a(bc) &= a' + bc & &\text{Th. 4} \\
&= (a' + b)(a' + c) & &\text{P3} \\
&= (a' + ab)(a' + c) & &\text{Th. 4} \\
&= a' + (ab)c & &\text{P3.}
\end{aligned}
$$

Then,
$$[a + a(bc)][a' + a(bc)] = [a + (ab)c][a' + (ab)c]$$

or

$$[a(bc) + a][a(bc) + a'] = [(ab)c + a][(ab)c + a'] \qquad \text{P1}$$
$$a(bc) + aa' = (ab)c + aa' \qquad \text{P3}$$
$$a(bc) + 0 = (ab)c + 0 \qquad \text{P4}$$
$$a(bc) = (ab)c \qquad \text{P2}$$

By Theorem 5, a sum or product of three or more terms can be written unambiguously without parentheses.

Theorem 6.   *The element a' associated with a by P4 is unique.*

Proof: Let x be any element of B such that

$$a + x = 1 \quad \text{and} \quad ax = 0.$$

We shall show that x is a'.

$$
\begin{aligned}
x &= 1x & \text{P2} \\
&= (a + a')x & \text{P4} \\
&= ax + a'x & \text{P3 and P1} \\
&= 0 + a'x & \text{assumed} \\
&= aa' + a'x & \text{P4} \\
&= a'a + a'x & \text{P1} \\
&= a'(a + x) & \text{P3} \\
&= a'(1) & \text{assumed} \\
&= a' & \text{P2}
\end{aligned}
$$

We shall call a' the *complement of a*.

Theorem 7.   *For every a in B,*

$$(a')' = a.$$

Proof: $a + a' = 1$ and $aa' = 0$ P4
$a' + a = 1$ and $a'a = 0$ P1

Thus, by the uniqueness proved in Theorem 6,

$$a = (a')'.$$

Theorem 8.   *In B,*

$$0' = 1 \quad \text{and} \quad 1' = 0.$$

Proof: $1 + 0 = 1$ and $1(0) = 0$ P2
Thus
$$0 = 1' \quad \text{and} \quad 1 = 0' \qquad \text{Th. 6 and P1}$$

Theorem 9. *For every a and b in B,*

$$(ab)' = a' + b' \quad \text{and} \quad (a + b)' = a'b'.$$

Proof:	$ab + (a' + b') = (ab + a') + b'$	Th. 5
	$= (a' + ab) + b'$	P1
	$= (a' + b) + b'$	Th. 4
	$= a' + (b + b')$	Th. 5
	$= a' + 1$	P4
	$= 1$	Th. 2
Also,	$ab(a' + b') = aba' + abb'$	P3
	$= 0b + a0$	P1 and P4
	$= 0 + 0 = 0$	Th. 2 and P2.
Thus	$(a' + b') = (ab)'$	

by Theorem 6.

3.19 EXERCISES

*1. In Theorem 2, prove the dual, that $a0 = 0$.

2. In Theorem 3, prove the dual, that $a(a + b) = a$,

*3. In Theorem 4, prove the remaining parts of the Theorem.

4. In Theorem 5, prove the dual, that $a + (b + c) = (a + b) + c$.

*5. In Theorem 9, prove the dual, that $(a + b)' = a'b'$. (Hint: derive the dual directly from the part that was proved in Theorem 9.)

3.20 PARTIAL ORDERING

We have seen that a Boolean algebra has a structure similar in many respects to the algebraic structure we found in the number systems. Since there is a natural ordering relation among the real numbers, we may wonder whether there is anything resembling it in a Boolean algebra. In Chapter 2 an example was given of a field that could not be ordered, and since a Boolean algebra differs somewhat from a field, there is no immediately obvious solution to our problem. Since Boolean algebra was abstracted from the algebra of sets, perhaps we should return to sets for inspiration. How could we order sets? A partial answer is given by set inclusion. If set A is contained in set B, we might say that A is "smaller" than B. But $A \subset B$ if and only if $AB' = \varnothing$. Thus we are led to the following definition of the symbol $\leq$, which we shall read as "precedes."

3.21 PRECEDENCE

Definition. In a Boolean algebra, $a \leq b$ if and only if $ab' = 0$.

This definition is only a partial answer to our problem, because if a and b are two distinct elements of a Boolean algebra such that $ab' \neq 0$ and $a'b \neq 0$, then a and b cannot be compared. That is, we do *not* have $a = b$, $a \leq b$, or $b \leq a$. However, a number of the properties of order are preserved. Let us state them in a theorem.

> **Theorem 10.** *If a, b, c, and d are arbitrary elements of a Boolean algebra,*
> (1) $a \leq a$.
> (2) *If $a \leq b$ and $b \leq a$, then $a = b$.*
> (3) *If $a \leq b$ and $b \leq c$, then $a \leq c$.*
> (4) *If $a \leq b$ and $a \leq c$, then $a \leq bc$.*
> (5) *If $a \leq b$ and $c \leq d$, then $a + c \leq b + d$ and $ac \leq bd$.*
> (6) *The following are equivalent:*
>
> $$a \leq b, \qquad b' \leq a', \qquad a' + b = 1, \qquad a + b = b, \quad \text{and} \quad ab = a.$$

Proof: We must use only the definition of $\leq$ and the postulates and theorems of Boolean algebra. In most of what follows the reasons will be omitted. It will be a task for the student to cite the appropriate theorems or postulates.

1. Since $aa' = 0$ by P4,

$$a \leq a.$$

2. If $a \leq b$ and $b \leq a$, then

$$ab' = 0, \quad \text{and} \quad ba' = 0.$$

By Theorem 9, $a + b' = 1$. Thus, by Theorem 6, b' is the complement of a, $b' = a'$, or $a = b$.

3. If $a \leq b$ and $b \leq c$, then $ab' = 0$ and $bc' = 0$. But

$$ac' = ac'(b + b') = ac'b + ac'b' = a(bc') + c'(ab') = 0 + 0 = 0.$$

Thus,

$$a \leq c.$$

4. If $a \leq b$ and $a \leq c$, then $ab' = 0$ and $ac' = 0$. But

$$a(bc)' = a(b' + c') = ab' + ac' = 0 + 0 = 0.$$

Thus,

$$a \leq bc.$$

5. If $a \leq b$ and $c \leq d$, then $ab' = 0$ and $cd' = 0$. But

$$ac(bd)' = ac(b' + d') = (ab')c + a(cd') = 0 + 0 = 0.$$

Thus

$$ac \leq bd.$$

The second part is proved in a similar way.

6. By definition, $a \leq b$ if and only if $ab' = 0$. By P1 and Theorem 7, ab' may be written as $b'(a')'$. But $b'(a')' = 0$ if and only if $b' \leq a'$. Also, $ab' = 0$ if and only if $(ab')' = 1$, or $a' + b = 1$. Next, if $ab' = 0$, then $ab' + b = b$, or, by Theorem 4, $a + b = b$. Conversely, if $a + b = b$, then

$$(a + b)b' = bb',$$

or

$$ab' + bb' = bb',$$

or

$$ab' + 0 = 0,$$

or

$$ab' = 0.$$

Thus $a + b = b$ is equivalent to $ab' = 0$. The proof of the remaining part is left for the student.

Since some elements may not be comparable, our ordering is not a complete ordering. Thus we shall say that a Boolean algebra is *partially ordered* by $\leq$. The relation of set inclusion provides a partial ordering of a set of subsets of a universe. Two sets, A and B, are comparable only if one is a subset of the other.

3.22 A COMMENT

We have treated a Boolean algebra as an abstract, formal system. Thus, nothing is to be accepted as intuitively obvious. We insist on a careful, logical proof of everything. It is necessary to proceed in a completely formal way through definitions and theorems whose proofs consist of showing that the statements made are logical consequences of previous definitions, postulates, and theorems. Each element in the system is meaningless in itself; the only thing we know about it is how it is related to other members of the Boolean algebra.

The theorems given here by no means exhaust the subject. There is a large body of material that could be developed and has been developed in books and papers on Boolean algebra. The theorems and their proofs were given to illustrate one important activity of the mathematician, the logical investigation of an abstract system. Moreover, the system was motivated by observed relationships among the subsets comprising some universal set. Meaning can now be poured into the empty symbols of a Boolean algebra. When this is done, every statement in the Boolean algebra takes on meaning. If 1 and 0 are now assigned meanings as a universal and empty set, respectively; if the alphabetical symbols are taken as subsets of the universal set; if $+$ and $\cdot$ are taken as set union and intersection; if a' is taken to mean the set of points of the universal set that are not in a; and if $\leq$ is taken to mean set inclusion, then, because the postulates are true statements in the assigned language, the algebra of sets becomes a *realization* of a Boolean algebra in which all of our theorems have meaning in terms of sets. In the next section we shall show other possible realizations of Boolean algebras.

3.23   EXERCISES

In Exercises 1–10 simplify the expressions as much as possible, supplying a reason for each step.

*1. $(a + b)(a' + b)$ 2. $ac + abc + ac'$
*3. $ab + ab' + a'b + a'b'$ 4. $abc + a' + b' + c'$
*5. $(a + ab + abc)(a + b + c)$ 6. $(ab' + a'b)'(ab + a'b')'$
*7. $(ab + ab' + a'b')'$ 8. $a'c + b'c + abcd'$
*9. $(a + b' + c)(ab + a'c')'$ *10. $[(a' + b')' + a']'$

11. Supply the missing reasons in the proofs of the parts of Theorem 10.
*12. What conclusion can you draw if for elements a, b, and c in B, $a \leq b$, $b \leq c$, and $c \leq a$?

3.24   THE TWO-VALUED BOOLEAN ALGEBRA

Let us consider the simplest of all Boolean algebras, one containing only two elements, 0 and 1. Since these are the only elements in the algebra, we can display all relations by means of the following tables:

(+)			(·)			(')	(≤)
	0	1		0	1		
0	0	1	0	0	0	$0' = 1$	$0 \leq 0$
1	1	1	1	0	1	$1' = 0$	$0 \leq 1$
							$1 \leq 1$

Simple though these tables are, are there any realizations of the two-valued Boolean algebra? We might suspect that any realization might be trivial, but if we did so, we would be surprised to learn the truth.

3.25 SWITCHING CIRCUITS

In the figures that follow, let the capital letters represent simple switches that are either open or closed. If A is a switch, let it have the value 0 if it is open and 1 if it is closed. Denote two switches, A and B, connected in parallel, by $A + B$ and, if connected in series, by AB.

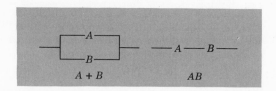

$$A + B \qquad\qquad AB$$

If A and B are connected in parallel, they represent a closed path if either A or B is closed. Hence we shall read $A + B$ as A or B. If A and B are connected in series, they represent a closed path if and only if both A and B are closed. Hence we shall read AB as A and B. Let us now extend our use of the capital letters to entire switching circuits made up of simple switches connected in parallel or in series. We can then combine these circuits by our operations of "or" and "and" to get larger switching circuits.

Two switching circuits are said to be *equivalent* (written $=$) if they have the same values, open or closed, for every possible combination of values for the switches involved.

A given switch may have several sets of contacts. That is, in a diagram representing a connection of a number of switches, a given letter may appear more than once. A switch that is closed whenever A is open and open whenever A is closed is denoted by A'. That is, the circuit defined by $A + A'$, where A is in parallel with A', is always equivalent to a short circuit (a closed switch) because one of the two switches, A or A', must be closed. Similarly, the circuit defined by AA', where A is in series with A', is always equivalent to an open switch because one of the two must be open.

In our algebra of switching circuits, let us introduce two special switches. One of these, denoted by 1, will be a switch that is permanently closed. The other, denoted by 0, will be a switch that is permanently open. Thus, if the closed switch, 1, is connected in series with a switching circuit A, there is no change in the circuit. That is, the new circuit is equivalent to the former, or

$$A1 = A.$$

Similarly, if an open switch is connected in parallel with a switching circuit, the result is equivalent to the original circuit, or

$$A + 0 = A.$$

Observe that with our new notation for the permanently closed or open switches we can write

$$A + A' = 1 \quad \text{and} \quad AA' = 0.$$

Is such a switching circuit a realization of a Boolean algebra? To answer this we must determine whether the four postulates are satisfied. Let us check.

P1. Both operations are commutative. If A is in parallel (or in series) with B, then B is in parallel (or in series) with A.

P2. There are identities for both operations. A switch that is permanently open, 0, is the identity for $+$, and the permanently closed switch, 1, is the identity for $\cdot$.

P3. Each operation distributes over the other. $AB + AC$ represents a closed path if and only if A and B are both closed or A and C are both closed. That is, A must be closed and B or C must be closed. Hence

$$AB + AC = A(B + C).$$

Similarly, $(A + B)(A + C)$ represents a closed path if and only if A or B is closed and A or C is closed. Thus either A is closed or, if not, both B and C must be closed. Hence

$$(A + B)(A + C) = A + BC.$$

P4. In terms of switches, A is either open or closed. That is, either A or A' has the value 1. Hence

$$A + A' = 1.$$

But a switch is never both open and closed. Hence

$$AA' = 0.$$

Since the postulates are satisfied, the switching circuits do provide a realization of a Boolean algebra. In fact, since the switches have only two positions, represented by 0 and 1, the arithmetic that we do in the system is based on the two-valued Boolean algebra. The significance of this is that we can write an algebraic expression that represents a certain switching circuit, manipulate this expression by means of the theorems of Boolean algebra to obtain a possibly simpler expression, and then translate the result into a switching circuit that may require less hardware than the original. For example, Theorem 3 states that

$$a + ab = a(a + b) = a.$$

In terms of switching circuits, this says that the following three circuits are equivalent:

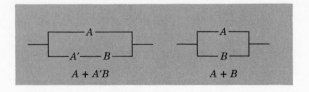

Theorem 4 says that

$$a + a'b = a + b,$$

which can be interpreted to mean that the following are equivalent:

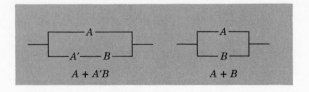

Some of the theorems are trivial indeed in this context. Theorem 7, for instance, merely says that a switch that is not open is closed, or if it is not closed it is open.

Let us try to simplify a switching circuit. Consider the following figure:

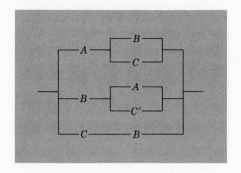

We can write this as

$$A(B + C) + B(A + C') + CB.$$

By using our postulates and theorems of Boolean algebra, we can reduce this to

$$
\begin{aligned}
AB + AC + BA + BC' + CB &= (AB + AB) + AC + BC' + BC \\
&= AB + AC + B(C' + C) \\
&= AB + AC + B \\
&= (B + AB) + AC \\
&= B + AC.
\end{aligned}
$$

This tells us that a simpler but completely equivalent circuit is

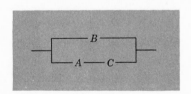

3.26   EXERCISES

*1. Draw a circuit corresponding to $(A + B)(A' + B)$.
*2. Draw a circuit corresponding to $AC + ABC + AC'$.
 3. Draw a circuit corresponding to $(A + B' + C)(AB + A'C')$.
 4. Draw a circuit corresponding to $ABC + A'BC' + A(B + C)$.
*5. Draw a circuit corresponding to $(A + B)(A' + C)(B' + C')$.

6–10. In each case draw an equivalent circuit that is simpler than the one shown

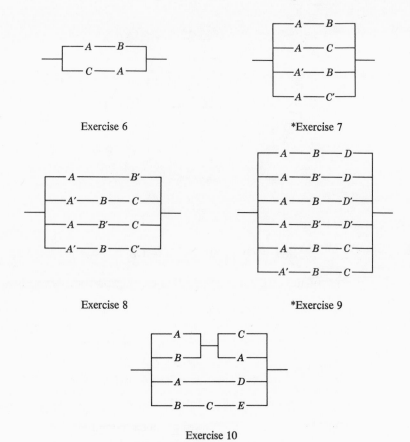

Exercise 6

*Exercise 7

Exercise 8

*Exercise 9

Exercise 10

*11. Write a Boolean algebra expression representing the following circuit. This amounts to replacing it by an equivalent series-parallel circuit.

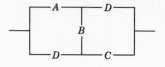

Exercise 11

3.27 EQUIVALENCE TABLES

The definition of equivalent circuits suggests a method of proof that two circuits are equivalent. To be equivalent, two circuits must behave alike for every possible set of values of their switches. Since a circuit has only a finite number of switches, this means that only a finite number of possibilities exist and that we can list them in a table. Let us show that

$$A + BC = (A + B)(A + C).$$

We first list the variables A, B, and C. Under them we list all possible combinations of values that A, B, and C can have. We then form the values of the indicated expressions. See Table 1. Since the columns headed $A + BC$

Table 1

A	B	C	BC	$A + BC$	$A + B$	$A + C$	$(A + B)(A + C)$
0	0	0	0	0	0	0	0
0	0	1	0	0	0	1	0
0	1	0	0	0	1	0	0
0	1	1	1	1	1	1	1
1	0	0	0	1	1	1	1
1	0	1	0	1	1	1	1
1	1	0	0	1	1	1	1
1	1	1	1	1	1	1	1

and $(A + B)(A + C)$ agree for every possible set of values for A, B, and C, they represent equivalent circuits. The use of equivalence tables will turn out to be quite important in another realization of the two-valued Boolean algebra, the algebra of logic.

3.28 PARTIAL ORDER IN SWITCHING CIRCUITS

Suppose that two switches, A and B, are so connected that A cannot be turned on unless B is also turned on. That is, A is never on when B is off, or $AB' = 0$. If switches A and B are connected in this way, we shall say that A *requires* B and write $A \leq B$. Then the relation $\leq$ for switching circuits satisfies the definition of a partial order in the Boolean algebra of switching circuits. Consequently, the conclusions of Theorem 10 hold for switching circuits. B plays the role of a master switch for A. When B is off, A cannot be turned on. This is the principle of a number of electronic locks. Suppose that a door is unlocked by switch A, and suppose that A, B, and C are connected so that $A \leq B$ and $B \leq C$. Then, in order to turn A on, it is necessary to turn on B, but B cannot be turned on until C is turned on. Thus, in order to open the door, the switches must be turned on in a particular order, first C, then B, and then A.

3.29 EXERCISES

In Exercises 1 to 8 use equivalence tables to prove that the two sides of each equation describe equivalent circuits.

*1. $A + A'B = A + B$

2. $A + AB = A$

*3. $B(A + A'B') = AB$

4. $(A + B)' = A'B'$

*5. $(AB)' = A' + B'$

6. $A(B + C') + A'C' = AB + C'$

*7. $AB + AC + BC' + BC = AC + B$

8. $(AB + AB' + A'B')' = A'B$

*9. In how many different orders can three switches be thrown?

10. In how many different orders can four switches be thrown?

*11. In how many different orders can n switches be thrown?

3.30 THE ALGEBRA OF LOGIC

We shall conclude this chapter by constructing one more realization of a Boolean algebra, the algebra of logic. Instead of switches or sets our objects will now be sentences that are true or false but not both. Such sentences will be called *propositions*. Examples of propositions are: "$2 + 2 = 4$," "Ice is cold," "The moon is made of green cheese," and "6 is a prime number." We shall not attempt to define truth or falsity; it is required only that a proposition have one but not both of these qualities. Not all simple declarative sentences are propositions, however. Consider the following:

The sentence on this line is false.

If the sentence is true, it is false, and if it is false, it is true. Hence it is not a proposition. We shall try to avoid such confusing sentences.

3.31 DISJUNCTION, CONJUNCTION, AND NEGATION

It is possible to combine propositions through the use of common connectives. Let us represent propositions by the letters a, b, c, etc. Then "a or b" is a perfectly good proposition. Unfortunately, we use the word "or" in two different senses in English. One usage is inclusive, meaning one or the other or both, and the other usage is exclusive, meaning one or the other but *not* both. It is better for our purposes to use "or" in the inclusive sense. In studying sets we used the symbol $+$ to indicate the set of points belonging to one set or another or to both. Thus let us use the same symbol to designate the inclusive "or." That is, $a + b$ is to be interpreted as the sentence "a or b

or both." We shall call $a + b$ the *disjunction* of a and b. For example, if a is the proposition "Ice is cold," and b is the proposition "$2 + 2 = 5$," then $a + b$, the disjunction of the two, is the proposition "Ice is cold, or $2 + 2 = 5$." In this case $a + b$ is true because a is true. The disjunction of a and b is true, then, whenever a is true or b is true or both.

Another connective is "and." If a and b are propositions, then "a and b" is also a proposition that is true if and only if a is true *and* b is true. Let us write "a and b" as ab. We shall call ab the *conjunction* of a and b. This usage corresponds with our treatment of sets, where an indicated multiplication represented the set of points common to one set *and* another. If a and b are the propositions of the last example, then ab, the conjunction of the two, is the sentence "Ice is cold, and $2 + 2 = 5$." In this case ab is false because a and b are not both true.

Next, if a is any proposition, there is a corresponding proposition that states that a is false. We shall call this new proposition the *negation* of a and write it as a'. It follows, then, that a' is a proposition that is true if a is false and false if a is true. If a is the proposition "Ice is cold," then a' is the proposition "Ice is not cold."

3.32   PROPOSITIONAL VARIABLES

We study the algebra of a number system by investigating those laws that hold for all numbers in the system. We use two kinds of symbols in this process, one, like 2, for the name of specific numbers, and another, like x, to represent an *arbitrary* number or an *unspecified* number. In our algebra of logic we shall use two kinds of symbols. One kind, like a, b, c, . . . , will be used as names for specific propositions. For the second kind we shall use the symbols u, v, x, . . . , to represent arbitrary propositions, and we shall call these symbols *propositional variables*. In a sense they are placeholders. In our algebra of numbers, when we say that $xy = yx$ is always true, we mean that a true equation results when any numbers are substituted for x and y. We wish to find just such statements in the algebra of logic, statements about propositional variables that will be valid when any propositions are substituted for the variables.

We can combine propositional variables to obtain meaningful expressions. For instance, $x + y$ represents the disjunction of arbitrary propositions. The expression $x + y$, then, becomes a true proposition when specific propositions are substituted for x and y, provided at least one of the propositions that we substitute is true. Otherwise the result is false.

3.33 EQUIVALENCE

We shall use the symbol $\equiv$ between two expressions involving propositional variables that are either both true or both false for *every* possible set of propositions that can be substituted for the variables. We shall say that two such expressions are *equivalent*. For instance, we can write $x + y \equiv y + x$ and $xy \equiv yx$. The equivalences in the algebraic logic correspond to the identities of algebra or trigonometry. We shall often read $\equiv$ as "if and only if."

3.34 1 AND 0

We shall use the symbol 1 in two ways, but this dual use should cause no confusion. As in switching circuits, where 1 represented a permanently closed switch, in the algebra of logic 1 will represent a proposition that is permanently true. (We ignore the philosophical question about the existence of absolute truth. In our system it isn't necessary to know what "truth" means.) Similarly, 0 will represent a permanently false proposition. Thus the statement that an expression involving propositional variables is equivalent to 1 is to be interpreted as meaning that the expression is a true proposition for *every* set of propositions that can be substituted for the variables. Such an equivalence will be called a *tautology*, and much of our work in the algebra of logic will consist of a search for tautologies. For example, the definition of the negation of a proposition yields a tautology, $x + x' \equiv 1$. An equivalence in which an algebraic expression is equivalent to 0 will indicate that the expression is false for *every* set of propositions that can be substituted for the variables involved. For example, $xx' \equiv 0$, because the conjunction of any proposition and its negation is always false. 1 and 0 are the constants in the algebra of logic.

We shall also use the symbols 1 and 0 to indicate the truth or falsity of a particular proposition. In this use we employ the symbol $=$ rather than $\equiv$. For instance, if a is the proposition "$2 + 2 = 4$," then we can write $a = 1$ and $a' = 0$. On the other hand, we cannot legitimately write $x \equiv 1$, for this would say that all propositions are true. We can, however, write $x = 1$. This is not a tautology. It is a statement in the algebra of logic that is satisfied if and only if a true proposition is substituted for x. Similarly, the proposition "Ice is hot" satisfies the equation $x = 0$. The equation $x = y$ is satisfied by any two propositions that are both true or are both false. That is,

$$(x = y) \equiv xy + x'y'.$$

3.35   LOGIC AS A BOOLEAN ALGEBRA

In order to manipulate the symbols representing propositional variables we must have some rules to follow. Fortunately, the rules have already been developed. They are the rules of Boolean algebra. To show that this is the case, we must show that the algebra of logic satisfies Huntington's postulates. Let us ascertain that it does this. We take as our set of elements all propositional variables, together with the logical constants 0 and 1. Our binary operations + and · are disjunction and conjunction, respectively.

P1.   If x and y are propositional variables, it follows from the definitions of + and · that

$$x + y \equiv y + x \quad \text{and} \quad xy \equiv yx.$$

Thus the operations are commutative.

P2.   If x is any propositional variable,

$$x + 0 \equiv x \quad \text{and} \quad x(1) \equiv x.$$

That is, $x + 0$ and $x(1)$ are true when a true proposition is substituted for x and false when a false proposition is substituted for x.

P3.   If x, y, and z are propositional variables,

$$x(y + z) \equiv xy + xz \quad \text{and} \quad x + yz \equiv (x + y)(x + z).$$

To demonstrate these equivalences, let us construct an equivalence table for each. We shall write 1 to indicate that a true proposition is substituted for a variable and 0 to indicate that a false proposition is substituted for a variable. See Table 2.

Table 2

x	y	z	$y + z$	$x(y + z)$	xy	xz	$xy + xz$
0	0	0	0	0	0	0	0
0	0	1	1	0	0	0	0
0	1	0	1	0	0	0	0
0	1	1	1	0	0	0	0
1	0	0	0	0	0	0	0
1	0	1	1	1	0	1	1
1	1	0	1	1	1	0	1
1	1	1	1	1	1	1	1

Since the columns headed $x(y + z)$ and $xy + xz$ have the same truth value for every possible combination of truth values for propositions substituted for x, y, and z, it follows that

$$x(y + z) \equiv xy + xz.$$

The student should verify that the other distributive law holds as well.

P4. By the definition of a proposition and its negation, if x is any propositional variable,

$$x + x' \equiv 1 \quad \text{and} \quad xx' \equiv 0.$$

Since Huntington's postulates are satisfied, we can conclude that the algebra of logic is a Boolean algebra. Hence all the theorems previously proved hold for propositions, and we have constructed a realization of a Boolean algebra.

Up to this point we have been deliberately formal in our approach to logic. The reason for this should be apparent. The sooner we can show that the algebra of logic is a Boolean algebra, the sooner we are free to use the theorems. For instance, we know from Theorem 6 that, except for variations in wording, there is one and only one negation for each proposition. Also, from Theorem 9 we know that the negation of xy is $x' + y'$ and that the negation of $x + y$ is $x'y'$. Theorem 8 is almost trivial. If a proposition is not false, it is true, and if it is not true, it is false. This, of course, depends heavily on our definition of a proposition. In a sense, if we want this theorem to hold we are forced to define the objects of our algebraic logic in just the way we did.

When we replace the symbols that appear in the theorems by actual propositions, the conclusions that we can draw seem "logical." From Theorem 4, if x and y are any two propositional variables,

$$x + x'y \equiv x + y.$$

Let the proposition "The grass is green" be substituted for x and the proposition "There is snow on the ground" be substituted for y. Then $x + x'y$ represents the proposition "The grass is green, or the grass is not green and there is snow on the ground." From Theorem 4 we know that this proposition is logically equivalent to "The grass is green, or there is snow on the ground."

3.36 EXERCISES

*1. Construct two true propositions. Call them m and n.
2. Check the definition of negation and then write the negations m' and n' of the propositions of Exercise 1.

*3. Construct two false propositions. Call them p and q.

4. Construct the negations p' and q' of the propositions of Problem 3.

Exercises 5 to 9 refer to the propositions constructed in Problems 1 to 4.

5. Illustrate Theorem 1 in words, using each of the propositions m, n, p, and q in place of a.

6. Illustrate Theorems 3, 4, and 9 in words, using propositions m for a and n for b.

*7. Illustrate Theorems 3, 4, and 9 in words, using propositions p for a and q for b.

8. Illustrate Theorems 3, 4, and 9 in words, using propositions m for a and p for b.

*9. Illustrate Theorems 3, 4, and 9 in words, using propositions q for a and n for b.

10. Carry out the proof that was omitted under P3, that $x + yz \equiv (x + y)(x + z)$, by forming an equivalence table.

3.37 NEGATION

If p is a proposition, then p', the negation of p, is defined to be the proposition "p is false." Unfortunately, when p is a proposition written in English the negation is usually awkward in this form. We should attempt to state the negation as simply and directly as possible. Sometimes, when the given proposition consists of several parts or asserts that something is true of every member of some class, the negation is not immediately obvious. However, there is a check that should always be used. Of a proposition and its negation, exactly one must be true and one false. The following examples illustrate some of these difficulties.

1. a: It is raining.

   a': It is not raining.

2. b: 7 is not greater than 5.

   b': 7 is greater than 5.

3. c: There is a real number x such that $2x = 5$.

   c': There is no real number x such that $2x = 5$, or

   c': For all real numbers x, $2x \neq 5$.

4. d: There is a rational number x such that $x^2 = 2$.

   d': There is no rational number whose square is 2, or

   d': The square of every rational number is different from 2.

5. e: All odd numbers are divisible by 3.

   e': Not all odd numbers are divisible by 3, or

   e': There exists an odd number that is not divisible by 3.

6. a: 5 is odd and 7 is even. (Hint: Use Theorem 9.)

   a': 5 is even or 7 is odd.

7. b: 5 is odd or 7 is even.

   b': 5 is even and 7 is odd.

8. c: No apple is red.

   c': Some apple is red.

9. d: All men are created equal.

   d': Not all men are created equal, or

   d': There are at least two men who were created unequal to each other.

10. e: Either all men have full civil rights or no man is free.

   e': Some man does not have full civil rights and some man is free.

Observe that the negation of a proposition suggests a way that can be used to prove theorems. If you can demonstrate that the negation of a theorem is false, you have demonstrated that the theorem is true. This is usually called a "proof by contradiction."

3.38 PROBLEMS

In Exercises 1–10 give the negation of the stated propositions.

*1. There is a real number x such that $x^2 - 4x - 7 = 0$.

2. For every real number x, $x^2 - 9 = (x - 3)(x + 3)$.

*3. There is no real number x such that $x^2 + x + 1 = 0$.

4. For every integer x, $x^2 + 41x - 41$ is a prime number.

*5. There is no rational number whose square is 3.

6. If x is an even integer, x^2 is divisible by 4.

*7. There is an odd integer whose square is even.

8. It is cold and cloudy today.

*9. All our texts are either heavy or expensive.

10. A pilot is old or careless, but not both.

Let p be a proposition stating a property about certain objects, denoted by x. In Exercises 11–14 give the negation of the stated proposition.

*11. There exists an x such that p is true.

12. For all x, p is true.

*13. There is no x for which p is true.

14. For some x, p is true.

3.39 IMPLICATION

It is very common in mathematics to state a theorem in the form, "If a, then b," where a and b are propositions. Frequently some causal relationship is implied by such a statement, but causation is outside the realm of our discussion. If we are to investigate such sentences, we must state explicitly what relation is involved in our Boolean algebra of logic. First, we shall introduce the symbol $\rightarrow$ and interpret $a \rightarrow b$, read as "a implies b," to mean "if a, then b." The sentence $a \rightarrow b$, then, is true whenever a and b are true propositions or whenever a is false, regardless of b. In the remaining case, in which a is true and b is false, $a \rightarrow b$ is a false sentence. That is, $(a \rightarrow b) = 1$ if and only if $ab' = 0$. If x and y are propositional variables, $x \rightarrow y \equiv (xy')'$. That is, whenever x and y represent propositions that make $x \rightarrow y$ true, then xy' is false, and conversely. By Theorem 9, we know that $(xy')'$ can be written as $x' + y$. Consequently, x implies y if and only if x represents a false proposition or y a true one,

$$x \rightarrow y \equiv x' + y.$$

Let us construct a table for $x \rightarrow y$.

Table 3

x	y	$x \rightarrow y$
0	0	1
0	1	1
1	0	0
1	1	1

The negation of $x \rightarrow y$ is given by $(x \rightarrow y)' \equiv xy'$. That is, the only case in which it is false that x implies y is that in which x represents a true proposition and y a false one. This may seem a little odd at first, because it is true that a false proposition implies any conclusion whatsoever. However, observe that if a is a true proposition and $a \rightarrow b$ is true, then b is true. This is the way that implication is customarily used.

By definition, $x \rightarrow y \equiv (xy')'$. That is, for given propositions a and b, $a \rightarrow b$ if and only if $ab' = 0$. Does this look familiar? In an abstract Boolean algebra, $a \leq b$ is true if and only if $ab' = 0$. Hence all of the parts of Theorem 10 carry over to implication, for implication is the partial ordering relationship in the Boolean algebra of logic. Let us restate Theorem 10 in the language of the logic of propositions.

Theorem 10. *If x, y, z, and w are propositional variables,*

1. $x \rightarrow x$;
2. *If $x \rightarrow y$ and $y \rightarrow x$, then*

$$x = y,$$

    or

$$(x \rightarrow y)(y \rightarrow x) \rightarrow (x = y);$$

3. *If $x \rightarrow y$ and $y \rightarrow z$, then*

$$x \rightarrow z,$$

    or

$$(x \rightarrow y)(y \rightarrow z) \rightarrow (x \rightarrow z);$$

4. *If $x \to y$ and $x \to z$, then*

$$x \to yz,$$

or

$$(x \to y)(x \to z) \to (x \to yz).$$

5. *If $x \to y$ and $z \to w$, then*

$$x + z \to y + w \quad and \quad xz \to yw,$$

or

$$(x \to y)(z \to w) \to (x + z \to y + w)(xz \to yw);$$

6. *The following are equivalent:*

$$x \to y, \quad xy' = 0, \quad x' + y = 1, \quad y' \to x', \quad x + y = y,$$
$$and \quad xy = x.$$

Since $xy' = 0$ merely states that xy' is false, as does $(xy')'$, the two are equivalent. Also, $x' + y = 1$ merely states that $x' + y$ is true, as does $x' + y$. Hence we may write

$$x \to y \equiv (xy')' \equiv x' + y \equiv y' \to x' \equiv (x + y = y) \equiv (xy = x).$$

Let us interpret these symbolic statements. Part 1 states that every proposition implies itself. For instance, let p be the proposition "Ice is cold." Then $p \to p$ is the proposition "If ice is cold, then ice is cold."

Part 2 states that if two propositions imply each other, they have the same truth value.

Part 3 is the transitive law. It is used in logical arguments to form a chain of deductions. If $a \to b$, $b \to c$, $c \to d$, and $d \to e$, which we shall write as $a \to b \to c \to d \to e$, then $a \to e$. We call a the "hypothesis" and e the "conclusion" that is drawn from the argument. For example, if the temperature is over 90° I am too warm, and if I am too warm I remove my coat. Hence, by Part 3, if the temperature is over 90° I remove my coat.

Part 4 is trivial. It merely states that a proposition implies each of two other propositions if and only if it implies them both.

Part 5 says that if a implies b and c implies d, then the disjunction of a and c implies the disjunction of b and d, and the conjunction of a and c implies the conjunction of b and d.

Part 6 tells us that implication may be written in six different ways. $x \to y \equiv (xy')'$ is merely definition and says that x implies y if and only if it is false that x is true and y is false. This, in turn, is true if and only if x is false or y is true. In applications of implication to logical arguments, we frequently wish to eliminate the sign of implication. This is done by replacing $x \to y$ by either $(xy')'$ or $x' + y$.

The statement that

$$x \rightarrow y \equiv y' \rightarrow x'$$

is particularly important. The second form is called the *contrapositive* of the first. Since $x'' \equiv x$ and $y'' \equiv y$, $x \rightarrow y$ and $y' \rightarrow x'$ are contrapositives of each other. Frequently an implication is seen in a different light if it is stated in the contrapositive form. For instance, "If it rains today, I shall get wet," is equivalent to "If I didn't get wet today, it didn't rain." "If the moon is made of green cheese, then $2 + 2$ is not 4" is equivalent to "If $2 + 2 = 4$, then the moon is not made of green cheese."

The last two parts of 6 say that $x \rightarrow y$ is equivalent to the statement that the disjunction of x and y has the truth value of y, and the conjunction of x and y has the truth value of x.

Since we have already shown that the algebra of logic satisfies Huntington's postulates, it is not necessary to prove the theorems again. However, let us prove that

$$x \rightarrow y \equiv (x + y = y)$$

as an illustration of the techniques of Boolean algebra. The logical statement that $x + y = y$ asserts that $x + y$ and y are both true or both false. That is,

$$(x + y = y) \equiv (x + y)y + (x + y)'y'.$$

Let us show that the right side is equivalent to $x' + y$. If we can do this, we shall have proved that

$$(x + y = y) \equiv x \rightarrow y.$$

By Theorem 3, $y(x + y) \equiv y$. By Theorem 9, $(x + y)' \equiv x'y'$. Thus

$$(x + y)'y' \equiv x'y'y' \equiv x'y'.$$

Hence

$$(x + y)y + (x + y)'y' \equiv y + x'y' \equiv x' + y$$

by Theorem 4, and we are done.

For another example, let us prove Part 3, that

$$(x \rightarrow y)(y \rightarrow z) \rightarrow (x \rightarrow z).$$

One method of proof is to show that this statement is a tautology, true for any propositions that can be substituted for x and y. In order to show the given expression is a tautology we must show that it is equivalent to 1. Our first task is to remove the implication signs. There are two ways to do this. One way is to use the fact that

$$x \rightarrow y \equiv x' + y, \quad y \rightarrow z \equiv y' + z, \quad \text{and} \quad x \rightarrow z \equiv x' + z.$$

Then we have

$$(x' + y)(y' + z) \rightarrow (x' + z),$$

or

$$(x'y' + x'z + yz) \rightarrow (x' + z).$$

Using the same method to remove the last arrow yields

$$\begin{aligned}
(x'y' + x'z + yz)' + x' + z &\equiv (x + y)(x + z')(y' + z') + x' + z \\
&\equiv (x + yz')(y' + z') + x' + z \\
&\equiv xy' + xz' + yz' + x' + z \\
&\equiv y' + z' + y + x' + z \\
&\equiv 1 + 1 + x' \equiv 1.
\end{aligned}$$

The other approach is to use

$$x \rightarrow y \equiv (xy')', \quad y \rightarrow z \equiv (yz')', \quad \text{and} \quad x \rightarrow z \equiv x' + z.$$

Then

$$\begin{aligned}
(xy')'(yz')' \rightarrow (x' + z) &\equiv [(xy')'(yz')']' + x' + z \\
&\equiv xy' + yz' + x' + z \\
&\equiv y' + y + x' + z \equiv 1.
\end{aligned}$$

As a final example of algebraic methods of proof, let us show that

$$(x \rightarrow y)(x \rightarrow z) \equiv (x \rightarrow yz).$$

By Part 6 of Theorem 10, we must show that

$$(x' + y)(x' + z) \equiv x' + yz.$$

By P3, we have

$$x' + yz \equiv x' + yz.$$

Let us observe again that no proof is required for Theorem 10. The proofs given here are, however, illustrative of the methods we can use in logic.

Let us prove that $x \rightarrow y \equiv (xy = x)$ by another technique, the equivalence table (Table 4). Since the columns headed $x \rightarrow y$ and $xy = x$ are identical,

Table 4

x	y	$x \rightarrow y$	xy	$xy = x$
0	0	1	0	1
0	1	1	0	1
1	0	0	0	0
1	1	1	1	1

the equivalence has been proved.

3.40 EXERCISES

*1. Let a be the proposition "I study hard," and let b be the proposition "I receive a good grade." Translate each of the following into reasonable English.

    (a) $a \rightarrow b$ (b) $b' \rightarrow a'$ (c) $a' + b = 1$

    (d) $ab' = 0$ (e) $ab = a$.

2. Give the contrapositive of $x \rightarrow (y + z)$.

*3. Give the contrapositive of $x \rightarrow yz$.

4. Give the contrapositive of $(x + y) \rightarrow z$.

*5. Give the contrapositive of $xy \rightarrow z$.

6. Given the statement, "Every integer that is prime is either odd or is 2."

    (a) Reduce this to a symbolic statement. Define the propositions involved.

    (b) State the contrapositive in English.

*7. Construct propositions a, b, and c such that $a = 1$, $b = 0$, and $c = 1$.

    (a) State Part 2 of Theorem 10 in English with a substituted for x and b for y.

    (b) Does $(a \rightarrow b)$ equal 0 or 1?

    (c) Does $(b \rightarrow a)$ equal 0 or 1?

    (d) State Part 3 of Theorem 10 in English with b replacing x, a replacing y, and c replacing z.

    (e) Does $(b \rightarrow ac)$ equal 0 or 1?

8. Given the statement, "The base angles of an isosceles triangle are equal."

    (a) Change the wording of the statement so that it is in the form "If a, then b."

    (b) Write the contrapositive of the given statement.

*9. If a and b are propositions such that $a = 1$ and $(a \rightarrow b) = 1$, what can you conclude about b?

10. If a, b, and c are propositions such that $a = 1$, $b = 0$, and $[a \rightarrow (b + c)] = 1$, what can you conclude about c?

3.41 VALID ARGUMENTS

In mathematics, truth is a relative matter. When we say that a certain theorem is true, we mean that it is possible to show that the theorem is the logical consequence of certain postulates. These postulates are not accepted as absolute truths but rather as hypotheses. Our theorems are all of the form, perhaps implicitly, "If a certain set of postulates is valid, then this conclusion can be drawn." The question now is, how do we know how to draw these conclusions? What arguments are valid? We define a *valid argument* to be one in which the conjunction of the premises implies the conclusion. Abstractly, if a and b are premises from which the conclusion c can be drawn, $ab \rightarrow c$ is a true sentence, or $(ab \rightarrow c) = 1$.

3.42   TAUTOLOGIES

Our study of valid arguments leads us to examine the sentences involving propositional variables that are logically true for any propositions that may be substituted for the variables. Such sentences are tautologies. Tautological reasoning is of great importance, then, because it always leads to a valid argument. We shall restrict our attention to four tautologies.

1. *Modus ponens.* A simple form of logical reasoning that has been recognized for thousands of years is the modus ponens, in which the conjunction of x and $x \rightarrow y$ implies y. Let us show that $x(x \rightarrow y) \rightarrow y$ is a tautology. We shall proceed to remove the symbols for implication by using the fact that $x \rightarrow y$ can be written either as $(xy')'$ or as $x' + y$. Thus

$$
\begin{aligned}
x(x \rightarrow y) \rightarrow y &\equiv x(xy')' \rightarrow y && \text{first form} \\
&\equiv (x' + xy') + y && \text{second form} \\
&\equiv x' + (xy' + y) && \text{Th. 5} \\
&\equiv x' + x + y && \text{Th. 4} \\
&\equiv 1 + y && \text{P4} \\
&\equiv 1 && \text{Th. 2}
\end{aligned}
$$

Since we have shown that $x(x \rightarrow y) \rightarrow y$ is a tautology, modus ponens is a valid argument.

2. *Syllogism.* Another ancient form of argument is the syllogism. There are many varieties of the syllogism, but one version is essentially Part 3 of Theorem 10; if $x \rightarrow y$ and $y \rightarrow z$, then $x \rightarrow z$.

Two proofs were given earlier that syllogistic reasoning is tautological. We must distinguish between correct logical reasoning and arriving at a true conclusion. If the hypothesis is false, the eventual conclusion may be either true or false, even if the logical reasoning is correct. A chain of logical deductions is only as good as its hypotheses.

3. A simple argument is that if x or y is true and x is false, then y is true.

$$(x + y)x' \rightarrow y \equiv (xx' + x'y) \rightarrow y$$
$$\equiv x'y \rightarrow y$$
$$\equiv x + y' + y$$
$$\equiv x + 1 \equiv 1.$$

4. The next argument is rather strange. It is not particularly useful, but it is a consequence of our logical system. A true conclusion is implied by any premise, true or false. We shall show that $y \rightarrow (x \rightarrow y)$ is a tautology by constructing an equivalence table (Table 5). Since the last column consists

Table 5

x	y	$x \rightarrow y$	$y \rightarrow (x \rightarrow y)$
0	0	1	1
0	1	1	1
1	0	0	1
1	1	1	1

entirely of 1's, we have shown that the proposition is a tautology. From this it follows that if a true proposition is substituted for y, then $x \rightarrow y$ is true no matter what proposition is substituted for x.

3.43   APPLICATIONS

The very richness of the English language is the source of most logical difficulties. If every time one wished to state that a implies b he wrote $a \rightarrow b$, our problem would be simple. The techniques used in proving the tautological nature of an argument would suffice. Thus a major task is to recognize $a \rightarrow b$ when it appears in various disguises. The following list of synonyms for $a \rightarrow b$ will at least indicate the problem.

If a, then b.
b if a.
a only if b.
b unless a'.
a is a sufficient condition for b.
A sufficient condition for b is a.
b is a necessary condition for a.
A necessary condition for a is b.
In order that b it is sufficient that a.
In order that a it is necessary that b.

Example 1. Consider the following collection of statements:
 (a) A trout is a fish.
 (b) If an animal is a fish, then it swims well.
 (c) An animal is clumsy only if it does not swim well.
 (d) All animals are either clumsy or agile but not both.
What conclusions can we draw from these four statements, if they are assumed to be correct? First, we must introduce a symbolism for the propositions. Let

$$t = \text{A certain animal is a trout.}$$
$$f = \text{A certain animal is a fish.}$$
$$c = \text{A certain animal is clumsy.}$$
$$s = \text{A certain animal swims well.}$$
$$a = \text{A certain animal is agile.}$$

Then (a) can be translated as $t \to f$, or $f' \to t'$; (b) can be translated as $f \to s$, or $s' \to f'$; (c) can be translated as $c \to s'$, or $s \to c'$; (d) can be translated as $c' = a$, or $a' = c$.

Let us try now to connect our symbols in a chain of implications, using Part 3 of Theorem 10 or tautology 2. We find that

$$t \to f \to s \to c',$$
or, since $c' = a$,
$$t \to f \to s \to a.$$

In English, this says, "A trout is a fish that swims well and is agile."

Example 2. A man about to be electrocuted is given a chance for his life. In the execution chamber are two chairs, labeled 1 and 2, and a jailer. One chair is electrified; the other is not. The prisoner must sit in one of the chairs, but before doing so he may ask the jailer one question, which the jailer must answer yes or no. The jailer is a consistent liar or else a consistent truth teller, but the prisoner does not know which. Knowing that the jailer deliberately lies or faithfully tells the truth, what question should the prisoner ask?

Let p be the proposition, "Number 1 is the hot seat." Let q be the proposition, "You are telling the truth." Now, consider how the jailer would answer the question, "Is it true that number 1 is the hot seat if and only if you are telling the truth?" Symbolically, the question is, "Is $p = q$ true?"

We shall form an equivalence table (Table 6) for all possible combinations of truth or falsity of the propositions involved with one additional column, the answer the jailer gives, remembering to give a false answer if he is a consistent liar (when $q = 0$), and a true answer if he consistently tells the truth ($q = 1$). We observe from the last column that the jailer

Table 6

p	q	$p = q$	Answer
0	0	1	no
0	1	0	no
1	0	0	yes
1	1	1	yes

answers "yes" if number one is the hot seat and "no" if it is not.

Example 3. The person who is consistently a liar or a truth teller appears often in the folklore of logic. Many logical puzzles are similar to the following:

In a certain country the populace consists entirely of mathematicians and salesmen. The mathematicians (naturally) always speak the truth. The salesmen, on the other hand, are consistent liars. One day three men of the country are out for an evening stroll. Their names, oddly enough, are Mr. A, Mr. B, and Mr. C. Mr. A, in a whisper to Mr. B, states that he is a mathematician or that he is a salesman. Mr. B then turns to Mr. C and says that A claims he is a mathematician. Mr. C replies indignantly that A is not a mathematician; he is a salesman. How many mathematicians and how many salesmen are in the party?

To solve this knotty problem, we list all possible cases in the form of a table where 0 indicates a salesman and 1 indicates a mathematician (Table 7).

Table 7

A	B	C
0	0	0
0	0	1
0	1	0
0	1	1
1	0	0
1	0	1
1	1	0
1	1	1

We now proceed to rule out all the cases that are inconsistent with the given facts. First, if Mr. A were a mathematician, he would identify himself as such to Mr. B. On the other hand, if Mr. A were a salesman, he would lie to Mr. B and state that he is a mathematician. In either event, then, Mr. A tells Mr. B that he is a mathematician. Consequently, Mr. B, who has truthfully relayed this assertion to Mr. C, must be a mathematician. Hence we can rule out half the potential cases, leaving only those entries in the table in which a 1 appears under B. Finally, if Mr. C is a mathematician, his retort is true, and Mr. *A* is a salesman. If Mr. *C* is lying, however, then Mr. *A* is a mathematician. In either case, Mr. *A* and Mr. *C* comprise one mathematician and one salesman. Since Mr. *B* is known to be a mathematician, we can conclude that there are two mathematicians and a salesman in the party.

3.44 EXERCISES

*1. Prove tautology 1 by using an equivalence table.
2. Prove tautology 2 by using an equivalence table.
*3. Prove tautology 3 by using an equivalence table.
4. Prove tautology 4 by the techniques of Boolean algebra.
*5. Prove that $xy \rightarrow x$ is a tautology.
6. Prove that $x \rightarrow x + y$ is a tautology.
*7. Prove that if x, $x \rightarrow y$, and $y \rightarrow z$ are all true, then z is true.
*8. Given: (a) I either ride a bus or drive to work. (b) My car always starts unless it is raining. (c) I ride a bus to work if my car won't start. (d) There wasn't a cloud in the sky all day last Friday. What conclusion, if any, can you draw about what I did last Friday?
9. In Exercise 8, change (c) to: I ride a bus to work only if my car won't start. Does this change the conclusion that can be drawn?
*10. The rain in Spain does not fall on the plain only if the wind is not from the south.
   (a) What happens when the wind is from the south?
   (b) What happens when the wind is from the north?
   (c) The rain in Spain fell on the plain. What can you say about the wind?
   (d) There was no rain on the plains of Spain. What about the wind?
   (e) Restate the sentence in a simpler, direct way.

3.45 RECOMMENDED READING

Arnold, B. H., *Logic and Boolean Algebra*, New York, Prentice-Hall, 1962.

Christian, R. R., *Introduction to Logic and Sets*, Boston, Ginn, 1958.

Davis, R. L. (ed.), *Elementary Mathematics of Sets with Applications*, CUP, Math. Assoc. of America, 1958.

Hohn, F. E., *Applied Boolean Algebra*, New York, Macmillan, 1960.

Krickenberger, W. R., and Pearson, H. R., *An Introduction to Sets and the Structure of Algebra*, Boston, Ginn, 1958.

Stanton, R. G., and Fryer, K. D., *Topics in Modern Mathematics*, New York, Prentice-Hall, 1964.

Whitesitt, J. E., *Boolean Algebra and Its Applications*, Reading, Mass., Addison-Wesley, 1962.

Young, F. H., *Digital Computers and Related Mathematics*, Boston, Ginn, 1961.

4

Philip Gendreau

The arithmetic of the hours; the integers modulo 12.

4.1 INTRODUCTION

In Chapter 2 an exploration was made into the algebraic properties of various number systems. We found, for instance, that the rational numbers form an ordered field. Some mention was made of number systems consisting of only a finite number of elements. In this chapter we shall investigate more thoroughly those number systems whose elements are *classes* of integers, where a class consists of the set of all integers that leave the same remainder after division by some integer, say m. For example, every integer leaves a remainder of 0, 1, or 2 when divided by 3. Thus, when $m = 3$, we are led to a number system having only three elements. Each element consists of an infinite set of integers sharing a common property: they leave the same remainder when divided by 3.

4.2 NOTATION, CONGRUENCE MODULO m

We need a set of symbols to represent these classes. The obvious choice is the remainder itself. This choice can lead to confusion, but it is quite simple to use if we are careful. In the example above, where $m = 3$, the symbol **2** can represent the set of all integers that leave a remainder of 2 when divided by 3. In this sense, **2** is used as a class, not an integer. In general, for any integer m greater than 1, the m symbols **0, 1, 2, . . . , m − 1** can represent

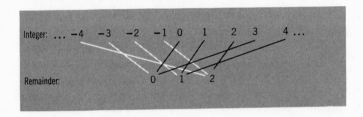

the classes of integers having the corresponding remainder when divided by m. We shall call these the *residue classes modulo m*.

Let us introduce the symbol $\equiv$, defined as follows:

> **Definition of** $\equiv$. If a and b are integers and $m > 1$, then $a \equiv b$ (modulo m) means that a and b leave the same remainder when divided by m.

We shall call m the *modulus* of the finite number system obtained. It is customary to abbreviate "modulo" to "mod," so that we can write $a \equiv b$ (mod m). For $m = 3$, we have $5 \equiv 11$ (mod 3), $-6 \equiv 0$ (mod 3), and so forth. We shall read the symbol $\equiv$ as "is congruent to," so that $a \equiv b$ (mod m) is read "a is congruent to b modulo m." Thus a set consisting of all integers congruent to each other forms a residue class modulo m.

We know that, if x is any integer, then x divided by m yields a quotient q and a remainder r, with $0 \leq r < m$, satisfying the relation $x = qm + r$. The remainder r is an integer in the set $0, 1, \ldots, m - 1$. Hence, if $a = q_1 m + r_1$ and $b = q_2 m + r_2$, then $a \equiv b$ (mod m) if and only if $r_1 = r_2$. Moreover, if $r_1 = r_2$, then

$$a - b = q_1 m - q_2 m = (q_1 - q_2)m.$$

That is, $a \equiv b$ (mod m) if and only if $a - b$ is a multiple of m.

Suppose that m is a modulus. Then we are led to a number system of m elements represented by the symbols $\mathbf{0, 1, 2, \ldots, m - 1}$, where each symbol represents an infinite residue class. Since each integer leaves a unique remainder between 0 and $m - 1$ when divided by m, each integer belongs to one and only one of the m classes. Two integers in the same class are congruent modulo m. Two integers in different classes are said to be *incongruent* modulo m. We are now ready to explore the algebraic structure of a *modular number system*, the system consisting of m elements.

4.3 EQUALITY AND ADDITION MODULO m

Let $\mathbf{0, 1, 2, \ldots, m - 1}$ be residue classes modulo m. If $\mathbf{r}_1$ and $\mathbf{r}_2$ are elements of the system, then we shall say that $\mathbf{r}_1 = \mathbf{r}_2$ if and only if the sets of integers forming $\mathbf{r}_1$ and $\mathbf{r}_2$ are identical. If this is true, and a and b are any two integers in the set, then

$$a \equiv b \ (\text{mod } m).$$

Hence we know what equality means in the system.

What meaning can be attached to addition in such a system? Our task is to seek a meaningful interpretation of the addition of two *classes* of integers. If r_1 and r_2 are residue classes modulo m, let a be any integer belonging to r_1 and b any integer belonging to r_2. Let $a + b = c$. Then c belongs to some class r_3. If we can show that the resulting r_3 is independent of the selection of a and b, then we have a logical basis for defining $r_1 + r_2$ to be r_3. By the rule for division, if a is any integer in r_1, then there exists a q_1 such that

$$a = q_1 m + r_1.$$

(Note that in this equation r_1 is an integer, not a class.) Also, if b is any integer in r_2, there exists a q_2 such that

$$b = q_2 m + r_2.$$

Then

$$a + b = q_1 m + r_1 + q_2 m + r_2 = (q_1 + q_2)m + r_1 + r_2.$$

Now, $r_1 + r_2$ may exceed m, but, since $r_1 + r_2$ is an integer, there are a q_3 and r_3 such that

$$r_1 + r_2 = q_3 m + r_3.$$

Thus,

$$a + b = (q_1 + q_2)m + q_3 m + r_3 = (q_1 + q_2 + q_3)m + r_3.$$

Hence

$$a + b \equiv r_3 \,(\text{mod } m)$$

for any a belonging to class r_1 and b belonging to class r_2.

For example, let us consider the residue classes modulo 13. If we wish to add the residue classes 7 and 9, we can add any two integers, one congruent to 7 modulo 13 and the other congruent to 9 modulo 13. Two obvious integers in this class are 7 and 9. As integers, their sum is 16, which is congruent to 3 modulo 13. Thus, in the residue classes modulo 13, $7 + 9 = 3$. The work of the previous paragraph assures us that, had we chosen any other integers in classes 7 and 9, the result would have been in the same class. For instance,

$$46 \equiv 7 \,(\text{mod } 13), \qquad 165 \equiv 9 \,(\text{mod } 13),$$

and

$$46 + 165 = 211 = 13 \cdot 16 + 3 \equiv 3 \,(\text{mod } 13).$$

What we have done is establish that we obtain a unique sum for two residue classes by adding any two elements of the residue classes and finding the residue class to which the sum belongs. Because this operation can always be performed we have shown that a modular number system is *closed under addition*.

To make sure that we understand this addition of residue classes, let us construct the table of addition for a modulus of 3 (Table 1). As residue classes,

Table 1.   + (mod 3)

	0	1	2
0	0	1	2
1	1	2	0
2	2	0	1

$2 + 2 = 1$ because as integers, $2 + 2 = 4 \equiv 1$ (mod 3).

Let us illustrate further what we have done. Suppose that we wish to add the residue classes **2** and **3** modulo 7. Our definition says that we can choose any element of the class **2**, such as 16, and any element of class **3**, such as 10, and the sum will always be in the same class, in this case **5**. We may think of the members of class **2** being written in one row and the members of class **3** in a row below with the 10 occurring just below the 16:

$$\downarrow$$

Class 2:	...	−5	2	9	16	23	30	37	...
Class 3:	...	−11	−4	3	10	17	24	31	...
Sum:	...	−16	−2	12	26	40	54	68	... (all elements of class 5)

We would like to show that *addition of residue classes is commutative*. As with closure, we must show that for any a in r_1 and b in r_2, $a + b$ and $b + a$ fall in the same residue class. Since we know from the work of Chapter 2 that

$$a + b = b + a$$

for any integers, this is trivial.

Next, is it true that *addition of residue classes is associative?* This is left as an exercise for the student.

The next field property is *the existence of an additive identity*. One residue class modulo m, represented by **0**, is the set of all multiples of m. Let km be any member of the class **0**. If **r** is any residue class, and a belongs to **r**, then $a + km \equiv a$ (mod m). Thus, as residue classes, $r + 0 = r$. The class **0** is the additive identity.

Finally, let a be any element of a class **r**, where **r** is not the **0** class. Let b be any member of the class **m** − **r**. Then

$$a = q_1 m + r \quad \text{and} \quad b = q_2 m + m - r,$$

so that

$$a + b = q_1 m + r + q_2 m + m - r = (q_1 + q_2 + 1)m.$$

Hence,

$$a + b \equiv 0 \pmod{m}.$$

Since $a + b$ belongs to the **0** class, it follows that **m** − **r** is the additive inverse of the class **r**. It is trivial to show that the **0** class is its own additive inverse. Thus *every element of a modular number system has an additive inverse.*

We have shown that with our definition of addition every modular number system satisfies all the field properties for addition.

Examples.

$$10 \equiv 5 \pmod{5}, \quad 15 \equiv -24 \pmod{13}, \quad 9 + 13 = 22 \equiv 1 \pmod{7},$$
$$47 + 13 = 60 \equiv 0 \pmod{12}, \quad -17 - 42 - 10 = -69 \equiv 3 \pmod{12}.$$

4.4 EXERCISES

*1. Prove that addition is associative in the set of residue classes modulo m.

2. What sort of system results if one forms the set of residue classes modulo 1?

*3. What sort of system results if one forms the set of residue classes modulo 0?

4. Give five integers congruent to 6 modulo 7.

*5. Give five integers congruent to 3 modulo 12.

6. Give five integers congruent to 0 modulo 15.

*7. Give five integers congruent to 16 modulo 17.

8. If $m > 1$ and $3 \equiv 5 \pmod{m}$, what is m?

*9. If $m > 1$ and $13 \equiv 19 \pmod{m}$, what are the possible values of m?

10. If $m > 1$ and $-7 \equiv 11 \pmod{m}$, what are the possible values of m?

*11. Every integer can be represented as $3n$, $3n + 1$, or $3n - 1$ for some n. Use this to show that every square is congruent to either 0 or 1 modulo 3.

12. Into what residue classes modulo 4 do the squares fall?

*13. The solutions of $x + 15 \equiv 2 \pmod{8}$ form what residue class?

14. The solutions of $x - 15 \equiv 2 \pmod{8}$ form what residue class?

*15. Let r_1 and r_2 be residue classes modulo 7 and let $r_1 + r_2 = 6$, where 6 is a residue class modulo 7. Form a table of all possible classes for r_1 and r_2.

16. Find an integer x such that $2x \equiv 5 \pmod{7}$.

*17. Find an integer x such that $3x \equiv 4 \pmod{11}$.

18. Find three integers x such that $3x \equiv 1 \pmod{7}$.

*19. Find three integers x such that $3x \equiv 1 \pmod{11}$.

20. Is there an integer x such that $3x \equiv 4 \pmod{6}$?

4.5   MULTIPLICATION MODULO m

Let r_1 and r_2 be residue classes modulo m. Is it possible to define multiplication of residue classes in the same manner that addition was defined? Let us try. Let a be any integer in class r_1 and b any integer in class r_2. Then there exist q_1 and q_2 such that

$$a = q_1 m + r_1 \quad \text{and} \quad b = q_2 m + r_2.$$

From this it follows that

$$ab = (q_1 m + r_1)(q_2 m + r_2) = q_1 q_2 m^2 + q_1 r_2 m + q_2 r_1 m + r_1 r_2$$
$$= (q_1 q_2 m + q_1 r_2 + q_2 r_1)m + r_1 r_2,$$

or

$$ab \equiv r_1 r_2 \ (\text{mod } m).$$

Now $r_1 r_2$, as a product of integers, may exceed m, but there exist q_3 and r_3 such that

$$r_1 r_2 = q_3 m + r_3.$$

Hence

$$ab \equiv r_3 \ (\text{mod } m)$$

for any a in r_1 and b in r_2. Consequently, the resulting product is unique, and we can define $r_1 r_2$ to be the class r_3. Residue classes are *closed under multiplication*.

The same argument used for addition shows that *multiplication is commutative and associative* in the system of residue classes modulo m. In fact, since the product of two residue classes is independent of the representative elements chosen, these properties are inherited from the integers, as was shown in the examples of Chapter 2.

The residue class **1** modulo m consists of all integers one greater than a multiple of m. Let a belong to the class **1**, so that

$$a = q_1 m + 1.$$

Let **r** be any residue class modulo m, and let b belong to **r**, so that

$$b = q_2 m + r.$$

Then

$$ab = (q_1 m + 1)(q_2 m + r) = q_1 q_2 m^2 + q_1 r m + q_2 m + r$$
$$= (q_1 q_2 m + q_1 r + q_2)m + r.$$

That is,

$$ab \equiv r \pmod{m},$$

or the product of any integer in class **1** with any member of class **r** is in class **r**. This demonstrates that *class* **1** *is the multiplicative identity* of the system of residue classes modulo m.

There remains the problem of multiplicative inverses, and it is here that we first encounter a real barrier. For any nonzero class **r**, we would like to find a class $\mathbf{r}^{-1}$ such that $\mathbf{rr}^{-1}$ is the class **1**. We shall find that this is not possible for every value of the modulus. For example, if $m = 4$, the inverse of **2** would be the class of all integers x such that $2x \equiv 1 \pmod 4$. Since $2x$ is always even, but every integer congruent to 1 modulo 4 is odd, there is no solution. Obviously, the modulus must be restricted in some way to insure the existence of an inverse.

Let $\mathbf{r}_1$ and $\mathbf{r}_2$ be any nonzero residue classes modulo m. What must be true of m if $\mathbf{r}_1\mathbf{r}_2 = \mathbf{1}$? If a and b are any integers in classes $\mathbf{r}_1$ and $\mathbf{r}_2$ respectively, we must have

$$ab \equiv 1 \pmod{m}.$$

That is, there exists q such that

$$ab = qm + 1 \quad \text{or} \quad ab - qm = 1.$$

If a and m had a common divisor $d > 1$, then d would be a factor of the left side. This would imply that d is a factor of 1, but this is impossible. Hence, a and m must have no factor in common. Since this condition must be true for every integer a in every nonzero residue class, we can conclude that no natural number greater than 1 and less than m has a factor in common with m. This says that m must be a prime number. We have shown that a necessary condition for the existence of a multiplicative inverse for every nonzero class is that the modulus be a prime number. Hereafter, whenever the symbol p is used for a modulus, we shall understand that p is a prime number.

It is necessary that the modulus be prime for multiplicative inverses for all nonzero classes to exist. Is it also sufficient? That is, is it true that for any integer a not a multiple of a prime p we can find a b such that $ab \equiv 1 \pmod p$? If so, the residue class to which b belongs is $\mathbf{r}^{-1}$, the inverse of $\mathbf{r}$, the class to which a belongs. We shall show that a unique class $\mathbf{r}^{-1}$ exists for every nonzero residue class $\mathbf{r}$ modulo p.

Let us call two integers relatively prime if they have no factor other than ± 1 in common. For example, 8 and 15 are relatively prime, even though neither is a prime number. Consider the set

$$\{a, 2a, 3a, \ldots, (p - 1)a\}.$$

If a is relatively prime to p, all $p - 1$ numbers in the set are also relatively prime to p. That is, none of them has a factor in common with p. This will be proved in Section 4.8. Hence, when divided by p, they leave remainders in the set $\{1, 2, \ldots, p - 1\}$. Can two of them leave the same remainder? If so, there are some n_1 and n_2 between 1 and $p - 1$ such that

$$n_1 a \equiv n_2 a \pmod{p},$$

or there is some q such that

$$n_1 a = qp + n_2 a, \quad \text{or} \quad n_1 a - n_2 a = qp, \quad \text{or} \quad (n_1 - n_2)a = qp.$$

Since a is relatively prime to p, it must be a factor of q, so that $q = ka$. Then

$$(n_1 - n_2)a = kap, \quad \text{or} \quad n_1 - n_2 = kp.$$

But this says that $n_1 \equiv n_2 \pmod{p}$. Since n_1 and n_2 are both less than p, they cannot be congruent unless they are equal. Hence, $n_1 a$ is not congruent to $n_2 a$ modulo p unless $n_1 = n_2$. From this we conclude that all $p - 1$ numbers in the set $\{a, 2a, \ldots, (p - 1)a\}$ fall in separate residue classes modulo p. Since there are only $p - 1$ nonzero residue classes, exactly one of the numbers of the set must fall in the residue class 1. That is, there is an n such that $na \equiv 1 \pmod{p}$. Then the residue class to which n belongs is the inverse of the class to which a belongs. We have proved that for every nonzero residue class $\mathbf{r}$ modulo a prime p there is a unique residue class $\mathbf{r}^{-1}$ such that $\mathbf{rr}^{-1} = \mathbf{1}$.

We have shown that the set of residue classes modulo any prime p satisfy all the field properties of multiplication. The requirement that the modulus be prime is necessary only for one property, the existence of multiplicative inverses. If we can now show that the system of residue classes modulo p satisfies the distributive law, we shall have shown that the system is actually a field.

4.6 THE DISTRIBUTIVE LAW

We shall show that *multiplication distributes over addition* in the set of residue classes modulo m, where m need not necessarily be a prime. From our definitions of addition and multiplication, all we must show is that for any integers a, b, and c,

$$a(b + c) \equiv ab + ac \pmod{m}.$$

Since the distributive law holds for integers, it is always true that $a(b + c) = ab + ac$. Consequently, it is trivially true that $a(b + c)$ and $ab + ac$, being equal, fall in the same residue class modulo m. In other words distributivity, like commutativity and associativity, is inherited from the integers. This completes our proof that the set of residue classes modulo any prime p forms a field.

4.7   EXERCISES

*1. Prove that multiplication is commutative in the set of residue classes modulo m.
 2. Prove that multiplication is associative in the set of residue classes modulo m.
*3. Recall that a prime number is an integer greater than 1 with no factor greater than 1 except itself. Give the first ten prime numbers.
 4. Form addition and multiplication tables for the residue classes modulo 3.
*5. Form addition and multiplication tables for the residue classes modulo 5.
 6. Form addition and multiplication tables for the residue classes modulo 7.
*7. Form addition and multiplication tables for the residue classes modulo 12.
 8. In the set of residue classes modulo 12, which classes do not have multiplicative inverses?
*9. If p is a prime, is it true that $ax \equiv ay \pmod{p}$ implies $x \equiv y \pmod{p}$ whenever $a \not\equiv 0 \pmod{p}$?
10. If m is not a prime, is it true that $ax \equiv ay \pmod{m}$ implies $x \equiv y \pmod{m}$ whenever $a \not\equiv 0 \pmod{m}$? Give an example.
*11. Can the set of residue classes modulo m be ordered? Review the properties of order in Chapter 2 and show that the residue classes modulo 3 cannot be ordered.

4.8   BASIC THEOREMS, DIVISIBILITY

Our next task is to determine when the solutions of congruences exist, what the solutions are, and how to find them. For this purpose we need three basic theorems about factorization of integers. The first, which will be given without proof, is called the *fundamental theorem of arithmetic*.

> **Theorem 1.** *Every integer not equal to 0, 1, or -1 can be factored in only one way as a product of primes, except for the order of the factors.*

The positive prime numbers are 2, 3, 5, 7, 11, ... Let us denote the first of these by p_1, the second by p_2, and, in general, the nth by p_n. Since Euclid proved that there are infinitely many primes, our sequence is endless. Theorem 1 implies that any integer n not 0 or ± 1 may be written in the form $n = \pm p_1^{\alpha_1} p_2^{\alpha_2} \cdots p_k^{\alpha_k}$, where α_i is the number of times that p_i occurs in the factorization of n. Since n is an integer, all α_i are 0 for i sufficiently large. For example,

$$200 = 2^3 \cdot 3^0 \cdot 5^2, \quad \text{and} \quad -63 = -2^0 \cdot 3^2 \cdot 5^0 \cdot 7.$$

We shall say that a *divides* b, written $a|b$, if a is a factor of b. That is, $a|b$ if and only if there is some integer c such that $b = ac$. For example, $3|72$ and $5|-200$. Clearly, every nonzero integer divides itself, 1 divides every integer, and every integer divides 0. The last is true because $0 = 0 \cdot a$ for any a. If a does not divide b, we shall write $a \nmid b$. Another way of looking at divisibility is provided by the fundamental theorem: $a|b$ if and only if every prime factor of a occurs at least as often in b as it does in a. This leads to our second theorem.

Theorem 2. *If $a|bc$ and a and b are relatively prime, then $a|c$.*

Proof: Let the integer bc be written in its completely factored form. Since bc is a multiple of a, every prime factor of a is a factor of bc. Since a and b are relatively prime, none of the factors of a is a factor of b. Hence, the factors of a are among the factors of bc contributed by c. Thus $a|c$.

As a corollary of Theorem 2, let us note that if p is any prime dividing a product bc, then p must divide b or c.

4.9 GREATEST COMMON DIVISORS

If a and b are any integers, the greatest common divisor of a and b is a nonnegative integer d with the following two properties:

1. $d|a$ and $d|b$;
2. if $c|a$ and $c|b$, then $c|d$.

Let us denote the greatest common divisor of a and b by (a, b). Then $(16, 24) = 8, (27, 15) = 3$, and $(11, 7) = 1$. We can now say that a and b are relatively prime if and only if $(a, b) = 1$.

An interesting and useful fact about greatest common divisors is given in the following theorem.

Theorem 3. *If $(a, b) = d$, then there exist integers s and t such that $as + bt = d$.*

Proof: Let us suppose that $b < a$. Then, by the division algorithm, there exist integers q_1 and r_1, with $0 \leq r_1 < b$, such that

$$a = q_1 b + r_1.$$

Since $d|a$ and $d|b$, it follows that $d|r_1$. A repetition of the division algorithm yields integers q_2 and r_2, with $0 \le r_2 < r_1$, such that

$$b = q_2r_1 + r_2.$$

Since $d|b$ and $d|r_1$, it follows that $d|r_2$. The next step in this process is

$$r_1 = q_3r_2 + r_3, \qquad 0 \le r_3 < r_2, \quad \text{and} \quad d|r_3.$$

This process yields a succession of decreasing remainders, each divisible by d. Since a sequence of decreasing positive remainders must have a least element r_k, the next remainder, r_{k+1}, must be zero. Thus the final two steps appear as

$$r_{k-2} = q_kr_{k-1} + r_k, \qquad 0 < r_k < r_{k-1}, \quad \text{and} \quad d|r_k;$$

$$r_{k-1} = q_{k+1}r_k + 0.$$

From the last step we see that $r_k|r_{k-1}$. Therefore, from the preceding step, we find that $r_k|r_{k-2}$. By working backward we find that r_k divides each of the previous remainders. From the second step we find that since r_k divides r_2 and r_1, $r_k|b$. Thus, from the first step, since r_k divides r_1 and b, $r_k|a$. Since $r_k|b$ and $r_k|a$, r_k is a common divisor of a and b, so that $r_k|d$. Thus we have found that

$$d|r_k \quad \text{and} \quad r_k|d.$$

If two positive integers divide each other, they are equal, so that

$$r_k = d.$$

To complete our proof, we must show that d (or r_k) can be expressed in terms of a and b. In the first equation, $r_1 = a - q_1b$. Substituting this expression for r_1 in the second equation gives r_2 in terms of a and b. Repeated substitution finally leads to d in the desired form.

Let us illustrate Theorem 3 for $(78, 32)$.

$$78 = 2 \cdot 32 + 14$$
$$32 = 2 \cdot 14 + 4$$
$$14 = 3 \cdot 4 + 2$$
$$4 = 2 \cdot 2 + 0.$$

Hence, $(78, 32) = 2$. Next,

$$14 = 78 - 2 \cdot 32.$$

Thus,
$$4 = 32 - 2(78 - 2 \cdot 32) = 5 \cdot 32 - 2 \cdot 78,$$

and
$$2 = 14 - 3 \cdot 4 = (78 - 2 \cdot 32) - 3(5 \cdot 32 - 2 \cdot 78)$$
$$= 7 \cdot 78 - 17 \cdot 32.$$

We have found that the s and t of Theorem 3 are 7 and -17, respectively.

A consequence of Theorem 3 is of such importance that we shall call it a corollary.

Corollary. If $(a, m) = d$, then $ax \equiv d \pmod{m}$ has a solution.

Proof: By Theorem 3, if $(a, m) = d$, there exist integers s and t such that $as + mt = d$. Then $as = d - mt$, or $as \equiv d \pmod{m}$. Thus s is a solution.

In particular, let us notice that if $(a, m) = 1$, then there is an x such that $ax \equiv 1 \pmod{m}$.

4.10 SOLUTION OF CONGRUENCES

We observe that $2x \equiv 1 \pmod{3}$ is satisfied for $x = 2, 5, -1$, and, in fact, for any $x \equiv 2 \pmod{3}$. On the other hand, $2x \equiv 1 \pmod{4}$ does not have a solution. In this section we wish to accomplish two things. One is to find a criterion for determining whether a solution exists to a congruence of the form $ax \equiv b \pmod{m}$. The second is to establish a means of finding the solution. The first is embodied in the following theorem.

Theorem 4. $ax \equiv b \pmod{m}$ *has a solution if and only if* $(a, m)|b$.

Proof: If $ax \equiv b \pmod{m}$, there is some k such that

$$ax - b = km, \quad \text{or} \quad ax - km = b.$$

Let $d = (a, m)$. Since $d|a$ and $d|m$, d divides the left side of the equation. Hence, d must divide b. The condition of the theorem is necessary. We must show that it is sufficient. By the Corollary, $(a, m) = d$ implies that there exists an x_1 such that $ax_1 \equiv d \pmod{m}$. Since $d|b$, $b = b_1 d$. Then, $ab_1 x_1 \equiv b_1 d \pmod{m}$, or $ab_1 x_1 \equiv b \pmod{m}$. Let $x = b_1 x_1$. Then $ax \equiv b \pmod{m}$.

Theorem 4 not only gives the criterion for the existence of a solution to a congruence, it also gives a method for finding a solution. However, the method has two drawbacks. One is that not all solutions are necessarily found, and the second is that the method is rather cumbersome to use. First, let us show that in some congruences the solution found in the proof of Theorem 4 is not complete.

Example 1. Let us solve

$$2x \equiv 4 \pmod{6}$$

by the method above. We have $d = (a, m) = (2, 6) = 2$, so that $d|b$. We observe that $2 \cdot 4 + 6(-1) = 2$. By Theorem 3, $2 \cdot 4 \equiv 2$ (mod 6). Since $b = 4 = 2 \cdot 2$, we multiply both sides by 2 to obtain $2 \cdot 8 \equiv 4$ (mod 6). We are led to the solution $x \equiv 8$ (mod 6) or, in simpler form, $x \equiv 2$ (mod 6). However, $x \equiv 5$ (mod 6) is also a solution.

The following theorem disposes of our difficulty.

Theorem 5. *If $(a, m) = d$ and $d|b$, then the general solution of $ax \equiv b$ (mod m) is given by the solutions of $(a/d)x \equiv b/d$ (mod m/d).*

Proof: Let
$$a = a_1 d, \quad b = b_1 d, \quad \text{and} \quad m = m_1 d.$$

We wish to show that any solution of $a_1 x \equiv b_1$ (mod m_1) is also a solution of $ax \equiv b$ (mod m) and that there are no other solutions. If $a_1 x \equiv b_1$ (mod m_1), there is some k such that
$$a_1 x - b_1 = km_1.$$
Then,
$$da_1 x - db_1 = km_1 d, \quad \text{or} \quad ax - b = km, \quad \text{or} \quad ax \equiv b \text{ (mod } m).$$

Part of our proof is complete. We must now show that there are no other solutions. Let x be any solution of $ax \equiv b$ (mod m), so that
$$ax = b + km.$$
Then
$$a_1 dx = b_1 d + km_1 d, \quad \text{or} \quad a_1 x = b_1 + km_1.$$

Thus x is also a solution of $a_1 x \equiv b_1$ (mod m_1). This completes our proof.

Example 1. Solve
$$2x \equiv 6 \text{ (mod 8)}.$$

Since $(2, 8) = 2$ and $6 = 2(3)$, the general solution is given by
$$x \equiv 3 \text{ (mod 4)}.$$

Example 2. Solve
$$6x \equiv 8 \text{ (mod 10)}.$$

Since $(6, 10) = 2$ and $8 = 2(4)$, the general solution is given by the solutions of
$$3x \equiv 4 \text{ (mod 5)}.$$

Since $4 \equiv 9$ (mod 5), we may write our congruence as
$$3x \equiv 9 \text{ (mod 5)}.$$

Since $x \equiv 3 \pmod 5$ is an obvious solution to this last congruence, we have found the general solution.

Example 3. Solve

$$6x \equiv 7 \pmod{10}.$$

Since $(6, 10) = 2$ and $2 \nmid 7$, there is no solution to the congruence.

4.11 EXERCISES

*1. Express each of the following numbers as a product of primes:

    (a) 72   (b) 484   (c) 1215

    (d) 187   (e) -1449

*2. Find each of the following greatest common divisors:

    (a) $(45, 63)$ (b) $(102, 78)$ (c) $(91, 36)$

    (d) $(168, 147)$ (e) $(180, 108)$

*3. What can you say about $(n, n + 1)$ for any natural number n? (Hint: $n + 1 - n = 1$.)

4. Prove that if $a|bc$ and $(a, b) = 1$, then $a|c$.

*5. Prove that if $a|b$ and $b|c$, then $a|c$.

6. Prove that if $a|b$ and $b|a$, then $a = \pm b$.

*7. Find integers s and t such that $45s + 63t = 9$.

8. Find integers s and t such that $17s + 11t = 1$.

*9. Find integers s and t such that $13s + 31t = 1$.

10. Find integers s and t such that $78s + 102t = 6$.

11. Solve each of the following congruences:

    *(a) $2x \equiv 5 \pmod 7$ (b) $3x \equiv 7 \pmod{11}$ *(c) $3x \equiv -4 \pmod{11}$

    (d) $3x \equiv -7 \pmod{11}$ *(e) $3x \equiv 1 \pmod{11}$

12. Solve each of the following congruences:

    *(a) $2x \equiv 6 \pmod{12}$ (b) $3x \equiv 12 \pmod{15}$ *(c) $4x \equiv 6 \pmod{10}$

    (d) $6x \equiv 9 \pmod{15}$ *(e) $6x \equiv 8 \pmod{10}$

4.12 TECHNIQUES FOR SOLVING CONGRUENCES

Preceding sections have shown that the congruence $ax \equiv b \pmod m$ has a solution if and only if

$$(a, m)|b.$$

If the condition is satisfied, the general solution can be found by reducing the congruence to

$$a_1 x \equiv b_1 \pmod{m_1},$$

where $a = a_1 d, b = b_1 d, m = m_1 d$, and $d = (a, m)$. Further, since $(a_1, m_1) = 1$, the solution of $a_1 x \equiv b_1 \pmod{m_1}$ can be found by using the algorithm employed in the proof of Theorem 3 to find integers s and t such that

$$a_1 s + m_1 t = 1.$$

Then, since $a_1 s b_1 + m_1 t b_1 = b_1$, the general solution is given by

$$x \equiv s b_1 \pmod{m_1}.$$

The use of the algorithm of Theorem 3 is not particularly difficult, but it can frequently be long and messy. Since the process has a clearly defined algorithm, it is not difficult to program for a digital computer, and this is frequently done. However, in the absence of a computer there are a number of tricks that may be employed to reduce the amount of computation. The first of these is to simplify the given congruence as much as possible before attempting to find a solution.

Theorem 6. *If $(c, m) = 1$, the congruences $ax \equiv b \pmod{m}$ and $cax \equiv cb$ (mod m) have the same solution.*

Proof: Suppose $(c, m) = 1$. Let us show first that if x is any integer such that $ax \equiv b \pmod{m}$, then

$$cax \equiv cb \pmod{m}.$$

This is trivial and does not depend upon the fact that $(c, m) = 1$. If $ax \equiv b \pmod{m}$, there is an integer k such that

$$ax = b + km.$$

Then

$$cax = cb + ckm, \quad \text{or} \quad cax \equiv cb \pmod{m}.$$

The converse requires a little more argument. In essence, we wish to establish a cancellation law for congruences. If x is any integer such that $cax \equiv cb \pmod{m}$, then there is some integer k such that

$$cax = cb + km, \quad \text{or} \quad c(ax - b) = km.$$

Thus

$$c \mid km.$$

Since $(c, m) = 1$, it follows from Theorem 2 that $c \mid k$, or there is some k_1 such that $k = c k_1$. Thus

$$c(ax - b) = c k_1 m, \quad \text{or} \quad ax - b = k_1 m, \quad \text{or} \quad ax \equiv b \pmod{m}.$$

Example 1. Solve

$$6x \equiv 15 \pmod{27}.$$

Since $(6, 27) = 3$ and $3|15$, the congruence is solvable. Our first step is to use Theorem 5 to replace the given congruence by a simpler but equivalent one,

$$2x \equiv 5 \pmod{9}.$$

We now have several choices of action. One is to multiply both sides by some integer relatively prime to 9, where the multiplier is selected in such a way as to simplify the coefficient of x. We observe that

$$2(5) = 10 \equiv 1 \pmod{9}.$$

Hence, multiplying both sides of the congruence by 5 yields

$$10x \equiv 25 \pmod{9}, \quad \text{or} \quad x \equiv 7 \pmod{9}.$$

Another procedure is to replace the right side of the congruence, 5, by some number congruent to it that has a factor in common with the coefficient of x. In this problem we can replace 5 by 14. Then

$$2x \equiv 14 \pmod{9}.$$

Since $(2, 9) = 1$, Theorem 6 says that the common factor of 2 may be cancelled, leaving

$$x \equiv 7 \pmod{9}.$$

Both methods are useful.

Example 2. Solve

$$7x \equiv 11 \pmod{29}.$$

Since $(7, 29) = 1$, we cannot reduce the modulus. Let us look for a multiple of 7 that is close to the modulus. In this problem, we observe that $7(4) = 28$. Hence, multiplying both sides by 4, which is permissible since $(4, 29) = 1$, we have

$$28x \equiv 44 \pmod{29}, \quad \text{or} \quad -x \equiv 15 \pmod{29}.$$

Finally, multiplying by -1, we find

$$x \equiv -15 \pmod{29}, \quad \text{or} \quad x \equiv 14 \pmod{29}.$$

Example 3. Solve

$$327x \equiv 543 \pmod{825}.$$

We find that
$$(327, 825) = 3, \quad \text{and} \quad 543 = 3(181).$$

Thus our reduced congruence is

$$109x \equiv 181 \pmod{275}.$$

We note, for future reference, that the prime factors of 275 are 5 and 11. We look for a multiple of 109 that is close to 275 or a multiple of 275, being careful to choose multiples that are relatively prime to 275. If one is not immediately obvious we can try another trick, which is to replace 109 and 181 by $109 - 275$ and $181 - 275$, respectively. Then we have

$$-166x \equiv -94 \pmod{275}.$$

We can now cancel the factor -2 on both sides, leaving

$$83x \equiv 47 \pmod{275}.$$

Let us now multiply both sides by 3, obtaining

$$249x \equiv 141 \pmod{275},$$

or, repeating the previous trick,

$$-26x \equiv -134 \pmod{275},$$

so that
$$13x \equiv 67 \pmod{275}.$$

We now observe that 13(21) is almost 275. Multiplying both sides by 21 yields
$$273x \equiv 1407 \pmod{275},$$

or
$$-2x \equiv 32 \pmod{275},$$

which finally leads to $\quad x \equiv -16 \equiv 259 \pmod{275}.$

We have finally found the general solution. The technique that has been demonstrated is not very definite. It depends on the observation and astuteness of the person using the technique. All that can be said in its favor is that when it works it saves considerable time. However, it is comforting to know that there is still a guaranteed algorithm to fall back on if necessary.

Why are we so careful to avoid multiplying both sides of a congruence by a number not relatively prime to the modulus? The reason is that extraneous solutions can be introduced in this way. For example, consider

$$x \equiv 9 \pmod{16}.$$

If we were to multiply both sides by 2, we would have $2x \equiv 18 \equiv 2 \pmod{16}$, which has the solution

$$x \equiv 1 \pmod 8$$

by Theorem 5. Obviously 1 is not a solution of the original congruence. However, the set of integers congruent to 1 modulo 8 include all solutions of the original congruence. Thus it is sometimes useful to multiply by some number not relatively prime to the modulus, provided we are careful to test all resulting solutions in order to eliminate the extraneous ones.

4.13 EXERCISES

In Exercises 1 through 10 solve the given congruences.

*1. $6x \equiv 15 \pmod{29}$ 2. $5x \equiv 29 \pmod{31}$

*3. $17x \equiv 10 \pmod{37}$ 4. $15x \equiv 25 \pmod{31}$

*5. $12x \equiv 23 \pmod{41}$ 6. $24x \equiv 15 \pmod{27}$

*7. $10x \equiv 34 \pmod{36}$ 8. $24x \equiv 18 \pmod{34}$

*9. $18x \equiv 84 \pmod{114}$ 10. $56x \equiv 98 \pmod{147}$

*11. Prove that for any m, $(m, -1) = 1$.

12. Prove that if m is odd, so that $m = 2n + 1$ for some n, then $(m, -2) = 1$.

*13. Prove that if $(a, m) = 1$, then $(-a, m) = 1$.

*14. Prove that if $x^2 \equiv n \pmod{65}$ has a solution for some n, then $x^2 \equiv -n \pmod{65}$ also has a solution. (Hint: if x is any solution of the first congruence, show that $8x$ satisfies the second.)

15. Prove that there are infinitely many primes. (Hint: let $p_1 p_2 \cdots p_n$ be the product of any n primes. Consider $p_1 p_2 \cdots p_n + 1$. Show that the latter is either a prime or has a prime factor different from the factors of the first. Why does this constitute the desired proof?)

4.14 SIMULTANEOUS CONGRUENCES

Suppose that two congruences with different moduli are given, and that each can be solved. Let $x \equiv a \pmod m$ and $x \equiv b \pmod n$ be the resulting solutions. Thus a certain set of integers satisfies $x \equiv a \pmod m$ and another set satisfies $x \equiv b \pmod n$. This leads us to ask whether a common solution exists and, if so, what it is. The following theorem answers these questions for the case where m and n are relatively prime.

> **Theorem 7.** *If $(m, n) = 1$, the congruences $x \equiv a \pmod m$ and $x \equiv b \pmod n$ have a common solution. If x is any common solution, the set of all solutions is given by the residue class of integers congruent to x modulo mn.*

Proof: The set of all integers satisfying the first congruence consists of all integers of the form $a + km$. If an integer of this set satisfies the second congruence, then

$$a + km \equiv b \pmod{n}$$

for some k, or

$$km \equiv (b - a) \pmod{n}.$$

Since $(m, n) = 1$, this congruence can be solved for k. Thus common solutions exist. Next, let x_1 and x_2 be any two common solutions. Since x_1 and x_2 are solutions of $x \equiv a \pmod{m}$, it is necessarily true that

$$x_1 \equiv x_2 \pmod{m},$$

or $x_1 - x_2$ is divisible by m. Similarly, since x_1 and x_2 are solutions of the second congruence, $x_1 - x_2$ is divisible by n. Since m and n have no factors in common, $x_1 - x_2$ is divisible by mn, or

$$x_1 \equiv x_2 \pmod{mn}.$$

Finally, if x is any common solution of the congruences, then we must prove that *any* integer congruent to x modulo mn is a solution. This is easily done. If x is a common solution, there exist integers k and j such that

$$x = a + km \quad \text{and} \quad x = b + jn.$$

If y is any integer congruent to x modulo mn, there is an integer r such that

$$y = x + rmn.$$

Then,

$$y = a + km + rmn = a + m(k + rn), \quad \text{or} \quad y \equiv a \pmod{m},$$

and

$$y = b + jn + rmn = b + n(j + rm), \quad \text{or} \quad y \equiv b \pmod{n}.$$

Thus y is also a common solution.

One method of solving $x \equiv a \pmod{m}$ and $x \equiv b \pmod{n}$ is based directly on the proof of Theorem 7. The first congruence is satisfied by

$$x = a + km$$

for any k. Let us actually find a k such that $a + km$ is a solution of the second congruence, or

$$a + km \equiv b \pmod{n}.$$

Any such k will serve.

Example 1. Let us find a common solution of

$$x \equiv 3 \pmod 5 \quad \text{and} \quad x \equiv 2 \pmod 3.$$

Our work is simplest if we choose the congruence with largest modulus as a starting point. In this case, x is of the form $3 + 5k$, and we wish to find a k such that

$$3 + 5k \equiv 2 \pmod 3.$$

Then $5k \equiv -1 \pmod 3$, which may be written

$$2k \equiv 2 \pmod 3.$$

Hence, any $k \equiv 1 \pmod 3$ will give us a solution. Thus,

$$x \equiv 3 + 5 \cdot 1 \pmod{15}, \quad \text{or} \quad x \equiv 8 \pmod{15}$$

is the desired solution.

Example 2. Find the common solution of

$$x \equiv 5 \pmod{11} \quad \text{and} \quad x \equiv 3 \pmod 7.$$

From the first congruence,

$$x = 5 + 11k.$$

From the second,

$$5 + 11k \equiv 3 \pmod 7,$$

which may be written as

$$4k \equiv -2 \pmod 7, \quad 2k \equiv -1 \equiv 6 \pmod 7, \quad \text{or} \quad k \equiv 3 \pmod 7.$$

Thus the general common solution is given by

$$x \equiv 5 + 11 \cdot 3 \equiv 38 \pmod{77}.$$

There is another method for solving such simultaneous congruences that is particularly easy to use when one of the moduli is small. This consists of writing all integers between 0 and $mn - 1$ that are solutions of the congruence with the largest modulus. Since, by Theorem 7, one and only one of these is also a solution of the other congruence, the common solution can be found by testing each of the integers in turn until one is found that satisfies the second congruence.

Example 3. Let us return to

$$x \equiv 3 \pmod 5 \quad \text{and} \quad x \equiv 2 \pmod 3.$$

From the first congruence we know that the desired solution is to be found among 3, 8, and 13. Of these, only 8 is congruent to 2 modulo 3.

Example 4.   Let us use this method to solve

$$x \equiv 5 \,(\text{mod } 11) \quad \text{and} \quad x \equiv 3 \,(\text{mod } 7).$$

The solution is to be found among 5, 16, 27, 38, 49, 60, and 71. By testing, we find that the desired common solution is

$$x \equiv 38 \,(\text{mod } 77).$$

4.15   SIMULTANEOUS CONGRUENCES IN MORE THAN ONE VARIABLE

Let us investigate simultaneous congruences similar to our ordinary simultaneous equations. In order to simplify our work, we shall assume that p is a prime. We wish to find the common solutions to

$$a_1 x + b_1 y \equiv c_1 \,(\text{mod } p)$$
$$a_2 x + b_2 y \equiv c_2 \,(\text{mod } p).$$

Since p is a prime, the residue classes modulo p form a field. The importance of this is that we can employ the same methods of solution that we would use in ordinary equations. If one of the coefficients is congruent to 0 modulo p, the problem is trivial. Suppose, then, that all coefficients are incongruent to 0 modulo p. Let us eliminate y from the pair of congruences. Since $b_1 \not\equiv 0$ $(\text{mod } p)$, there is an integer b_1^{-1} such that $b_1 b_1^{-1} \equiv 1 \,(\text{mod } p)$. Similarly, there is a b_2^{-1} such that $b_2 b_2^{-1} \equiv 1 \,(\text{mod } p)$. Multiplying the first congruence by b_1^{-1} and the second by b_2^{-1} yields

$$a_1 b_1^{-1} x + y \equiv b_1^{-1} c_1 \,(\text{mod } p)$$
$$a_2 b_2^{-1} x + y \equiv b_2^{-1} c_2 \,(\text{mod } p).$$

Subtracting, we find

$$(a_1 b_1^{-1} - a_2 b_2^{-1})x \equiv (b_1^{-1} c_1 - b_2^{-1} c_2) \,(\text{mod } p).$$

If $a_1 b_1^{-1} - a_2 b_2^{-1}$ is not a multiple of p, a solution exists. Substituting this value of x in either congruence permits us to solve for y. Alternatively, we could have multiplied the first congruence by b_2 and the second by b_1 before subtracting. This method works as well to eliminate y.

Example 1. Let us find the common solution of

$$3x + 2y \equiv 1 \pmod 5$$
$$4x + 3y \equiv 2 \pmod 5.$$

Multiplying the first congruence by 3 and the second by 2, we find

$$9x + 6y \equiv 3 \pmod 5, \quad \text{or} \quad 4x + y \equiv 3 \pmod 5$$
$$8x + 6y \equiv 4 \pmod 5, \quad \text{or} \quad 3x + y \equiv 4 \pmod 5.$$

Subtracting the second congruence from the first yields

$$x \equiv -1 \equiv 4 \pmod 5.$$

Substituting 4 for x in the first congruence gives

$$12 + 2y \equiv 1 \pmod 5, \quad \text{or} \quad 2y \equiv -11 \equiv 4 \pmod 5.$$

The last congruence is satisfied by $y \equiv 2 \pmod 5$.

For a check, we substitute these values in the second congruence. We find

$$16 + 6 = 22 \equiv 2 \pmod 5.$$

Thus our solution is correct.

Example 2. Solve

$$(1) \quad \begin{cases} 2x + y - 3z \equiv 3 \pmod{11} \\ x - 2y + z \equiv 1 \pmod{11} \\ 3x + 2y + 4z \equiv 10 \pmod{11}. \end{cases}$$

We wish to eliminate one variable to obtain two congruences in two variables. It is simple to eliminate y by adding the second congruence to the third and twice the first to the second. This gives us

$$(2) \quad \begin{cases} 5x - 5z \equiv 7 \pmod{11} \\ 4x + 5z \equiv 0 \pmod{11}. \end{cases}$$

Adding these two congruences gives

$$9x \equiv 7 \pmod{11}, \quad \text{or} \quad -2x \equiv -4 \pmod{11}, \quad \text{so that} \quad x \equiv 2 \pmod{11}.$$

Substituting for x in the second of the congruences of (2), we find

$$5z \equiv -8 \pmod{11}, \quad \text{or} \quad 5z \equiv 3 \pmod{11}.$$

Multiplying both sides by 2 yields

$$10z \equiv 6 \pmod{11}.$$

Thus,

$$-z \equiv 6 \equiv -5 \ (\text{mod } 11), \quad \text{or} \quad z \equiv 5 \ (\text{mod } 11).$$

Substituting in the first of the congruences of (1), we find

$$4 + y - 15 \equiv 3 \ (\text{mod } 11), \quad \text{or} \quad y \equiv 3 \ (\text{mod } 11).$$

We have found the solution:

$$x \equiv 2 \ (\text{mod } 11), \quad y \equiv 3 \ (\text{mod } 11), \quad \text{and} \quad z \equiv 5 \ (\text{mod } 11).$$

Solving simultaneous congruences is easier than solving simultaneous equations. For one thing, we never encounter fractions. For another, we need never use minus signs, although their use in intermediate steps is convenient. Finally, since all coefficients and constants can be reduced to integers smaller than the modulus in magnitude, the arithmetic remains relatively simple.

4.16   EXERCISES

In Exercises 1–20, solve the given simultaneous congruences.

*1. $x \equiv 5 \ (\text{mod } 11)$
    $x \equiv 3 \ (\text{mod } 7)$

2. $x \equiv 2 \ (\text{mod } 9)$
    $x \equiv 3 \ (\text{mod } 10)$

*3. $x \equiv 1 \ (\text{mod } 8)$
    $x \equiv 1 \ (\text{mod } 9)$

4. $x \equiv 8 \ (\text{mod } 9)$
    $x \equiv 7 \ (\text{mod } 8)$

*5. $x \equiv 4 \ (\text{mod } 5)$
    $x \equiv 3 \ (\text{mod } 11)$

6. $3x + 2 \equiv 1 \ (\text{mod } 5)$
    $2x + 1 \equiv 3 \ (\text{mod } 7)$

*7. $2x - 1 \equiv 5 \ (\text{mod } 7)$
    $2x + 1 \equiv 4 \ (\text{mod } 5)$

8. $2x - 1 \equiv 4 \ (\text{mod } 7)$
    $2x + 1 \equiv 0 \ (\text{mod } 5)$

*9. $3x - 2 \equiv 4 \ (\text{mod } 7)$
    $2x + 1 \equiv 2 \ (\text{mod } 3)$

10. $6x - 1 \equiv 2 \ (\text{mod } 7)$
    $4x + 3 \equiv 1 \ (\text{mod } 11)$

*11. $x + 2y \equiv 2 \ (\text{mod } 3)$
    $2x + 2y \equiv 1 \ (\text{mod } 3)$

12. $2x + 3y \equiv 1 \ (\text{mod } 5)$
    $x + y \equiv 2 \ (\text{mod } 5)$

*13. $2x + 3y \equiv 1 \ (\text{mod } 5)$
    $3x - y \equiv 3 \ (\text{mod } 5)$

14. $4x + 3y \equiv 2 \ (\text{mod } 7)$
    $3x + 5y \equiv 1 \ (\text{mod } 7)$

*15. $3x + y \equiv 4 \ (\text{mod } 11)$
    $5x - 3y \equiv 9 \ (\text{mod } 11)$

16. $5x - y \equiv 2 \ (\text{mod } 11)$
    $7x + 5y \equiv 5 \ (\text{mod } 11)$

*17. $5x - 7y \equiv 1 \ (\text{mod } 13)$
    $6x + 5y \equiv 9 \ (\text{mod } 13)$

18. $5x - 7y \equiv 1 \ (\text{mod } 17)$
    $6x + 5y \equiv 9 \ (\text{mod } 17)$

*19. $2x + 3y - z \equiv 2 \ (\text{mod } 7)$
    $3x - y + z \equiv 3 \ (\text{mod } 7)$
    $4x + y + 2z \equiv 6 \ (\text{mod } 7)$

20. $x + 2y - z \equiv 1 \ (\text{mod } 11)$
    $2x - y + 2z \equiv 3 \ (\text{mod } 11)$
    $3x + 2y - z \equiv 5 \ (\text{mod } 11)$

Show that the simultaneous congruences of Exercises 21 and 22 do not have a common solution.

*21. $2x + 3y \equiv 5 \pmod{7}$
$\quad\;\; 4x - \;\, y \equiv 1 \pmod{7}$

22. $2x + \;\, y - z \equiv 1 \pmod{11}$
$\quad\;\;\; x + \;\, y + z \equiv 2 \pmod{11}$
$\quad\; 5x + 3y - z \equiv 3 \pmod{11}$

4.17 ON BEING CRYPTIC

C. C. MacDuffee, in his book, *Introduction to Abstract Algebra*, gives an interesting application of simultaneous congruences. Let us establish a one-to-one correspondence between the residue classes modulo 29 and a set of 29 characters consisting of the letters of the alphabet, the hyphen, the asterisk, and the period as shown in the table below:

$-$	a	b	c	d	e	$\cdot$	$\cdot$	$\cdot$	v	w	x	y	z	$*$	$\cdot$
0	1	2	3	4	5	$\cdot$	$\cdot$	$\cdot$	22	23	24	25	26	27	28

It can be shown that the system of congruences

$$2x + \;\, y \equiv c_1 \quad (\text{mod } 29)$$
$$\;\; x - 3y \equiv c_2$$

has a solution for every c_1 and c_2. In fact, the methods of the previous sections will show that a solution is given by

$$x \equiv -4c_2 - 12c_1 \quad (\text{mod } 29).$$
$$y \equiv \quad\; 8c_2 - \;\, 4c_1$$

These congruences can be used to encode and decipher messages in such a way that it is extremely difficult for anyone without the key to break the code. In order to encode a message, break it into groups of 2 consecutive characters, including a blank by use of a hyphen if necessary to complete a group. Each pair of characters corresponds to a pair of numbers. Substitute the first for x and the second for y. The resulting values for c_1 and c_2 in turn determine a pair of characters in the encoded message. The merit of this coding system is that the residue class into which a character is transformed depends not only on the character but on the other character of the pair in which it appears *and* on the order within the pair. The decoding process is exactly the reverse. The first two characters of a coded message are used to assign values to c_1 and c_2. When the congruences are solved, the first character of the decoded message is given by the residue class to which x belongs and the second by the class to which y belongs.

Let us encode the word *cat*. This will be done in two parts, first encoding *ca* and then *t–*. Referring to the correspondence table, we find that $c \leftrightarrow 3$ and $a \leftrightarrow 1$. Substituting 3 for x and 1 for y, we have

$$\begin{aligned} 2x + y &\equiv 6 + 1 \equiv 7 \\ x - 3y &\equiv 3 - 3 \equiv 0 \end{aligned} \quad \text{(mod 29)}.$$

Since $7 \leftrightarrow g$ and $0 \leftrightarrow -$, *ca* is encoded as *g–*. For the second pair, we use the fact that $t \leftrightarrow 20$ and $- \leftrightarrow 0$. Substituting 20 for x and 0 for y, we have

$$\begin{aligned} 2x + y &\equiv 40 + 0 \equiv 11 \\ x - 3y &\equiv 20 - 0 \equiv 20 \end{aligned} \quad \text{(mod 29)}.$$

Since $11 \leftrightarrow k$ and $20 \leftrightarrow t$, *t–* is encoded as *kt*. Thus the entire message *cat–* is encoded as *g–kt*.

Let us try the reverse process. Suppose a message is *mr.i*. Since we have found that the solution to the congruences is given by

$$\begin{aligned} x &\equiv -4c_2 - 12c_1 \\ y &\equiv 8c_2 - 4c_1 \end{aligned} \quad \text{(mod 29)},$$

we need only substitute the proper values for c_1 and c_2. Since $m \leftrightarrow 13$ and $r \leftrightarrow 18$, we substitute 13 for c_1 and 18 for c_2.

$$\begin{aligned} x &\equiv -4(18) - 12(13) \equiv -228 \equiv 4 \\ y &\equiv 8(18) - 4(13) \equiv 92 \equiv 5 \end{aligned} \quad \text{(mod 29)}$$

Since $4 \leftrightarrow d$ and $5 \leftrightarrow e$, the first half of the message is *de*. For the second part, $. \leftrightarrow 28 = c_1$, and $i \leftrightarrow 9 = c_2$. Since $28 \equiv -1 \pmod{29}$, it will be easier to use -1 for c_1. Then

$$\begin{aligned} x &\equiv -4(9) - 12(-1) \equiv -24 \equiv 5 \\ y &\equiv 8(9) - 4(-1) \equiv 76 \equiv 18 \end{aligned} \quad \text{(mod 29)}.$$

Since $5 \leftrightarrow e$ and $18 \leftrightarrow r$, the second half of the message is *er*. The entire coded word was *deer*. Notice that the two occurrences of *e* in *deer* were encoded as different symbols. This is a very hard code to break, but it can be made even harder by using three congruences in three unknowns.

4.18   EXERCISES

1. Use the pair of simultaneous congruences of the last section to encode your name. Check your work by decoding the result.

*2. Use the pair of simultaneous congruences of the last section to decode the message *uvkv*.

*3. Use the following pair of congruences to encode the word *book*.

$$3x - 2y \equiv c_1$$
$$3x + 8y \equiv c_2 \quad (\text{mod } 29)$$

4. Use the congruences of Exercise 3 to decode the message *cyotwl*.

5. Use the following simultaneous congruences to encode the word *hello*.

$$2x + y - z \equiv c_1$$
$$3x - 2y + z \equiv c_2 \quad (\text{mod } 29)$$
$$x + 2y - 3z \equiv c_3$$

*6. Use the congruences of Exercise 5 to decode the message *–cp–tifgj*.

4.19 RECOMMENDED READING

Beaumont, R., and Ball, R., *Introduction to Modern Algebra and Matrix Theory*, New York, Rinehart, 1954.

Birkhoff, G., and MacLane, S., *A Brief Survey of Modern Algebra*, New York, Macmillan, 1953.

Kahn, D., "Modern Cryptology," *Scientific American*, July 1966.

MacDuffee, C. C., *Introduction to Abstract Algebra*, New York, Wiley, 1940.

Whitesitt, J. E., *Principles of Modern Algebra*, Reading, Mass., Addison-Wesley, 1964.

5

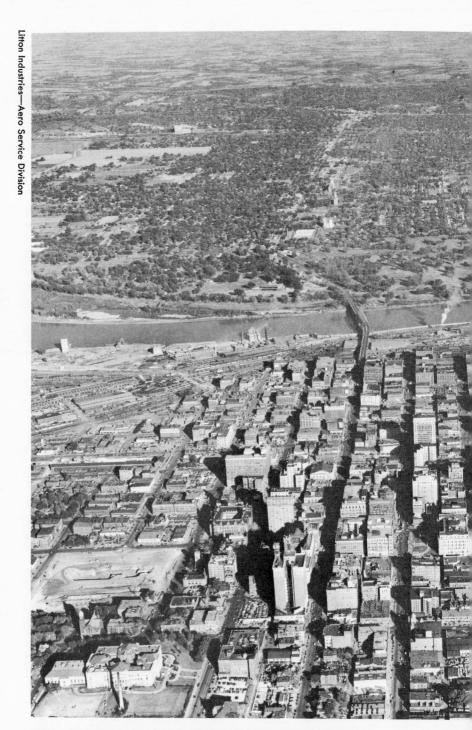

The coordinate system of Descartes displayed by an American city.

5.1 INTRODUCTION

Toward the end of the seventeenth century a development occurred in mathematics that changed the entire world. This development, on which modern technological society is based, was the invention of the calculus by Sir Isaac Newton (1642–1727) and Gottfried Leibniz (1646–1716), independently. This momentous discovery, however, was not without roots. The groundwork for calculus was laid by René Descartes in his *Geometry* of 1637. Here for the first time was a systematic treatment of geometry from an algebraic standpoint. Others contributed to this field both before and after Descartes, but the credit for the world's awareness of it must go to the French philosopher and mathematician. We, too, in our approach to calculus must retrace these steps and gain some degree of familiarity with and some manipulative skill in *analytic geometry*, as it has come to be called. We were introduced to this subject very briefly in Chapter 1. In this chapter we shall explore the area in greater depth.

5.2 THE CARTESIAN COORDINATE SYSTEM

The basis for analytic geometry is the one-to-one correspondence that we have seen between the real numbers and the points on a line. Thus we can refer to a *number line* where each point has associated with it a corresponding real number. Let us construct two number lines in a plane, lines that intersect at right angles at the point corresponding to zero on both lines. They will be oriented so that positive numbers lie along the right part of a horizontal line and the upper part of a vertical line. We shall call the horizontal line the *x-axis*, the vertical line the *y-axis*, and the point where they intersect the *origin*. Then each point in the plane can be specified by an ordered pair of numbers, the first giving its distance to the right (if positive) or to the left

159

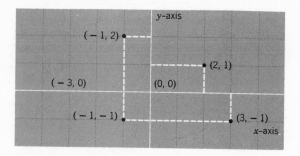

(if negative) of the y-axis, and the second giving its distance above (if positive) or below (if negative) the x-axis.

If (p, q) specifies a point we call p and q the *coordinates* of the point and we shall refer to the first as the x-coordinate, the second as the y-coordinate. To locate a point (p, q), then, we go p units in the x direction and q units in the y direction. Such an assignment of ordered pairs of real numbers to points in a plane is called a *cartesian coordinate system*, after Descartes. There are other possible coordinate systems, but we shall restrict our attention to the cartesian coordinate system.

A *graph* is the set of all points whose coordinates satisfy a given equation. For instance, the point $(4, -1)$ is on the graph of the equation $2x + 3y = 5$ because $2(4) + 3(-1) = 5$. On the other hand, the point $(4, 1)$ is not on the graph because $2(4) + 3(1) \neq 5$.

5.3 EQUATION OF A LINE

Let us consider a straight line through the points $(1, 2)$ and $(4, 4)$. Let (x, y) be any other point on the line. With (x, y) as shown above, let us draw horizontal or vertical lines through $(1, 2)$, $(4, 4)$, and (x, y) to form similar triangles as in the figure below. The right triangle with vertices $(1, 2)$ and $(4, 4)$

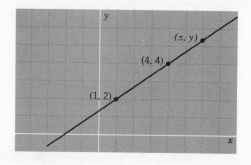

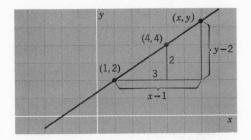

has legs of length 3 and 2. The right triangle with vertices (1, 2) and (x, y) has legs of length $x - 1$ and $y - 2$. Since the two triangles are similar, the ratios of corresponding sides are equal, or

$$\frac{y - 2}{2} = \frac{x - 1}{3}.$$

Algebraically we can reduce this equation to

$$3y - 6 = 2x - 2, \quad \text{or} \quad 2x - 3y + 4 = 0.$$

The point (x, y) is fully arbitrary. The equation $2x - 3y + 4 = 0$ is satisfied by the coordinates of *every* point on the line and by no others. Thus we call $2x - 3y + 4 = 0$ an *equation of the line*. This equation can assume many forms that are algebraically equivalent. For instance, the following equations are all equivalent in the sense that each is satisfied by the coordinates of the points on the given line and by no others.

$$2x - 3y = -4 \qquad\qquad 10x - 15y + 20 = 0$$

$$\frac{x}{-2} + \frac{y}{4/3} = 1 \qquad\qquad y - 4 = \frac{2}{3}(x - 4)$$

$$y - 2 = \frac{2}{3}(x - 1)$$

We shall show that for any real numbers A, B, and C, with A and B not both zero, the equation $Ax + By = C$ is satisfied by the points lying on a straight line. First, if $A = 0$, the equation reduces to $y = C/B$, which is satisfied by those points and only those points on a line parallel to the x-axis. That is, the graph of $y = C/B$ is the set of all points of the form $(x, C/B)$ for any x.

Example 1.   Let us find the graph of

$$3y = 12.$$

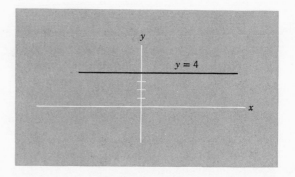

The equation $3y = 12$ is equivalent to $y = 4$. The graph consists of all (x, y) for which $y = 4$, or all points of the form $(x, 4)$. The graph is a line parallel to the x-axis and 4 units above it.

If $B = 0$, the equation $Ax + By = C$ reduces to $x = C/A$. An argument similar to the preceding one leads us to conclude that the graph of the equation is a line parallel to the y-axis and C/A units away from it, to the right if C/A is positive, to the left if C/A is negative.

The x-axis itself consists of all points whose coordinates satisfy the equation $y = 0$. Similarly, an equation of the y-axis is $x = 0$.

Let us now consider the equation $Ax + By = C$ in which neither A, B, nor C is zero. We can verify by direct substitution that the points

$$\left(\frac{C}{A}, 0\right) \quad \text{and} \quad \left(0, \frac{C}{B}\right)$$

lie on the graph of the equation. Let us draw the line through the two points and let (x, y) be any other point on the line. The similar triangles formed in the figure have their sides in equal ratios. We observe that in the figure C/A

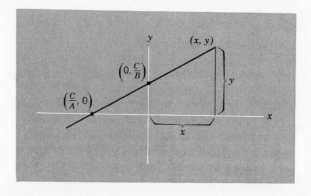

is negative. Hence the base of the right triangle with vertices $(C/A, 0)$ and (x, y) has length $x - C/A$. Then

$$\frac{x - C/A}{-C/A} = \frac{y}{C/B}, \quad \text{or} \quad A\left(x - \frac{C}{A}\right) = -By, \quad \text{or} \quad Ax + By = C.$$

Thus the coordinates of any point on the line satisfy the equation $Ax + By = C$. Further, for any (x, y) not on the line, the triangles formed above are not similar, so that the given equation is not satisfied.

We have shown that every equation of the form $Ax + By = C$ has a graph that is a straight line. Also, every straight line satisfies an equation of this form. Thus we shall call $Ax + By = C$ the *general linear equation*. Our next task is to find ways to obtain geometric information about a line from its equation and to find simple ways to write the equation of a line specified by geometric conditions.

5.4 SLOPES AND INTERCEPTS

Let us consider a general linear equation, $Ax + By = C$, for some real numbers A, B, and C. If $B \neq 0$, we can solve the equation for y and obtain

$$y = \left(-\frac{A}{B}\right)x + \frac{C}{B}.$$

Let us denote $(-A/B)$ by m and C/B by b. Then

$$y = mx + b.$$

Since every point on the y-axis has x-coordinate zero, we can find the point where the line crosses the y-axis by setting $x = 0$ in the equation $y = mx + b$. Then $y = b$, or $(0, b)$ is the point where the line cuts the y-axis. Let us call b the *y-intercept* of the line. For example, if $2x + 3y = 12$, we can solve for y and find that

$$y = \left(-\frac{2}{3}\right)x + 4.$$

For this line, the y-intercept is 4.

What interpretation can we give to m? If $y = mx + b$, then $y = b$ when $x = 0$. When $x = 1$, $y = m + b$. When $x = 2$, $y = 2m + b$. In general, whenever x is increased by 1, y is changed by m. If $m > 0$ this change is positive, or the line slopes upward from left to right. If $m < 0$ the change is negative, or the line slopes downward. If $m = 0$ the line is horizontal. We

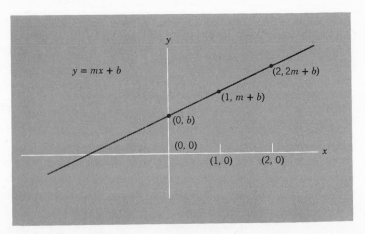

call *m* the *slope* of the line, and an equation of the form $y = mx + b$ is said to be the *slope-intercept form* of the linear equation.

It should be reasonably obvious that two distinct lines are parallel if and only if they have the same slope. This will be proved later.

To draw the graph of a linear equation, we need only two distinct points on it. In the slope-intercept form, $y = mx + b$, one convenient point is $(0, b)$, and another can be obtained by giving x an arbitrary value. For instance, $(2, 2m + b)$ is another point on the line.

Example 1. Draw the graph of

$$4x - 3y = 10.$$

Solving for y, we find that

$$y = \left(\frac{4}{3}\right) x - \frac{10}{3}.$$

One point on the line is $(0, -10/3)$. Another is $(4, 2)$.

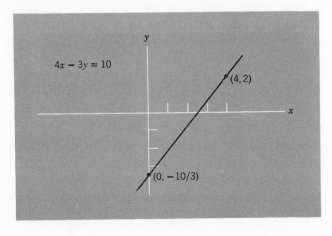

Let us go the other way. What equations can we find for a line passing through two points? Suppose that (x_1, y_1) and (x_2, y_2) are two distinct points in the plane and that $x_1 \neq x_2$. Let us draw the line through the points. Since $x_1 \neq x_2$, this line is not vertical. Let (x, y) be any arbitrary point on the line. From ratios in similar triangles, we find that

$$\frac{y - y_1}{x - x_1} = \frac{y_2 - y_1}{x_2 - x_1},$$

or

$$(x_2 - x_1)(y - y_1) = (y_2 - y_1)(x - x_1).$$

Since this is a linear equation satisfied by the coordinates of the two given points, it is an equation of the line through the points. Notice, moreover, that the slope of the line is $(y_2 - y_1)/(x_2 - x_1)$, or the difference of the y's divided by the difference of the x's taken in the same order.

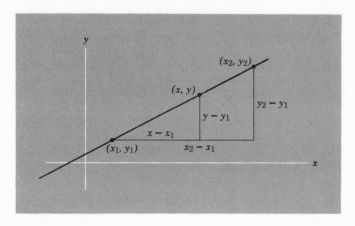

Example 2. Find an equation of the line through $(2, -1)$ and $(-3, 6)$.
By the method above,

$$(-3 - 2)[y - (-1)] = [6 - (-1)](x - 2),$$

or

$$(-5)(y + 1) = 7(x - 2),$$

or

$$7x + 5y = 9.$$

Example 3. Find an equation of the line through (2, 3) and (5, 3).

We have

$$(5 - 2)(y - 3) = (3 - 3)(x - 2), \quad \text{or} \quad 3(y - 3) = 0, \quad \text{or} \quad y = 3.$$

This result may be surprising, but it states a condition satisfied by precisely those points that lie on the line. The line is horizontal, with slope $m = 0$, and for every point (x, y) on the line, $y = 3$, regardless of x.

Example 4. Find an equation of the line through (3, 2) and (3, 5).

This time we have

$$(3 - 3)(y - 2) = (5 - 2)(x - 3),$$

which reduces to

$$x = 3.$$

The line is vertical, and the equation expresses the condition that for every point (x, y) on the line, $x = 3$. What is its slope? It is not defined. Indeed, for all nonvertical lines we can determine the slope either by solving the equation for y, in which case the slope is the coefficient of x, or by taking the ratio of the differences of the coordinates of two points on the line. Since neither process can be carried out for a vertical line, we shall leave its slope undefined.

Example 5. Find an equation of the line through $(-1, 2)$ with slope 3.

In the slope-intercept form, $y = mx + b$. Since the slope is 3, we have

$$y = 3x + b.$$

Since $(-1, 2)$ lies on the line, its coordinates satisfy the equation, or

$$2 = 3(-1) + b, \quad \text{or} \quad b = 5.$$

Thus

$$y = 3x + 5$$

is the desired equation.

Example 6. Find an equation of the line through $(-1, 2)$ that is parallel to $2x + 3y = 7$.

The slope of the line whose equation is $2x + 3y = 7$ is obtained by

$$y = \left(-\frac{2}{3}\right) x + \frac{7}{3}.$$

Thus

$$m = -\frac{2}{3}.$$

The equation of any line parallel to $2x + 3y = 7$, then, is given by

$$y = \left(-\frac{2}{3}\right)x + b.$$

To determine b we proceed as in the previous example and make use of the fact that the line passes through $(-1, 2)$. Thus

$$2 = \left(-\frac{2}{3}\right)(-1) + b, \quad \text{or} \quad b = \frac{4}{3}.$$

Hence the desired equation is

$$y = \left(-\frac{2}{3}\right)x + \frac{4}{3},$$

which may be written as

$$2x + 3y = 4.$$

5.5 EXERCISES

*1. The equation $3x + 4y = 12$ can be put in the form $x/4 + y/3 = 1$. How can this form be used in constructing the graph? (What is y if $x = 0$?)

2. Draw the graph of $2x - 3y = 24$. What is the slope of the line?

*3. Draw the graph of $x + 2y = 7$. What is the slope of the line?

4. Draw the graph of $8x - 3y = -6$. What is the slope of the line?

*5. Draw the graph of $3y = 2$. What is the slope of the line?

6. Draw the graph of $3x = 2$. What is the slope of the line?

*7. Find an equation and the slope of the line through $(-4, 3)$ and $(2, 7)$.

8. Find an equation and the slope of the line through $(-2, -5)$ and $(-1, 3)$.

*9. Find an equation and the slope of the line through $(0, 2)$ and $(2, 0)$.

10. Find an equation and the slope of the line through $(-6, 3)$ and $(-6, 7)$.

*11. Find an equation of the line through $(2, 3)$ with slope 2.

12. Find an equation of the line through $(-1, 4)$ with slope -2.

*13. Find an equation of the line through $(2, 3)$ with the same slope as $2x - 3y = 5$.

14. Find an equation of the line through $(-3, 7)$ with the same slope as $3x + y = 47$.

*15. Find an equation of the line through $(2, 3)$ with the same slope as the line through the origin and $(-3, 7)$.

16. Find an equation of the line through $(2, 3)$ with the same slope as the line through $(-1, 1)$ and $(2, 5)$.

5.6 PARALLEL LINES

Two distinct lines are said to be parallel if they do not intersect. Our approach permits us to replace this geometric condition by an algebraic one. Two distinct lines are parallel if their equations have no common solution.

Let two lines be graphs of the following equations:

$$A_1x + B_1y = C_1$$
$$A_2x + B_2y = C_2.$$

Let us try to solve this pair of equations by eliminating y. We multiply the first equation by B_2, the second by B_1, and subtract. This gives us

$$(A_1B_2 - A_2B_1)x = B_2C_1 - B_1C_2.$$

If $A_1B_2 - A_2B_1 \neq 0$, we can find x by dividing both sides of the equation by this quantity. Then the number found can be substituted for x in either equation to find y, completing the solution of the equations. But if the lines are parallel, their equations have no solution. The only thing that can prevent us from finding a solution is to have

$$A_1B_2 - A_2B_1 = 0.$$

Thus we have found a numerical condition on the coefficients that tells us when two lines are parallel. For example, the line whose equation is $2x + 3y = 7$ is parallel to the line whose equation is $4x + 6y = 13$ because $2(6) - 4(3) = 0$.

If $A_1B_2 - A_2B_1 = 0$ and neither B_1 nor B_2 is zero, then we can divide by B_1B_2 and have

$$\frac{A_1}{B_1} - \frac{A_2}{B_2} = 0, \quad \text{or} \quad -\frac{A_1}{B_1} = -\frac{A_2}{B_2}.$$

Since $-A_1/B_1$ and $-A_2/B_2$ are the slopes of the two lines, we conclude that if two lines are parallel, they have the same slope. When $B_1B_2 \neq 0$, the steps are reversible, so that the converse also holds. Of course, there is a string attached. In order to divide by B_1B_2 we must assume that neither B_1 nor B_2 is zero. We have found that both A and B cannot be zero in the equation of a line. Hence, if $B_1 = 0$ and $A_1B_2 - A_2B_1 = 0$, then

$$A_1B_2 = 0.$$

Since $A_1 \neq 0$, it follows that $B_2 = 0$. If $B_1 = B_2 = 0$, both lines are parallel to the y-axis, hence parallel to each other, even though the slope of neither line is defined. This demonstrates that the condition that

$$A_1B_2 - A_2B_1 = 0, \quad \text{or} \quad A_1B_2 = A_2B_1,$$

is a slightly more general condition for the parallelism of two lines than is the equality of their slopes.

Let a line be the graph of $Ax + By = C$. Consider the line whose equation is $Ax + By = k$, for any real k. If $k = C$, the lines are obviously identical, but what can we say if $k \neq C$? For each value of k there is a line. For all possible values of k, then, there is an entire family of lines. What do they have in common? Their equations satisfy the condition for parallelism. The set of lines in the family

$$\{Ax + By = k\}$$

is a set of lines parallel to the given line. It is left to the reader to show that this set actually includes *all* lines parallel to the given line.

Let (x_1, y_1) be any point in the plane. Then

$$Ax + By = Ax_1 + By_1$$

is the equation of a line for which two facts are evident. For one, it is parallel to the line $Ax + By = C$, and for the second it passes through the point (x_1, y_1), since the coordinates of the point satisfy the equation. Thus it is very simple to write the equation of a line through a given point parallel to a given line. It is always gratifying when the tortuous path from definition through theory leads to a simple solution for a class of problems.

> ***Example 1.*** Write an equation of the line through $(2, -1)$ parallel to $3x + 4y = 7$. A solution is given by
>
> $$3x + 4y = 3(2) + 4(-1) = 6 - 4 = 2.$$
>
> ***Example 2.*** Write an equation of the line through $(7, 5)$ parallel to $x = -3$. A solution is given by $x = 7$.

5.7 PERPENDICULAR LINES

Let

$$A_1x + B_1y = C_1 \quad \text{and} \quad A_2x + B_2y = C_2$$

be equations of two lines that are mutually perpendicular. Let us find an equivalent algebraic condition. The constants on the right, C_1 and C_2, merely

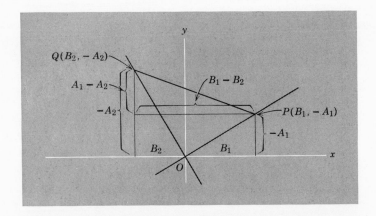

determine the location of the lines in the plane. The orientation of the lines is determined by the coefficients of x and y. Hence, we may consider two lines through the origin parallel to the given lines. The equations of these lines are

$$A_1 x + B_1 y = 0 \quad \text{and} \quad A_2 x + B_2 y = 0.$$

Since $x = B_1$, $y = -A_1$, are values satisfying the first equation, the point $(B_1, -A_1)$ is on the first line. Similarly, $(B_2, -A_2)$ is on the second line.

Denote the origin by O, the point $(B_1, -A_1)$ by P, and $(B_2, -A_2)$ by Q. The perpendicularity of the lines is equivalent to the condition that POQ is a right triangle with the right angle at O. By the Pythagorean theorem,

$$\overline{PQ}^2 = \overline{OP}^2 + \overline{OQ}^2,$$

or

$$(B_1 - B_2)^2 + (A_2 - A_1)^2 = B_1^2 + A_1^2 + B_2^2 + A_2^2,$$

or

$$B_1^2 - 2B_1 B_2 + B_2^2 + A_2^2 - 2A_1 A_2 + A_1^2 = B_1^2 + A_1^2 + B_2^2 + A_2^2,$$

or

$$-2B_1 B_2 - 2A_1 A_2 = 0,$$

or

$$A_1 A_2 + B_1 B_2 = 0.$$

This is the algebraic condition we sought. Two lines whose equations are $A_1 x + B_1 y = C_1$ and $A_2 x + B_2 y = C_2$ are perpendicular if and only if $A_1 A_2 + B_1 B_2 = 0$.

If one line, say the first, is parallel to the x-axis, then $A_1 = 0$. Then $B_1 B_2 = 0$. Since B_1 cannot be zero, it follows that $B_2 = 0$, or the second line is parallel to the y-axis. If one line is not parallel to an axis, then neither is the other, and A_1, B_1, A_2, and B_2 are all different from zero. In this case we can write

$$A_1 A_2 + B_1 B_2 = 0 \quad \text{as} \quad \frac{A_1 A_2}{B_1 B_2} + 1 = 0,$$

or,

$$\left(-\frac{A_1}{B_1}\right)\left(-\frac{A_2}{B_2}\right) = -1.$$

Since $-A_1/B_1$ and $-A_2/B_2$ are the slopes of the two lines, any two lines for which slope is defined are perpendicular if and only if the product of their slopes is -1, or the slopes are negative reciprocals of each other. Thus if m_1 and m_2 are the slopes of perpendicular lines,

$$m_2 = -\frac{1}{m_1}.$$

Let $Ax + By = C$ be the equation of a line. Consider the family of lines $\{Bx - Ay = k\}$, where k can assume any real value. Our test for perpendicularity shows that all members of this family of lines are perpendicular to the given line. If we wish to write the equation of a line through (x_1, y_1) perpendicular to $Ax + By = C$, we can write

$$Bx - Ay = Bx_1 - Ay_1.$$

Example 1.   Write an equation of the line through $(2, -1)$ perpendicular to $3x + 4y = 7$. A solution is given by

$$4x - 3y = 4(2) - 3(-1) = 11.$$

5.8   EXERCISES

*1. Write an equation of a line through $(2, 3)$ parallel to $2x - 3y = 5$.

2. Write an equation of a line through $(-3, 7)$ parallel to $3x + y = 47$.

*3. Write an equation of a line through $(-5, -2)$ parallel to $6x + y + 4 = 0$.

4. Write an equation of a line through the origin parallel to $6x + y + 4 = 0$.

*5. Write an equation of a line through $(2, 3)$ parallel to the line through $(4, 1)$ and $(2, -3)$.

6. Write an equation of a line through $(-3, 7)$ parallel to the line through $(-1, 1)$ and $(3, -1)$.

*7. Write an equation of a line through $(2, 3)$ perpendicular to $2x - 3y = 5$.

8. Write an equation of a line through $(-3, 7)$ perpendicular to $3x + y = 47$.

*9. Write an equation of a line through $(-5, -2)$ perpendicular to

$$6x + y + 4 = 0.$$

10. Write an equation of a line through the orign perpendicular to $6x + y + 4 = 0$.

*11. Write an equation of a line through $(2, 3)$ perpendicular to the line through $(4, 1)$ and $(2, -3)$.

12. Write an equation of a line through $(-3, 7)$ perpendicular to the line through $(-1, 1)$ and $(3, -1)$.

*13. Write an equation of a line through $(2, 3)$ parallel to $x = 4$.

14. Write an equation of a line through $(2, 3)$ parallel to $y = 5$.

*15. Write an equation of a line through $(2, 3)$ perpendicular to $x = 4$.

16. Write an equation of a line through $(2, 3)$ perpendicular to $y = 5$.

*17. What do the members of each of the following families of lines have in common?

(a) $y = 2x + k$ for all real k

(b) $y = kx + 2$ for all real k

(c) $a(x - 3) + b(y - 4) = 0$ for all real a and b

(d) $2x + 3y - 5 + k(x - y + 7) = 0$ for all real k

5.9 DISTANCE BETWEEN POINTS

Let (x_1, y_1) and (x_2, y_2) be two points in the plane. Draw the line segment between them and complete the right triangle as in the figure. Let d be the distance between the points. The distance d is easily found by the Pythagorean theorem. In fact, we have already done this in the preceding section on perpendicular lines. However, we should have a formula for reference. By the Pythagorean theorem,

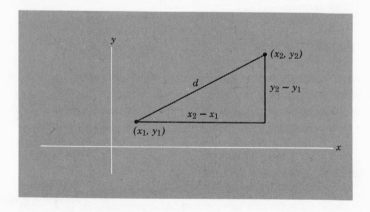

$$d^2 = (x_2 - x_1)^2 + (y_2 - y_1)^2,$$

or

$$d = \sqrt{(x_2 - x_1)^2 + (y_2 - y_1)^2}.$$

Although we have used points with positive coordinates in the illustration, the formula is valid for *any* two points. In all cases the sides of the triangle have lengths

$$\pm(x_2 - x_1) \quad \text{and} \quad \pm(y_2 - y_1).$$

When these are squared, the $\pm$ signs are dropped.

Example 1. Find the distance between $(-3, -2)$ and $(5, 1)$.

$$d = \sqrt{[5 - (-3)]^2 + [1 - (-2)]^2} = \sqrt{8^2 + 3^2} = \sqrt{64 + 9} = \sqrt{73}.$$

5.10 PERPENDICULAR BISECTORS OF LINE SEGMENTS

It is frequently necessary in geometry to construct a line or other curve having certain properties. In analytic geometry we must find the equation of the curve satisfying the given conditions. Since the equation of a curve merely states an algebraic condition that must be satisfied by the coordinates of exactly those points in the plane that possess the desired properties, we must translate the geometric conditions to algebraic ones. For example, suppose that we wish to find the perpendicular bisector of a line segment. In our analytic geometry the line segment is specified as the set of points on the line between points (x_1, y_1) and (x_2, y_2). Let (x, y) represent an arbitrary point on the desired bisector. What condition must be satisfied by the coordinates of this point? In plane geometry we would use a compass to mark off equal

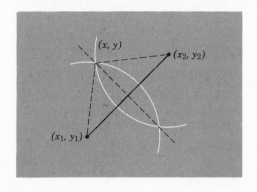

arcs from the given endpoints. The two points of intersection of the arcs determine the bisector. This is true because the points on the bisector are precisely those points that are equidistant from the two endpoints. But we can state this condition analytically, that the distance from (x, y) to (x_1, y_1) is equal to the distance from (x, y) to (x_2, y_2).

$$\sqrt{(x - x_1)^2 + (y - y_1)^2} = \sqrt{(x - x_2)^2 + (y - y_2)^2},$$

or, squaring,

$$x^2 - 2x_1x + x_1^2 + y^2 - 2y_1y + y_1^2 = x^2 - 2x_2x + x_2^2 + y^2 - 2y_2y + y_2^2.$$

In the last equation the x^2 and y^2 terms cancel, leaving a linear equation. This is the equation of the desired line.

Example 1. Find the equation of the perpendicular bisector of the line segment joining $(-1, 2)$ and $(5, -8)$.

Let (x, y) be any point equidistant from $(-1, 2)$ and $(5, -8)$. Then

$$\sqrt{(x + 1)^2 + (y - 2)^2} = \sqrt{(x - 5)^2 + (y + 8)^2}$$

$$x^2 + 2x + 1 + y^2 - 4y + 4 = x^2 - 10x + 25 + y^2 + 16x + 64$$

$$12x + 12y = 25 + 64 - 1 - 4 = 84$$

$$x + y = 7.$$

5.11 CIRCLES

By definition, a circle consists of all points in a plane that are a fixed distance r from a given point, the center. Let (h, k) be the center. Then, if (x, y) is an arbitrary point on the circle, its distance from (h, k) is r, or the square of the distance is r^2. That is,

$$(x - h)^2 + (y - k)^2 = r^2.$$

Since this is true for all points on the circle and for no others, we have found an equation for the desired circle.

Example 1. Find an equation for the circle with center at $(2, -3)$ and radius 4.

$$(x - 2)^2 + [y - (-3)]^2 = 4^2, \quad \text{or} \quad (x - 2)^2 + (y + 3)^2 = 16.$$

Example 2. Find an equation of the circle through (3, 4) with center at the origin.

Since the distance from the origin to (3, 4) is $\sqrt{9 + 16} = 5$, $r = 5$. Also, (h, k) is (0, 0). Hence the desired equation is

$$x^2 + y^2 = 25.$$

Example 3. Find the center and radius of the circle

$$x^2 + y^2 + 4x - 8y - 16 = 0.$$

This is the reverse of the previous examples. We wish to transform the equation into the form

$$(x - h)^2 + (y - k)^2 = r^2.$$

In order to do this, we *complete the square* on x and y. That is, we group the terms containing x and the terms containing y and add enough to each group to make a perfect square.

$$(x^2 + 4x + \quad) + (y^2 - 8y + \quad) = 16 +$$

Since $(x + a)^2 = x^2 + 2ax + a^2$, the quantity to be added in each group is the square of half the coefficient of the first-degree term. The same quantity must be added to both sides of the equation, of course. Thus

$$(x^2 + 4x + 4) + (y^2 - 8y + 16) = 16 + 4 + 16,$$

or $\qquad\qquad (x + 2)^2 + (y - 4)^2 = 36 = 6^2.$

Hence, the center is at $(-2, 4)$ and the radius is 6.

Not every equation of the form of those in the last example represent actual circles. In the process of completing the square we may find that $(x - h)^2 + (y - k)^2$ equals 0 or a negative number. In the case of 0, the circle is merely a point. If r^2 is negative, there is no point in the plane that satisfies the equation.

In plane geometry it is possible to construct a circle that passes through any three points that do not lie on the same line. We do this by finding the point of intersection of the perpendicular bisectors of the chords joining pairs of points. The distance from the center to any of the points provides the radius. These operations can all be carried out in our analytic geometry. In the following example the equations of the perpendicular bisectors will be found by a method somewhat different from that of Section 5.10. This illustrates the variety of techniques available to us.

Example 1. Find an equation of the circle passing through $(-1, 2)$, $(5, 0)$, and $(-1, 2)$.

First, the line through $(-1, 2)$ and $(5, 0)$ has slope $m = -1/3$. Its equation is easily found to be $x + 3y = 5$. The midpoint of the chord joining $(-1, 2)$ and $(5, 0)$ is $(2, 1)$. The equation of the line through $(2, 1)$ perpendicular to the line whose equation is $x + 3y = 5$ is

$$3x - y = 3 \cdot 2 - 1 = 5.$$

Next, the line through $(5, 0)$ and $(1, -2)$ has slope $m = 1/2$. Its equation is $x - 2y = 5$. The midpoint of the chord joining $(5, 0)$ and $(1, -2)$ is $(3, -1)$. The equation of the perpendicular bisector of the chord joining $(5, 0)$ and $(1, -2)$ is thus

$$2x + y = 2 \cdot 3 - 1 = 5.$$

If we add the two equations that we have derived, we find that $5x = 10$, or $x = 2$. From either equation, then, we find that $y = 1$. We have found that the center of the circle is at $(2, 1)$. The radius is the distance from $(2, 1)$ to any of the three points. Using $(5, 0)$, we find that

$$r^2 = (5 - 2)^2 + (0 - 1)^2 = 10.$$

Thus the desired equation is

$$(x - 2)^2 + (y - 1)^2 = 10.$$

We can check our result by showing that this equation is satisfied by the coordinates of the given points. This is left for the student.

5.12 EXERCISES

*1. Find the equation of the line that is the perpendicular bisector of the line segment joining $(2, 3)$ and $(-3, 5)$.

2. Find the equation of the perpendicular bisector of the line segment joining $(-3, 5)$ and $(7, -5)$.

*3. Write the equation of the circle with center at $(-3, 5)$ and radius 4.

4. Write the equation of the circle with center at $(4, 7)$ and radius 8.

*5. Write the equation of the circle with center at the origin that passes through the point $(3, -4)$.

6. Write the equation of the circle with center at $(-4, 1)$ that passes through the point $(6, 2)$.

*7. What is the center and radius of the circle whose equation is $x^2 + y^2 - 2x + 4y - 11 = 0$? Draw its graph.

8. What is the center and radius of the circle whose equation is $2x^2 + 2y^2 - 3x + 6y - 13/8 = 0$? Draw its graph.

*9. A square has vertices $(0, 0)$, $(4, 0)$, $(4, 4)$, and $(0, 4)$.
   (a) Find the equation of the circle inscribed in the square.
   (b) Find the equation of the circle circumscribed about the square.

10. Find the equation of the circle with center at $(2, 3)$ that
   (a) passes through the origin,
   (b) is tangent to the x-axis,
   (c) is tangent to the y-axis.

*11. Find an equation of the circle passing through $(4, 5)$, $(-4, 1)$, and $(5, -2)$.

12. Find an equation of the circle passing through $(-1, -2)$, $(2, -1)$, and $(3, 6)$.

*13. Find an equation of the line through the point of intersection of the circles $(x - 2)^2 + (y - 3)^2 = 9$ and $(x - 5)^2 + (y - 1)^2 = 16$.

14. Find an equation of the line tangent to $x^2 + y^2 = 100$ at $(-6, 8)$.

*15. (a) Find an equation of the line of intersection of $x^2 + y^2 = 100$ and $(x + 6)^2 + (y - 8)^2 = r^2$.
   (b) As r gets close to 0, what does the line of part (a) approach?

5.13 PARABOLAS

It is possible to draw straight lines and circles with the Euclidean tools of straight edge and compass, but that is the extent of it. We can find as many individual points as we like on other curves, but we cannot actually draw the curves. It is here that the power of analytic geometry comes forth. Our graphs are merely visual aids. Our mathematics consists of algebraic manipulation of equations. That is, the primary necessity in our present work is to find an equation representing a geometric concept. For instance, a *parabola* is defined to be the set of all points equidistant from a fixed point (the *focus*) and

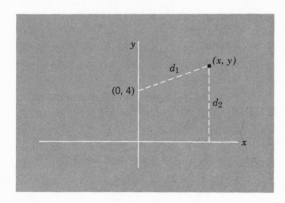

a fixed line (the *directrix*). Let the fixed point be (0, 4) and the fixed line be the x-axis. If (x, y) is any point on the parabola, then the distance from (x, y) to (0, 4) is equal to the distance from (x, y) to the x-axis. In the figure above,

$$d_1 = d_2, \quad \text{or} \quad \sqrt{(x - 0)^2 + (y - 4)^2} = y.$$

On squaring, we find that

$$x^2 + y^2 - 8y + 16 = y^2, \quad \text{or} \quad x^2 = 8y - 16 = 8(y - 2).$$

This is the equation of the parabola. Its graph is given below.

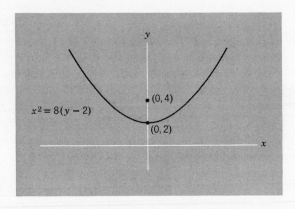

From $x^2 = 8y - 16$, we find that

$$y = 2 + \frac{x^2}{8}.$$

Since x^2 is never negative, the smallest value of y is that for which $x = 0$. Then $y = 2$. The point (0, 2) is rather special. It is midway between the focus and the directrix, and it is the point on the graph that is nearest the directrix. Such a point is called the *vertex* of the parabola.

> **Example 1.** Find the equation of the parabola with focus (3, 2) and directrix $x = 5$.
>
> Let (x, y) be any point on the parabola. Then the distance from (x, y) to (3, 2) is equal to the distance from (x, y) to the line $x = 5$. If we look at a graph, it is easy to see that the distance from (x, y) to $x = 5$ is $5 - x$. Hence,
>
> $$\sqrt{(x - 3)^2 + (y - 2)^2} = 5 - x$$
>
> $$x^2 - 6x + 9 + (y - 2)^2 = 25 - 10x + x^2$$
>
> $$(y - 2)^2 = -4x + 16 = -4(x - 4).$$

We may write the equation above in the form

$$x = 4 - \frac{(y - 2)^2}{4}.$$

Since $(y - 2)^2$ is never negative, its smallest value is 0, when $y = 2$. When the smallest possible value is subtracted from 4, the resulting value of x is the largest it can assume. Hence the point (4, 2) is the vertex of the parabola and is the rightmost point on the graph. Since the focus lies to the left of the directrix, so must all the points on the curve. Thus the graph of the parabola must open to the left. We can get a fair idea of what the graph looks like by plotting a few additional points besides the vertex.

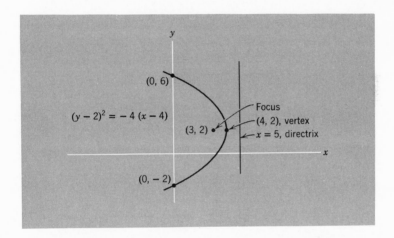

We see that if a parabola has a directrix that is either horizontal or vertical, then the resulting equation contains only one term that is a multiple of either x^2 or y^2 in addition to terms of lower degree. The resulting equation has one of the following two forms:

(a) $(x - h)^2 = c(y - k)$,

or

(b) $(y - k)^2 = c(x - h)$,

where c may be positive or negative, and the vertex is at (h, k). Conversely, if we have any equation in x and y that has only one squared term, we can complete the square in that variable to obtain one of the two forms above.

Example 2. Investigate

$$y = x^2 + 6x + 10.$$

To complete the square in x, we first write

$$y - 10 = x^2 + 6x.$$

We then add 9 to both sides to complete the square.

$$y - 10 + 9 = x^2 + 6x + 9, \quad \text{or} \quad y - 1 = (x + 3)^2$$

This is a parabola of type (b) with vertex at $(-3, 1)$. Since $(x + 3)^2$ is never negative, $y - 1$ is never negative, or y is never less than 1. Hence the parabola opens upward from the vertex.

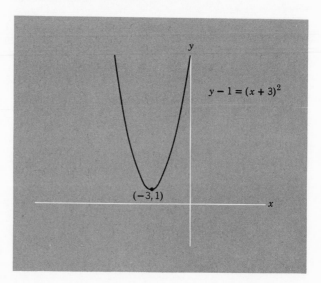

5.14 PHYSICAL PROPERTIES OF THE PARABOLA

The parabola is of considerable practical importance in the physical world because of two properties associated with it. One is the focusing property.

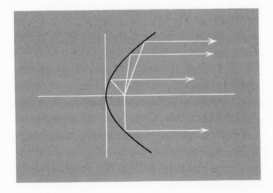

Let us call the line through the vertex and focus of a parabola the *axis* of the curve. Then from any point on the parabola the line drawn to the focus and the line parallel to the axis of the parabola make equal angles with the line tangent to the parabola at the given point. A physical interpretation of this is that all rays emanating from the focus are reflected in a single direction, parallel to the axis of the parabola. This fact is used in such parabolic reflectors as auto headlights, radar antennae, microwave transmission antennae, and remote audio pickups at sports events.

Another fact of physical importance is that the trajectory of a projectile, such as a bullet, when fired upward at an angle with the horizontal, is essentially a parabola. The deviation from a true parabola results primarily from the resistance of the air and the curvature of the earth.

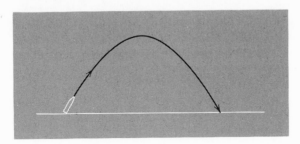

5.15 EXERCISES

*1. Find the equation of a parabola with focus (2, 4) and directrix $x = 8$.

2. Find the equation of a parabola with focus (2, 4) and directrix $x = -4$.

*3. Find the equation of a parabola with focus (2, 4) and directrix $y = 6$.

4. Find the equation of a parabola with focus (2, 4) and directrix $y = -6$.

*5. Find the vertex and sketch the graph of $y = x^2 + 2x$.

6. Find the vertex and sketch the graph of $y = x^2 - 4x - 1$.

*7. Find the vertex and sketch the graph of $2x^2 + 4x - y = 0$.

8. Find the vertex and sketch the graph of $3x^2 + 6x + y + 9 = 0$.

*9. Write an equation for the parabola opening upward with vertex at the origin and passing through $(2, 8)$.

10. Write an equation for the parabola opening to the right with vertex at the origin and passing through $(12, -6)$.

*11. Write an equation for the parabola opening downward with vertex at the origin and passing through $(-2, -1)$.

12. Write an equation for the parabola opening to the left with vertex at the origin and passing through $(-2, -1)$.

*13. A cable of a suspension bridge hangs in an arc of a parabola between two piers 200 feet apart. If the center of the cable dips 50 feet below the ends, write an equation for the cable in any suitable coordinate system.

14. Draw a careful graph of $y^2 = 4x$. From 4 points on the curve, draw as good an approximation to the tangent line as you can. Then draw the lines from each point to the focus $(1, 0)$ and the lines parallel to the axis. Compare the acute angles that each pair of lines at a point make with the tangent line.

*15. A formula of physics states that a body falling freely from rest in a vacuum will fall $gt^2/2$ feet in t seconds. Here, g is a physical constant that is approximately 32. Using $g = 32$, sketch a curve in which the distance fallen, s, is plotted against time, t.

16. Show that an equation of the parabola with focus at $(h + p, k)$ and directrix $x = h - p$ is $(y - k)^2 = 4p(x - h)$.

*17. Find an equation of the parabola with focus at $(h - p, k)$ and directrix $x = h + p$.

18. Find an equation of the parabola with focus at $(h, k + p)$ and directrix $y = k - p$.

*19. Find an equation of the parabola with focus at $(h, k - p)$ and directrix $y = k + p$.

5.16 ELLIPSES

Pin a sheet of paper to a drawing board with two thumbtacks placed about 6 inches apart. Do not push the pins all the way in. Tie a piece of string about 15 inches long into a loop and place the loop around the tacks. Insert a pencil in the loop and stretch it tight. Then, keeping the string taut, trace out a curve on the paper. This curve is called an *ellipse*.

In this section we shall develop equations for ellipses. To start, let us set up a coordinate system in such a way that the tacks lie on the x-axis and the origin is midway between them. Let us assign coordinates $(-c, 0)$ and $(c, 0)$

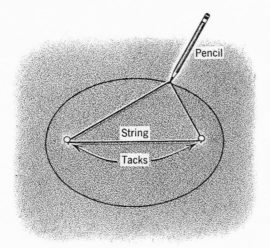

to the points where the tacks are located and call these points *foci* (plural of focus). Let our loop of string be of length $2c + 2a$, where $a > c$. Let a point on the ellipse be designated by (x, y). Let d_1 be the distance from (x, y) to the left focus and d_2 the distance to the right one. Then the sum of the distances from (x, y) to the foci is $2a$.

We are now ready to find an equation satisfied by the coordinates of precisely those points of the plane that lie on the ellipse. In our notation, $d_1 + d_2 = 2a$ for every point on the ellipse. Using the distance formula, we find

$$\sqrt{(x + c)^2 + y^2} + \sqrt{(x - c)^2 + y^2} = 2a.$$

Move one of the radicals to the right side and square. Then

$$(x + c)^2 + y^2 = 4a^2 - 4a\sqrt{(x - c)^2 + y^2} + (x - c)^2 + y^2,$$

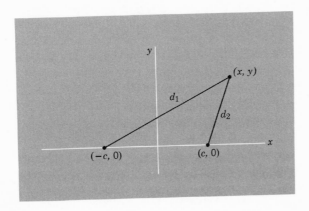

or

$$x^2 + 2cx + c^2 + y^2 = 4a^2 - 4a\sqrt{(x-c)^2 + y^2} + x^2 - 2cx + c^2 + y^2,$$

which simplifies to

$$a\sqrt{(x-c)^2 + y^2} = a^2 - cx.$$

Squaring again, we have

$$a^2(x^2 - 2cx + c^2) + a^2y^2 = a^4 - 2a^2cx + c^2x^2,$$

or

$$x^2(a^2 - c^2) + a^2y^2 = a^2(a^2 - c^2).$$

Since $a > c$, $a^2 - c^2$ is a positive number. Let us call it b^2. Then

$$b^2x^2 + a^2y^2 = a^2b^2,$$

or

$$\frac{x^2}{a^2} + \frac{y^2}{b^2} = 1.$$

This is the desired formula.

If $y = 0$, we find that $x = \pm a$. We call the points $(a, 0)$ and $(-a, 0)$ the *vertices* of the ellipse, and we call the line segment joining the vertices the *major axis*. If $x = 0$, we have $y = \pm b$. We call the line segment joining $(0, b)$ and $(0, -b)$ the *minor axis* of the ellipse.

An ellipse is a little like a circle with two centers. For a given value of a,

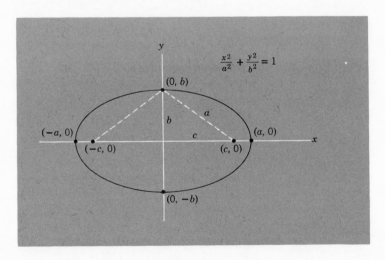

the ellipse is close to a circle when the foci are close together and less circular when the foci are farther apart. The ratio c/a measures, in a sense, how far an ellipse is from being circular. We denote c/a by e and call e the *eccentricity* of the ellipse. Since $c < a$, e lies between 0 and 1. The planets move in paths that are very nearly ellipses with the sun at one focus. The eccentricity of the earth's path, however, is extremely small. The path is nearly a circle. The comets, on the other hand, move in paths with an eccentricity that is close to 1. Their paths are greatly stretched out.

If the foci lie on the y-axis at $(0, c)$ and $(0, -c)$, the equation is

$$\frac{x^2}{b^2} + \frac{y^2}{a^2} = 1.$$

In this case the vertices are $(0, \pm a)$, and the major axis is parallel to the y-axis.

5.17 AWAY FROM THE ORIGIN

We first investigated an ellipse with center at the origin and foci $(\pm c, 0)$. We found its equation to be

$$\frac{x^2}{a^2} + \frac{y^2}{b^2} = 1.$$

Let us interpret this equation geometrically in terms of distances from lines in a plane, rather than in terms of coordinate axes. If (x, y) is a point on the

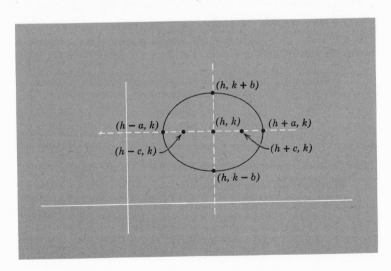

ellipse, the square of the distance from a vertical line through the center, divided by a^2, plus the square of the distance from a horizontal line through the center, divided by b^2, is 1. Suppose now that the center of the ellipse is at (h, k) and the foci are at $(h \pm c, k)$. The vertical line through the center has equation $x = h$, and the square of the distance from (x, y) to this line is $(x - h)^2$. The horizontal line through the center has equation $y = k$, and the square of the distance from (x, y) to this line is $(y - k)^2$. Thus our geometric conditions assert that

$$\frac{(x - h)^2}{a^2} + \frac{(y - k)^2}{b^2} = 1.$$

An ellipse with center at (h, k) and with its major axis parallel to the y-axis has an equation of the form

$$\frac{(x - h)^2}{b^2} + \frac{(y - k)^2}{a^2} = 1.$$

Any equation of the form

$$Ax^2 + By^2 + Cx + Dy + E = 0$$

formally represents an ellipse if A and B differ in value but have the same sign. This means that if the equation is satisfied by the coordinates of some points in the plane, these points form an ellipse. It is possible, however, for an equation of this form to have no points at all on its graph or just one point. The equation $x^2 + 2y^2 = 0$ is satisfied only by $(0, 0)$. The graph of $x^2 + 2y^2 = -1$ consists of the empty set. There are no points on it.

For any ellipse, the facts we wish to know about it include the location of the center, foci, and vertices, length of major and minor axes, and the eccentricity. With this information we can sketch the graph with ease. If we can reduce the equation

$$Ax^2 + By^2 + Cx + Dy + E = 0$$

to the form

$$\frac{(x - h)^2}{a^2} + \frac{(y - k)^2}{b^2} = 1,$$

we can list the following by inspection:

1. center: (h, k)
2. $c = \sqrt{a^2 - b^2}$
3. foci: $(h \pm c, k)$

4. vertices: $(h \pm a, k)$
5. major axis length: $2a$
6. minor axis length: $2b$
7. eccentricity: $e = c/a$.

If the major axis is parallel to the y-axis, a slight change is made in 3 and 4.

In order to transform a general equation of an ellipse into the desired form we complete the square, as we did with the circle. In the case of the ellipse, however, a slight complication is introduced by the fact that the coefficients of x^2 and y^2 are not alike. The following example illustrates the procedure.

Consider

$$9x^2 + 25y^2 + 36x - 50y - 164 = 0.$$

We first write

$$9(x^2 + 4x + \quad) + 25(y^2 - 2y + \quad) = 164.$$

We then complete the square within each pair of parentheses, adding the same quantity to both sides of the equation.

$$9(x^2 + 4x + 4) + 25(y^2 - 2y + 1) = 164 + 9(4) + 25(1)$$

$$9(x + 2)^2 + 25(y - 1)^2 = 225$$

$$\frac{(x + 2)^2}{25} + \frac{(y - 1)^2}{9} = 1.$$

We can now write the following:

1. center: $(-2, 1)$
2. $c = \sqrt{25 - 9} = 4$
3. foci: $(-2 \pm 4, 1)$, or $(-6, 1)$ and $(2, 1)$
4. vertices: $(-2 \pm 5, 1)$, or $(-7, 1)$ and $(3, 1)$
5. major axis length: 10
6. minor axis length: 6
7. eccentricity: $4/5$.

5.18   PHYSICAL PROPERTIES OF THE ELLIPSE

The ellipse has played a major role in astronomy. The German astronomer Johannes Kepler (1571–1630), using the data of his colleague Tycho Brahe (1546–1601), established his celestial laws early in the seventeenth century.

The first of these laws is that every planet describes an ellipse with the sun at a focus. Kepler's laws enabled Isaac Newton (1642–1727) to formulate his laws of gravitation. By Newton's theory, two celestial objects revolve about each other in elliptic paths with their common center of gravity as a focus. If one object is very much more massive than the other, as the sun relative to the earth, then the common center of gravity is very near the center of the larger body. Deviation from a true elliptic path results from the attraction of other heavenly bodies. The elliptic path of the earth has a very small eccentricity and is consequently nearly circular. The comets, on the other hand, follow paths with a relatively large eccentricity.

The ellipse, like the parabola, has a focusing property. Rays emanating from one focus in any direction are reflected through the other focus. It is this fact that accounts for the peculiar phenomenon of the "whispering gallery." This is an elliptic room in which words whispered at one focus can be heard distinctly at the other focus but not at a comparable distance away in other directions. In this country the best known examples of whispering galleries are the Mormon tabernacle at Salt Lake City and a hall at the Capitol in Washington, D.C.

5.19 EXERCISES

In Exercises 1 to 12 find the center, foci, vertices, and eccentricity of each ellipse and sketch its graph.

*1. $x^2/25 + y^2/16 = 1$

2. $x^2/16 + y^2/25 = 1$

*3. $2x^2 + y^2 = 2$

4. $x^2 + 4y^2 = 4$

*5. $(x - 2)^2/25 + (y - 3)^2/16 = 1$

6. $(x + 3)^2/16 + (y - 5)^2/25 = 1$

*7. $(x - 6)^2/2 + (y + 1)^2/4 = 1$

8. $(x + 2)^2/4 + (y + 3)^2/2 = 1$

*9. $9x^2 + 25y^2 + 18x - 100y - 116 = 0$

10. $4x^2 + 2y^2 - 8x + 4y + 2 = 0$

*11. $x^2 + 25y^2 - 50y = 0$

12. $169x^2 + 144y^2 + 338x - 288y - 24{,}023 = 0$

*13. Write an equation for an ellipse with vertices at $(\pm 6, 0)$ and minor axis of length 8.

14. Write an equation for an ellipse with vertices at $(0, \pm 5)$ and foci at $(0, \pm 3)$.

*15. Write an equation of an ellipse with center at $(2, 3)$, vertices at $(2 \pm 5, 3)$, and $e = 4/5$.

5.20 HYPERBOLAS

Let us try another drawing experiment. As with the ellipse, pin a sheet of paper to a drawing board with two thumbtacks about 6 inches apart, with the heads far enough out to let a string slide along the tacks. Tie a small loop in the middle of a length of string. From the loop measure 24 inches on one end of the string and 20 inches on the other. Tie the two ends together at this point. Arrange the string about the tacks as in the sketch and place a pencil in the loop. Hold the string by the knot. With the string taut, pull the pencil, which will follow an arc of a *hyperbola*. By reversing the strings on the tacks and by turning the drawing board, you will get four arcs that form the two branches of the hyperbola.

It should be clear that as the pencil is pulled along an arc of the hyperbola, the distance from the pencil to one tack is always two inches greater than the distance to the other. Let us introduce a coordinate system and obtain an equation for such a curve.

The hyperbola consists of all points in a plane for which the difference of the distances from two fixed points, represented by the tacks, is a constant. Let the fixed points, called the *foci*, be located at $(-c, 0)$ and $(c, 0)$. Let the distance from (x, y) to $(-c, 0)$ be d_1 and from (x, y) to $(c, 0)$ be d_2. Let $d_1 - d_2 = \pm 2a$, where $a < c$. Then,

$$\sqrt{(x + c)^2 + y^2} - \sqrt{(x - c)^2 + y^2} = \pm 2a,$$

or

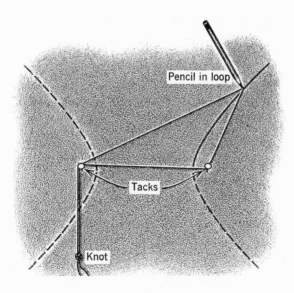

Pencil in loop

Tacks

Knot

$$\sqrt{(x+c)^2+y^2} = \sqrt{(x-c)^2+y^2} \pm 2a.$$

Then, squaring, we find

$$x^2 + 2cx + c^2 + y^2 = x^2 - 2cx + c^2 + y^2$$
$$\pm 4a\sqrt{(x-c)^2+y^2} + 4a^2,$$

which simplifies to

$$\pm a\sqrt{(x-c)^2+y^2} = cx - a^2.$$

Then, squaring again,

$$a^2x^2 - 2a^2cx + a^2c^2 + a^2y^2 = c^2x^2 - 2a^2cx + a^4,$$

or

$$x^2(c^2 - a^2) - a^2y^2 = a^2(c^2 - a^2).$$

Since $a < c$, $c^2 - a^2$ is a positive number. Let $c^2 - a^2 = b^2$. Then

$$b^2x^2 - a^2y^2 = a^2b^2,$$

or

$$\frac{x^2}{a^2} - \frac{y^2}{b^2} = 1.$$

This is the desired equation of the hyperbola.

If $y = 0$, we find that

$$x = \pm a.$$

We call the points $(a, 0)$ and $(-a, 0)$ the *vertices* of the hyperbola, and the line segment joining them is called the *transverse axis* of the curve. The point midway between the vertices, in this case the origin, is the *center* of the hyperbola. The lines $y = \pm(b/a)x$ are called the *asymptotes*. As we go farther and farther from the vertices the hyperbola gets closer and closer to the asymptotes, but the curve never quite touches these lines. With each hyperbola whose equation is $x^2/a^2 - y^2/b^2 = 1$ there is associated another curve, called the *conjugate hyperbola*, whose equation is

$$\frac{x^2}{a^2} - \frac{y^2}{b^2} = -1, \quad \text{or} \quad \frac{y^2}{b^2} - \frac{x^2}{a^2} = 1.$$

The vertices of this associated hyperbola are at $(0, \pm b)$. Thus we say that the *conjugate axis* of the original hyperbola has length $2b$. A hyperbola and its conjugate have the same asymptotes.

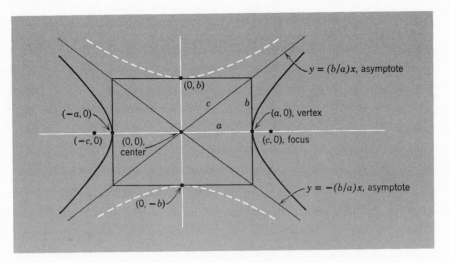

The *eccentricity*, *e*, of a hyperbola is defined to be c/a. Since $c > a$, *e* is always greater than 1. For a given value of c, when a is relatively small or *e* is relatively large, the hyperbola is quite pointed. When a is close to c, however, the asymptotes become steep, and the hyperbola is gently rounded at its vertices.

If the foci lie on the *y*-axis at $(0, \pm c)$, the equation reduces to

$$\frac{y^2}{a^2} - \frac{x^2}{b^2} = 1.$$

In this case the vertices are at $(0, \pm a)$, and the asymptotes are $y = \pm(a/b)x$. In either case the equations of the asymptotes can be found by replacing the number 1 on the right side of the equation of the hyperbola by 0 and then solving for *y*.

In the final form of the equation of the ellipse, a^2 was the larger of the two numbers appearing in the denominators. In the hyperbola, a^2 is the number appearing under the squared term that is positive. In the case of the hyperbola, a may be larger than, smaller than, or equal to b.

5.21 AWAY FROM THE ORIGIN

As with the ellipse, we find that the equation of a hyperbola with foci located c units left and right of the point (h, k) is

$$\frac{(x - h)^2}{a^2} - \frac{(y - k)^2}{b^2} = 1.$$

If the foci are at $(h, k \pm c)$, the equation is

$$\frac{(y - k)^2}{a^2} - \frac{(x - h)^2}{b^2} = 1.$$

The student should carry out the geometric argument to show this.
An equation of the form

$$Ax^2 + By^2 + Cx + Dy + E = 0$$

represents a hyperbola if A and B have different signs, except for the degenerate case of two intersecting straight lines. Such an equation can be reduced by completing the square to one of the two forms above, except for the degenerate case, in which 0 is obtained on the right instead of 1. Observe that, when the square is completed and the right side is reduced to 1 by an appropriate division, the number under the square with the positive sign is denoted by a^2 and under the other by b^2. In either case,

$$c^2 = a^2 + b^2.$$

When the equation of a hyperbola is reduced to the form

$$\frac{(x - h)^2}{a^2} - \frac{(y - k)^2}{b^2} = 1,$$

we can list the following by inspection:

1. center: (h, k)
2. foci: $(h \pm c, k)$
3. vertices: $(h \pm a, k)$
4. transverse axis length: $2a$
5. equations of asymptotes: $y - k = \pm (b/a)(x - h)$
6. eccentricity: $e = c/a$.

If the transverse axis is parallel to the y-axis, the type form is

$$\frac{(y - k)^2}{a^2} - \frac{(x - h)^2}{b^2} = 1,$$

and the following are changed:

2. foci: $(h, k \pm c)$
3. vertices: $(h, k \pm a)$
5. equations of asymptotes: $y - k = \pm (a/b)(x - h)$.

Example 1. Investigate

$$9x^2 - 16y^2 - 36x + 32y - 124 = 0.$$

First, we complete the square.

$$9(x^2 - 4x + 4) - 16(y^2 - 2y + 1) = 124 + 36 - 16 = 144,$$

or

$$\frac{(x - 2)^2}{16} - \frac{(y - 1)^2}{9} = 1.$$

From this form of the equation we see that $a = 4$ and $b = 3$. Hence $c = 5$. We can now list the following data about the hyperbola:

1. center: $(2, 1)$
2. foci: $(2 \pm 5, 1)$
3. vertices: $(2 \pm 4, 1)$
4. transverse axis length: 8
5. equations of asymptotes: $y - 1 = \pm(3/4)(x - 2)$
6. eccentricity: $e = 5/4$.

Example 2. Investigate

$$2x^2 - y^2 + 12x + 4y + 15 = 0.$$

First, we complete the square.

$$2(x^2 + 6x + 9) - (y^2 - 4y + 4) = -16 + 18 - 4 = -2.$$

The negative number on the right informs us that the hyperbola's trans-

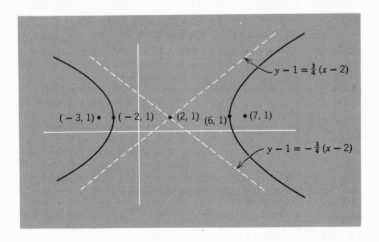

verse axis is vertical. When we divide by -2, we find the type form is

$$\frac{(y-2)^2}{2} - \frac{(x+3)^2}{1} = 1.$$

Here, $c = \sqrt{2+1} = \sqrt{3}$. Thus we have the following:

1. center: $(-3, 2)$
2. foci: $(-3, 2 \pm \sqrt{3})$
3. vertices: $(-3, 2 \pm \sqrt{2})$
4. transverse axis length: $2\sqrt{2}$
5. equations of asymptotes: $y - 2 = \pm\sqrt{2}(x + 3)$
6. eccentricity: $e = \sqrt{3}/\sqrt{2} = \sqrt{6}/2$.

5.22 CONIC SECTIONS

The circle, parabola, ellipse, and hyperbola were figures known and studied by the ancient Greeks. They observed that these figures were the possible intersections of a plane and a right circular cone. A cone of this sort is a surface obtained in the following way. Let a circle be drawn in a horizontal plane. Let P be a point directly above the center of the circle. A right circular cone is the set of all points in space that lie on some line through P and a point of the circle. A line through P and the center of the circle is the *axis* of the cone. The cone is divided into two *nappes* by the point P, which is the *vertex* of the cone. Each nappe is infinite in extent.

A plane perpendicular to the axis intersects the cone in a circle (or a point, if the plane passes through P). A slightly tilted plane intersects the cone in an ellipse (or a point, if the plane passes through P). A plane tilted so that it intersects only one nappe and is parallel to a line that generates the cone produces a parabola. A plane that intersects both nappes produces a hyperbola (or two intersecting lines if the plane passes through P). It is for this reason that the four curves mentioned are called *conic sections*.

The Greeks, of course, studied these curves strictly from a geometric standpoint. The algebraic approach did not come until many, many centuries later.

5.23 EXERCISES

In Exercises 1 to 15 find the center, foci, vertices, and equations of the asymptotes of each hyperbola and sketch its graph.

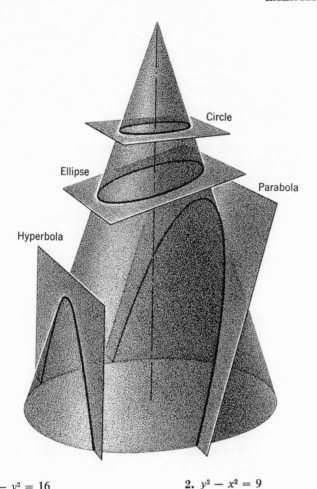

*1. $x^2 - y^2 = 16$

2. $y^2 - x^2 = 9$

*3. $x^2/9 - y^2/16 = 1$

4. $x^2/16 - y^2/9 = 1$

*5. $y^2/25 - x^2/144 = 1$

6. $144x^2 - 25y^2 = 3600$

*7. $(x - 2)^2/16 - (y - 3)^2/9 = 1$

8. $(x + 3)^2/9 - (y - 5)^2/16 = 1$

*9. $(y - 6)^2 - (x + 1)^2/8 = 1$

10. $7(y + 4)^2 - 9(x - 2)^2 = 63$

*11. $20(x - 5)^2 - 16(y + 1)^2 = 320$

12. $16x^2 - 9y^2 + 64x + 54y - 161 = 0$

*13. $x^2 - y^2 + 6x + 2y + 12 = 0$

14. $9x^2 - y^2 - 54x - 2y + 89 = 0$

*15. $12x^2 - 4y^2 - 48x - 8y - 4 = 0$

16. Give the geometric argument for obtaining the form for the equation of a hyperbola with foci at $(h \pm c, k)$.

*17. Sketch, in a single coordinate system, the graphs of the following four equations:

(a) $x^2/16 + y^2/9 = 1$ (b) $x^2/16 - y^2/9 = 1$
(c) $x^2/16 - y^2/9 = -1$ (d) $x^2/16 - y^2/9 = 0$

18. Consider $Ax^2 + By^2 + Cx + Dy + E = 0$. If A and B have different signs, we would classify the graph of the equation as a hyperbola. Suppose that when the square is completed, the constant on the right is 0. What conclusion can you draw?

*19. If $Ax^2 + By^2 + Cx + Dy + E = 0$ and A and B have different signs, what algebraic test will tell whether the graph is really a hyperbola or two intersecting lines? If A and B have the same sign, what does this same test tell you about the graph of the ellipse?

20. Sketch the graph of $xy = 1$.

5.24 ALGEBRA AND GEOMETRY

The operations of geometry are paralleled by operations of algebra. For instance, the problem of finding the point of intersection of two lines becomes the problem of finding the ordered pair of real numbers that satisfies two linear equations. The concept of parallelism is replaced by the concept of equal slope.

A familiar problem of geometry is to construct a circle passing through three noncollinear points. Algebraically, we must find an equation of a circle that is satisfied by the coordinates of three points. Let us do so. Suppose the three points are $(4, 6)$, $(5, -1)$, and $(-2, -2)$. First, since the center lies on the perpendicular bisector of the line segment joining any two points, and since such a perpendicular bisector is the set of all points equidistant from the points, let us find an equation for the perpendicular bisector of the line segment joining $(4, 6)$ and $(-2, -2)$. For an arbitrary (x, y) we set the squares of its distances from $(4, 6)$ and $(-2, -2)$ equal.

$$(x - 4)^2 + (y - 6)^2 = (x + 2)^2 + (y + 2)^2,$$

or

$$x^2 - 8x + 16 + y^2 - 12y + 36 = x^2 + 4x + 4 + y^2 + 4y + 4$$

$$12x + 16y = 44, \quad \text{or} \quad 3x + 4y = 11.$$

We repeat for the line segment joining $(5, -1)$ and $(-2, -2)$.

$$(x - 5)^2 + (y + 1)^2 = (x + 2)^2 + (y + 2)^2,$$

which reduces to

$$14x + 2y = 18, \quad \text{or} \quad 7x + y = 9.$$

We now find the solution to the pair of equations

$$3x + 4y = 11 \quad \text{and} \quad 7x + y = 9$$

to be

$$x = 1 \quad \text{and} \quad y = 2.$$

Thus the center of the circle is the point $(1, 2)$, and its radius is the distance to any of the points, say $(-2, -2)$. We find that

$$r = \sqrt{(1 + 2)^2 + (2 + 2)^2} = 5.$$

Thus the equation of the desired circle is

$$(x - 1)^2 + (y - 2)^2 = 25.$$

5.25   A THEOREM OF GEOMETRY

Finally, let us show that the medians of a triangle intersect in a point. Any triangle can be oriented with respect to a coordinate system so that one vertex is at the origin and another is on the positive x-axis. We shall label the vertices as indicated in the figure.

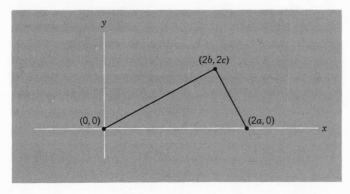

We have used $(2a, 0)$ and $(2b, 2c)$ to make the arithmetic that follows simpler. A median of a triangle is a line segment from any vertex to the midpoint of the opposite side. Let (p, q) be the midpoint of the line segment joining (x_1, y_1) and (x_2, y_2). Then, from the congruent triangles in the figure below, we find that

$$x_2 - p = p - x_1 \quad \text{and} \quad y_2 - q = q - y_1,$$

or

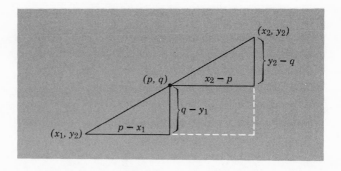

$$p = \frac{x_1 + x_2}{2} \quad \text{and} \quad q = \frac{y_1 + y_2}{2}.$$

Thus the coordinates of the midpoint of a line segment are the averages of the coordinates of the endpoints. Let us add the medians to the triangle of the preceding figure. We shall have proved the theorem if we show that the equations of the three medians have a common solution. Thus we shall write the equations of the medians and show that the solution of two of them satisfies the third.

The equation of the line through the origin and $(a + b, c)$ is

$$(a + b - 0)(y - 0) = (c - 0)(x - 0), \quad \text{or} \quad (a + b)y = cx. \qquad (1)$$

The equation of the line through $(2a, 0)$ and (b, c) is

$$(b - 2a)(y - 0) = (c - 0)(x - 2a), \quad \text{or} \quad (b - 2a)y = cx - 2ac. \qquad (2)$$

The equation of the line through $(a, 0)$ and $(2b, 2c)$ is

$$(2b - a)(y - 0) = (2c - 0)(x - a), \quad \text{or} \quad (2b - a)y = 2cx - 2ac. \qquad (3)$$

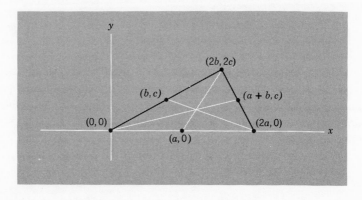

Equations (1) and (2) can be written in the form

$$(1) \quad ay + by = cx$$
$$(2) \quad -2ay + by = cx - 2ac$$

By subtraction, we find $\quad 3ay \quad = \quad 2ac,$

or

$$y = \frac{2c}{3}.$$

Then, from (1),

$$x = \frac{(a + b)y}{c} = \frac{2(a + b)}{3}.$$

If we substitute these values for x and y in equation (3), we find that

$$\frac{(2b - a)2c}{3} = \frac{4c(a + b)}{3} - 2ac,$$

or

$$4bc - 2ac = 4ac + 4bc - 6ac,$$

or

$$0 = 0.$$

Equation (3) is satisfied. Moreover, it can be shown that the common point of intersection, $[2(a + b)/3, 2c/3]$, is two thirds of the distance from each vertex to the midpoint of the opposite side. We have proved even more than was required.

Some theorems of geometry are easier to prove by geometric methods, some by algebraic methods. Having both methods at our disposal gives us greater freedom in our approach to theorems.

5.26 EXERCISES

*1. Find the equation of the circle through $(0, -1)$, $(-2, 5)$, and $(2, 3)$.
 2. Find the equation of the circle through $(-6, -3)$, $(3, 0)$, and $(2, 2)$.
*3. Let (a, b) be a point outside the circle with center at (h, k) and radius r. Let S be the length of the tangent line to the circle from (a, b). Find the length of S. (Hint: the triangle in the figure below is a right triangle.)
 4. Prove that a triangle inscribed in a semicircle is a right triangle. (Hint: Let the circle be $x^2 + y^2 = r^2$. Let (a, b) be a point on the circle, so that $a^2 + b^2 = r^2$. Prove that (a, b), $(r, 0)$, and $(-r, 0)$ are vertices of a right triangle by using the Pythagorean theorem.)

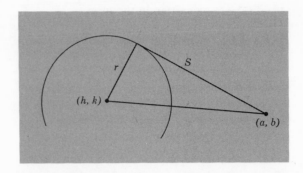

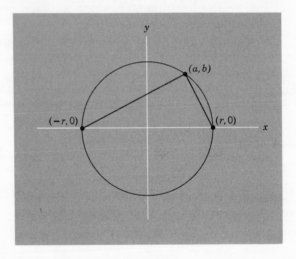

*5. Prove that the three altitudes of a triangle intersect in a single point. Let the triangle have vertices $(0, 0)$, (a, b) and $(c, 0)$.

5.27 RECOMMENDED READING

Allendoerfer, C. B., and Oakley, C. O., *Fundamentals of Freshman Mathematics*, New York, McGraw-Hill, 1959.

Lang, S., *A First Course in Calculus*, Reading, Mass., Addison-Wesley, 1964.

Milne, W. E., and Davis, D. R., *Introductory College Mathematics*, Boston, Ginn, 1962.

6

An electrocardiograph; illustration of a vital function.

6.1 RELATIONS AND FUNCTIONS

In Chapters 2 and 3 we studied the role that algebraic structure plays in mathematics. Another concept of fundamental importance is that of a *function*. First, however, let us look at a somewhat broader idea, that of a *relation*. Loosely, a relation is merely a rule that associates elements of some sort with each of a given set of elements. For instance, each person has a set (possibly empty) of blood relatives. Let Mr. X have relatives $Y_1, Y_2, \ldots, Y_n$. Then we can form a list of the following form:

$$\{(X, Y_1), (X, Y_2), \ldots, (X, Y_n)\}.$$

Furthermore, if we restrict our attention to a certain fixed population of people, we can form such a list for each person. In this way we get a collection of ordered pairs $\{(X, Y)\}$, where X is related to Y. The pair is said to be "ordered" because it is possible to distinguish which is the first element and which is the second. In order to determine whether or not John Jones is related to Hal Smith, we merely examine all the pairs whose first element is John Jones and find out whether Hal Smith's name appears as a second element. If so, they are related. If not, they are unrelated.

In our example, if X is related to Y, then Y is related to X. This restriction is too severe. We would like our concept to be general enough so that it will include relations like "is taller than" such that we may have X related to Y without necessarily having Y related to X. For the same population of people, let us form a new list (x, y), where each ordered pair (x, y) means that x is taller than y. In this example, if x is related to y, then y is not related to x. What conclusion can you draw if x is related to y, in this sense, and y is related to z?

It is not even necessary to have the first and second members of the ordered pairs from the same population. For example, let each person in a given set of students be associated with the courses he has taken. In this case we have a set of ordered pairs (x, y) where x is a student and y is a course he has taken.

We are ready to make a formal definition of a relation.

6.2 RELATIONS

A *relation* is a set of ordered pairs of elements (x, y) where x is an element of a set S_x and y is an element of a set S_y (S_x and S_y may or may not be distinct), together with a rule or criterion that can be used to determine which ordered pairs belong to the relation. If the number of ordered pairs in a relation is finite, the rule may consist merely of a list of the pairs. The set of all first elements is called the *domain* of the relation. The set of all second elements is called the *range* of the relation. If R is a relation and x is related to y, we shall write $(x, y) \in R$. We shall read $\in$ as "belongs to."

You will not be surprised to discover that most of our attention will be devoted to relations whose domain and range are sets of numbers. Let us examine some examples of relations, each of whose domain is the set of all real numbers for which the relation has meaning.

> *Example 1.* R is the relation "less than," written $<$.
> We have $(x, y) \in R$ if and only if $x < y$. Thus $(2, 7) \in R$, but $(10, -2)$ does not. In this case we write $(10, -2) \notin R$. Since every real number is greater than some real number, the range of R is the same as the domain, the set of all real numbers.

> *Example 2.* $(x, y) \in R$ if and only if $x^2 = y$.
> This example is different from any we have seen so far in that for each

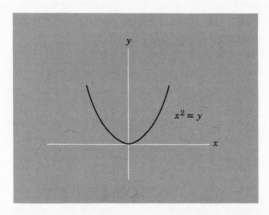

x there is only one y. Moreover, since x^2 is never negative, the range of R consists of only the nonnegative real numbers.

Example 3. $(x, y) \in R$ if and only if $y = 2$ or $y = -2$.

In this example the range of R consists of only two numbers, 2 and -2. Thus $(-0.6, 2)$ and $(3.7, -2) \in R$, but no pair of real numbers belongs to R if the second element is not 2 or -2.

In each of the previous examples the domain of the relation was the set of all real numbers. In those that follow the domain is restricted.

Example 4. $(x, y) \in R$ if and only if $x^2 + y^2 = 1$.

We recognize the graph of R to be the circle of radius 1 whose center is at the origin. Some members of R are $(0.6, 0.8)$, $(-1/\sqrt{2}, 1/\sqrt{2})$, $(5/13, -12/13)$, and $(-15/17, -8/17)$. Since x^2 and y^2 are nonnegative, neither can be larger than 1. Hence, the domain and range of R are the real numbers from -1 to 1.

Example 5. $(x, y) \in R$ if and only if $x = y^2$.

This relation is similar to that of Example 2, but the domain and range have been interchanged. The domain of R is the set of nonnegative reals, and the range consists of all reals.

6.3   EXERCISES

For each of the Exercises 1–18 give the domain and range of R, and give two ordered pairs that belong to R and two that do not.

*1. $(x, y) \in R$ if and only if $y = x + 2$.

2. $(x, y) \in R$ if and only if $y = x^2 + 4$.

*3. $(x, y) \in R$ if and only if $x = y^2 + 4$.

4. $(x, y) \in R$ if and only if $y = x$.

*5. $(x, y) \in R$ if and only if $x^2 + y^2 = 25$.

6. $(x, y) \in R$ if and only if $x^2 - y^2 = 25$.

*7. $(x, y) \in R$ if and only if $x + y = 1$.

8. $(x, y) \in R$ if and only if $y > x + 2$.

*9. $(x, y) \in R$ if and only if $y \leq x + 2$.

10. $(x, y) \in R$ if and only if $x = 7$.

*11. $(x, y) \in R$ if and only if $y = -5$.

12. $(x, y) \in R$ if and only if x and y are positive integers whose greatest common divisor is greater than 1.

*13. $(x, y) \in R$ if and only if x and y are positive integers with no common factor greater than 1.

14. $(x, y) \in R$ if and only if x and y are real numbers that differ by less than 2.

*15. $(x, y) \in R$ if and only if x and y differ by exactly 2.

16. $(A, B) \in R$ if and only if A and B are subsets of a universe U and $A \subset B$.

*17. $(A, B) \in R$ if and only if A and B are subsets of a universe U and $AB = \varnothing$.

18. $(p, q) \in R$ if and only if p and q are propositions and $p \rightarrow q$.

*19. Let R be the "equals" relation, $(x, y) \in R$ if and only if $x = y$. Show that R has the following properties:

(a) $(x, x) \in R$.

(b) If $(x, y) \in R$, then $(y, x) \in R$.

(c) If $(x, y) \in R$ and $(y, z) \in R$, then $(x, z) \in R$.

20. Let R be the "less than or equals" relation, $(x, y) \in R$ if and only if $x \leq y$. Show that R has the following properties:

(a) $(x, x) \in R$.

(b) If $(x, y) \in R$ and $(y, x) \in R$, then $x = y$.

(c) If $(x, y) \in R$ and $(y, z) \in R$, then $(x, z) \in R$.

6.4 FUNCTIONS

Among all relations there are some that are particularly useful in mathematics. These are the relations for which a single element of the range corresponds to each element of the domain. Such a relation is called a *function*.

> **Examples.** The relation of Example 2 of Section 6.2, where $(x, y) \in R$ if and only if $x^2 = y$, is a function because for each x there is a single y in the range. On the other hand, the relation of Example 5, where $(x, y) \in R$ if and only if $x = y^2$ is not a function because $(4, 2)$ and $(4, -2)$ are both elements of R.

6.5 NOTATION

If f is a function, we obtain a set of ordered pairs. If $(x, y) \in f$, then we shall write $y = f(x)$, read "y equals f of x." This notation, $f(x)$, is very convenient whenever we wish to replace x by a number or by another function. For example, suppose that a function is represented briefly by $f(x) = 2x^2 + 3$. By this, of course, we mean the function that consists of the ordered pairs (x, y) for which $y = 2x^2 + 3$. However, our notation permits us to attach meaning to expressions like $f(0), f(2), f(t)$, and $f(x + h)$ by substituting whatever appears in the parentheses for x in $f(x)$. That is,

$$f(0) = 2 \cdot 0^2 + 3 = 3,$$

$$f(2) = 2 \cdot 2^2 + 3 = 11,$$

$$f(t) = 2t^2 + 3,$$

and

$$f(x + h) = 2(x + h)^2 + 3.$$

In fact, we can even substitute symbols representing functions in this way. If $f(x)$ represents a function under discussion and $x = g(t)$, then $f(g(t))$ is a meaningful expression. For instance, if $f(x) = 2x^2 + 3$ and $x = g(t) = t - 5$, then

$$f(g(t)) = 2[g(t)]^2 + 3 = 2(t - 5)^2 + 3.$$

A somewhat more elaborate notation for a function is given by the "set-builder" notation:

$$f = \{(x, y): y = f(x), x \in \text{Domain}\}.$$

This says that f is a function that is a set of ordered pairs (x, y) in which y is obtained from x by the rule $y = f(x)$, where x belongs to a certain domain. If the domain is the set of all real numbers for which the relation is meaningful, the specification of the domain may be omitted.

Example 1. $f = \{(x, y): y = 2x, x > 0\}.$

f is the function that assigns to each positive x the number $2x$. Here,

$$f(x) = 2x.$$

Example 2. $g = \{(x, y): y = x^2\}.$

Since the domain of g is unspecified, we take it to be all real numbers. Then g is the function that assigns to every real number its square, $g(x) = x^2$. Note that $(3, 9)$ and $(-3, 9)$ belong to g, so that two different ordered pairs of g can have the same second elements, but the definition of a function says that any two different pairs of a function will have different *first* elements.

Example 3. $h = \{(u, v): v = 3 - 2u\}.$

Here, $v = h(u)$, where $h(u) = 3 - 2u$. It is clear that there is nothing sacred about the symbols x and y. The symbols u and v or any two distinguishable characters can be used in representing a function, and the name of the function is entirely arbitrary. We shall usually use f, g, and h as function names, but the choice is merely a convenience.

6.6 THE GRAPH OF A FUNCTION

We have seen that a function is a set of ordered pairs of elements determined by some rule. If the domain and range of a function are subsets of the set of real numbers, then the function defines a set of ordered pairs of real numbers. We saw in Chapter 5 that an ordered pair of real numbers can be represented by a point in a plane. It is natural, therefore, to call the set of points corresponding to the ordered pairs (x, y), determined by a function f, the *graph* of f.

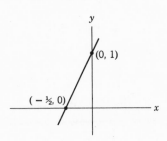

For example, the graph of

$$f = \{(x, y): y = 2x + 1\}$$

is a line with slope 2 and y-intercept 1. In general, the graph of

$$f = \{(x, y): y = mx + b\}$$

is a straight line with slope m and y-intercept b. It is very useful to be able to associate a graph with a function, for the graph is an enormous aid to our intuition when we are studying functions.

6.7 A FUNCTION AS A MAPPING

Another way to think of a function is as a *mapping*. That is, a function f transforms or "maps" every x in the domain of f into a y in the range. This is illustrated schematically in the figure. We call y the "image" of x under f.

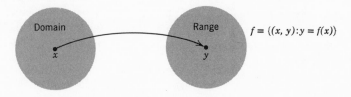

6.8 INVERSE OF A FUNCTION

Among all functions there are some that are particularly noteworthy. These are the functions for which each element of the range is the image of only one element of the domain. Such a function is said to be one-to-one (written 1–1). When this is true, we can devise a mapping (function) that maps each y into the x from which it came. If f is a mapping such that each y is the image of a single x, the function that maps y back into x is called the *inverse* of f and is written f^{-1}. Thus if $f = \{(x, y):y = f(x)\}$ and f is 1–1, then f has an inverse, and

$$f^{-1} = \{(y, x):x = f^{-1}(y)\}.$$

Observe that this is equivalent to saying that

$$f^{-1} = \{(x, y):y = f^{-1}(x)\}$$

because the names attached to the variables are arbitrary.

We have omitted any mention of the domain or range, but it is clear that the domain of f^{-1} is the range of f, and vice versa.

Example 4. If $f = \{(x, y):y = 2x\}$, then

$$f^{-1} = \{(x, y):y = x/2\}.$$

For instance, f maps 6 into 12, and f^{-1} maps 12 into 6.

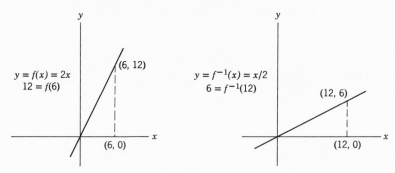

Example 5. If $f = \{(x, y):y = x^2, x \geq 0\}$, then

$$f^{-1} = \{(x, y):y = \sqrt{x}, x \geq 0\}.$$

Here, f maps 3 into 9, and f^{-1} maps 9 into 3.

In order to find the inverse of a function $f = \{(x, y):y = f(x)\}$, we attempt to solve the equation $y = f(x)$ for x in terms of y. If we can do this so that each y determines a single x, we have found the inverse of f.

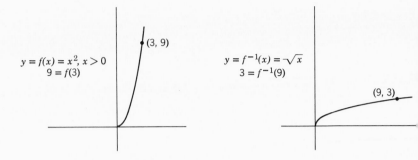

Example 6. Let

$$f = \{(x, y): y = 3x - 2\}.$$

Let us solve the equation $y = 3x - 2$ for x. We find that

$$3x = y + 2, \quad \text{or} \quad x = \frac{y + 2}{3}.$$

After interchanging x and y we can express f^{-1} in the form

$$f^{-1} = \left\{(x, y): y = \frac{x + 2}{3}\right\}.$$

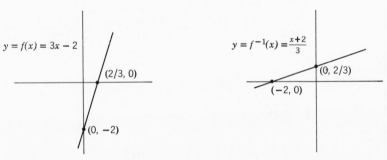

Example 7. Let us try to find the inverse of $f = \{(x, y): y = x^2\}$. Since the domain of f is unspecified, we take it to be all real numbers. The range of f is all nonnegative numbers. If we try to solve $y = x^2$ for x, we find that

$$x = \pm\sqrt{y}.$$

That is, for each positive y there are *two* x's that map into it. Thus f does not have an inverse. In Example 5 we had a similar function, but the domain was limited to nonnegative numbers. Then each y was the image of a single x, so that f had an inverse.

6.9   EXERCISES

*1. In Exercises 1 to 10 of the preceding problem set, which of the relations are functions?

2. Write in functional notation the function that maps every real number into five more than three times the number.

*3. Write in functional notation the function that maps every real number into the product of one more than the number times one less than the number.

4. Write in functional notation the function that maps every positive real number into half its fourth root.

*5. Write in functional notation the function that maps every real number into the negative of itself.

In Exercises 6–15 find the inverse of the given function, if it exists.

6. $f = \{(x, y):y = x + 3\}$ *7. $g = \{(x, y):y = 3x + 7\}$

8. $h = \{(u, v):v = 2u^2 - 1\}$ *9. $f = \{(r, s):s = 2r^3 - 1\}$

10. $g = \{(p, q):q = 100p - 17\}$ *11. $h = \{(x, y):2x - 3y = 5\}$

12. $f = \{(x, y):3x - 2y = 5\}$ *13. $g = \{(r, s):s = 3\}$

14. $h = \{(x, y):y = \sqrt{16 - x^2}, -4 \le x \le 4\}$

*15. $F = \{(x, y):y = (2/3)\sqrt{25 - x^2}, 0 \le x \le 5\}$

16. What function is its own inverse?

*17. Let $f = \{(x, y):y = x^2 - 4\}$. Find and simplify, where possible:

    *(a) $f(0)$ (b) $f(-x)$ *(c) $f(2)$

    (d) $f(t)$ *(e) $f(x^2)$ (f) $f(x + h)$

    *(g) $f(x + h) - f(x)$ (h) $\dfrac{f(x + h) - f(x)}{h}$ *(i) $\dfrac{f(x) - f(t)}{x - t}$

    (j) $f(f(x))$

18. Let $f = \{(x, y):y = x + 2\}$ and $g = \{(x, y):y = x^2\}$. Then f maps 3 into 5, and g maps 5 into 25. Let h be the function that maps every real number in the way that f followed by g does. Write h in functional notation, $h = \{(x, y):y = \ \}$.

*19. Let $f = \{(x, y):y = x^2\}$ and $g = \{(x, y):y = x + 2\}$. Then f maps 3 into 9, and g maps 9 into 11. Let h be the function that maps every real number in the way f followed by g does. Write h in functional notation.

20. If $f = \{(x, y):y = f(x)\}$ and $g = \{(x, y):y = g(x)\}$, how would you interpret $f(g(x))$? $g(f(x))$?

21. If $f = \{(x, y):y = x^2 + 2\}$ and $g = \{(x, y):y = 3x - 5\}$, evaluate the following:

    *(a) $f(g(2))$ (b) $g(f(2))$ *(c) $f(f(2))$

    (d) $g(g(2))$ *(e) $f(g(t))$ (f) $g(f(t))$

    *(g) $f(x + 3)$ (h) $g(t - 2)$ *(i) $f(g(x + h))$

    (j) $g(f(x + h)) - g(f(x))$

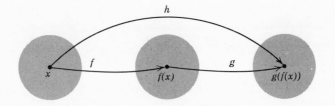

6.10 COMPOSITE FUNCTIONS

In Exercises 17–20 of Section 6.9 examples were given of expressions using functional notation in which the variable was itself a function. In Exercise 21, for example, f and g were defined as

$$f = \{(x, y): y = x^2 + 2\}, \qquad g = \{(x, y): y = 3x - 5\}.$$

According to our notation,

$$f(x) = x^2 + 2 \quad \text{and} \quad g(t) = 3t - 5.$$

Then

$$f(g(t)) = f(3t - 5) = (3t - 5)^2 + 2 = 9t^2 - 30t + 27.$$

In expressions of this sort f is a function of the function g. We call such a function of a function a *composition* of the functions. We shall say that $f(g(x))$ is a *composite* function. Also, we observe that $f(g(x))$ is not in general equal to $g(f(x))$. If we consider

$$h = \{(x, y): y = g(f(x))\},$$

the relations of the functions involved can be represented schematically as shown in the figure.

There are many places in elementary mathematics, particularly in calculus, where the concept and notation of the composition of functions is useful.

6.11 MORE GRAPHS OF RELATIONS AND FUNCTIONS

Relations as well as functions can be graphed, provided the domains and ranges consist of real numbers. For instance,

$$C = \{(x, y): x^2 + y^2 = 4\}$$

is a relation that is not a function, but it is clear that all of the points (x, y) for which $x^2 + y^2 = 4$ constitute a circle about the origin of radius 2.

The graph of a relation may not be a curve. It is quite possible that it is a region.

Example 1.   Let

$$A = \{(x, y): x^2 + y^2 \leq 4\}.$$

The set of all points (x, y) for which $x^2 + y^2 \leq 4$ constitutes the boundary and interior of the circle that is the graph of $x^2 + y^2 = 4$. This is true because $x^2 + y^2$ is the square of the distance from (x, y) to $(0, 0)$. Thus the set of points for which $x^2 + y^2 < 4$ consists of all points that are not more than 2 units away from the origin.

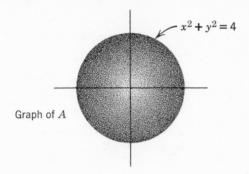

Graph of A

Example 2.   Let

$$P = \{(x, y): y \geq x\}.$$

We know that the points in the plane for which $y = x$ lie on the line making a 45° angle with the positive x-axis. Now consider any point (x, y) in the plane. If $y = x$, the point is on the line. If $y < x$, the point is below the line. But if $y > x$, the point lies above the line. Thus the graph of P is the half-plane consisting of all points on or above the line $y = x$.

In Chapter 5 the graph of a parabola was discussed. From the standpoint of functions we know that

$$f = \{(x, y): y = x^2 - 4x + 3\}$$

has a graph that is a parabola. By completing the square we can put f in the form

$$f = \{(x, y): y + 1 = (x - 2)^2\}.$$

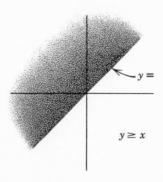

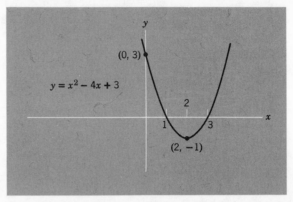

Polynomials are among the commonest functions encountered. The previous function was an example of a polynomial function of the second degree. Polynomials of higher order are more difficult to graph. The next chapter will give us some methods that can help in the construction of graphs of polynomials, but* until then we must plot the graphs point by point. Some special polynomials, of course, are quite easy to graph.

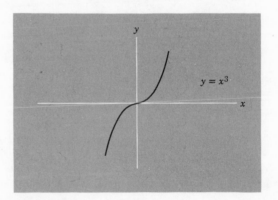

Example 3. $f = \{(x, y):y = x^3\}$.

Example 4. $g = \{(x, y):y = x^3 - 6x^2 + 11x - 6\}$
$$= \{(x, y):y = (x - 1)(x - 2)(x - 3)\}.$$

If $x = 1, 2$, or 3, the factored form shows that $y = 0$. If $x < 1$, all three factors, and hence their product, are negative. If $1 < x < 2$, only two factors are negative. Since the product of two negative numbers is positive, $y > 0$ for $1 < x < 2$. Similarly, $y < 0$ for $2 < x < 3$, and $y > 0$ for

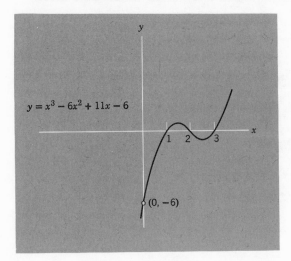

$x > 3$. Many problems in mathematics reduce to that of finding the values of the variable that make a function equal to zero.

How can we handle $\{(x, y): x = y^2 - 4y + 3\}$? This set of ordered pairs is not a function. That is, y is not a function of x because for some values of x there are two values of y. However, x can be expressed as a function of y. We can do this by interchanging the position of x and y to obtain

$$g = \{(y, x): x = y^2 - 4y + 3\}.$$

Its graph is given below.

If the axes are now returned to their customary position, we have the

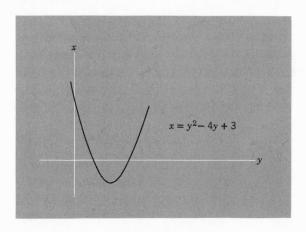

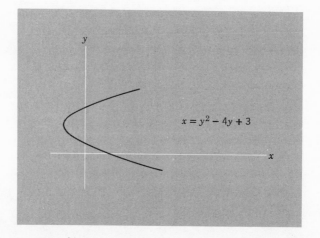

$$x = y^2 - 4y + 3$$

graph given above. This is actually the graph of a relation, not a function. That is, the set of ordered pairs (x, y) satisfying $x = y^2 - 4y + 3$ is a relation, but the set of ordered pairs (y, x) satisfying the same equation is a function, and this fact may be of use.

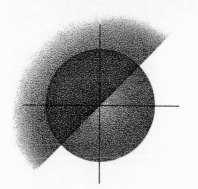

Many problems can be stated in terms of the points that satisfy two or more relations at the same time.

Example 5. Let S be the set of all points on the graph of $P = \{(x, y): y \geq x\}$ *and* $A = \{(x, y): x^2 + y^2 \leq 4\}$. The graph of S is the intersection of the graphs of P and A.

6.12 SIMULTANEOUS LINEAR INEQUALITIES

An area of mathematics that has appeared rather recently and has grown to considerable importance is called *linear programming*. A vital part of this subject is finding the region simultaneously satisfying several inequalities whose graphs are half-planes. As a very simple example, let us find the points that belong to all the graphs of the following three relations.

1. $R_1 = \{(x, y): y \leq 2x + 1\}$
2. $R_2 = \{(x, y): y \geq -x + 1\}$
3. $R_3 = \{(x, y): x \leq 1\}$

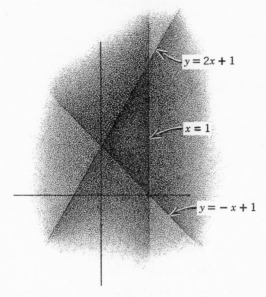

$y = 2x + 1$

$x = 1$

$y = -x + 1$

Let us graph these three relations. The desired graph consists of the boundary and interior of a triangle whose vertices are $(0, 1)$, $(1, 3)$, and $(1, 0)$.

A typical linear programming problem would seek the point or points satisfying all three of the inequalities above for which some linear expression like $x + y$ is a maximum. Since the graph of $x + y = c$ is a line with slope -1, we can think of the set of all lines with slope -1. Which one intersects the triangular region above and has maximum c? We visualize a line with slope -1 moving downward from above until it first intersects the triangle. This occurs at the point $(1, 3)$. Thus $(1, 3)$ is the point satisfying inequalities 1, 2, and 3 for which $x + y$ is a maximum.

If there are more than three inequalities, the region may be bounded by a polygon instead of a triangle, or, if some of the inequalities are reversed, the region may be unbounded. This would also happen if R_2, say, were omitted.

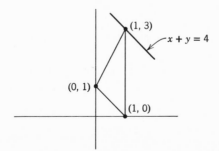

$(1, 3)$

$x + y = 4$

$(0, 1)$

$(1, 0)$

The discussion above is not intended to be even a bare introduction to the vast domain of linear programming. It does, however, show that the graphs of relations are not merely curiosities.

6.13 EXERCISES

Graph the relations of Exercises 1–15.

*1. $f = \{(x, y): y = 2x - 7\}$ 2. $g = \{(x, y): y = x^2\}$

*3. $h = \{(x, y): x^2 + y^2 = 4\}$ 4. $f = \{(x, y): x = y^2\}$

*5. $g = \{(x, y): y = \sqrt{4 - x^2}\}$ 6. $h = \{(x, y): y = 1/(x^2 - 1)\}$

*7. $f = \left\{(x, y): y = \dfrac{1}{(x - 1)(x - 2)}\right\}$ 8. $g = \{(x, y): y < x - 2\}$

*9. $h = \{(x, y): y > x - 2\}$ 10. $f = \{(x, y): x^2 + y^2 > 1\}$

*11. $g = \{(x, y): y > x^2\}$ 12. $h = \{(x, y): y < 2x - 1 \text{ and } y > x\}$

*13. $f = \{(x, y): 1 \leq x^2 + y^2 \leq 4\}$ 14. $g = \{(x, y): y < -x^2 \text{ and } y > -2\}$

*15. $h = \{(x, y): (x - 2)^2 + (y + 3)^2 = 4\}$

16. Write a set of relations whose graph is the set of points inside the triangle whose vertices are $(0, 0)$, $(0, 1)$, and $(1, 0)$.

*17. Write a set of relations whose graph is the set of points inside the triangle whose vertices are $(1, 0)$, $(0, 1)$, and $(2, 2)$.

18. Write a set of relations whose graph is the interior and boundary of the square whose vertices are $(0, 0)$, $(0, 1)$, $(1, 0)$, and $(1, 1)$.

*19. Write a set of relations whose graph is the interior and boundary of the square whose vertices are $(-1, 0)$, $(0, 1)$, $(1, 0)$, and $(0, -1)$.

20. Is the set $\{(1, 2), (2, -1), (3, 4), (2, 1)\}$ a relation? Is it a function?

6.14 SPECIAL FUNCTIONS

There are two rather simple functions, the greatest integer function and the absolute value function, that are frequently of use in various branches of mathematics. The first of these is a mapping from the real numbers to the integers. The second maps each real number into its magnitude, regardless of its sign.

6.15 GREATEST INTEGER FUNCTION

For any given real number x, let y be the largest integer that does not exceed x. For this we shall write $y = [x]$. Thus the greatest integer function is

$$\{(x, y): y = [x]\}.$$

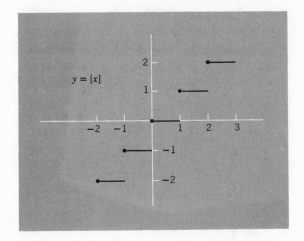

$y = [x]$

Examples. $[2] = 2$ $[\pi] = 3$
            $[2.5] = 2$ $[-\pi] = -4$
            $[-2.5] = -3$ $[-0.0001] = -1$

The graph of $\{(x, y) : y = [x]\}$ is rather interesting. It consists of a series of line segments of length 1, where each segment contains its left endpoint but not its right.

The postage on first class mail is at present five cents per ounce or fraction thereof. Thus if w is weight in ounces and p is postage in cents, we wish to find a function for which $p = 5$ for $0 < w \le 1$, $p = 10$ for $1 < w \le 2$, and so forth. This function is very similar to the greatest integer function. In fact, $p = 5[1 + w]$ is almost what we want. For each natural number n we have $p = 5n$ for $n - 1 < w < n$. The difficulty lies in the fact that for each integral value of w, our postage is calculated as five cents too much. The postage on one ounce, for example, is ten cents. It will be left for the student to verify that the function below rectifies the error.

$$p = 5\left(1 + [w] - \left[\frac{[w]}{w}\right]\right) \quad \text{for} \quad w > 0.$$

6.16   ABSOLUTE VALUE FUNCTION

For any given real number x, let $y = x$ if $x \ge 0$, and $y = -x$ if $x < 0$. For this we shall write $y = |x|$. We define the absolute value function to be

$$\{(x, y) : y = |x|\}.$$

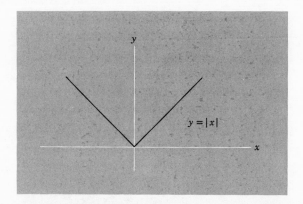

Observe that the slope of the graph of $y = |x|$ is 1 for $x > 0$ and -1 for $x < 0$. The slope is not defined at the origin.

Examples. $|3.7| = 3.7,$ $|-\pi| = \pi,$ $|0| = 0.$

Since $\sqrt{c}$ is defined, for each positive c, to be the positive number whose square is c, it follows that $\sqrt{x^2} = |x|$.

Some interesting conclusions can be deduced from the definition of the absolute value function. Let us state them as theorems.

Theorem 1. *For every real x and y, $|xy| = |x|\cdot|y|$.*

Proof: $|xy| = \sqrt{x^2y^2} = \sqrt{x^2}\sqrt{y^2} = |x|\cdot|y|$.

Theorem 2. *For any real x and y, $|x + y| \leq |x| + |y|$.*

Proof: Let us consider two cases.

1. If x and y have the same sign, the absolute value of their sum is the sum of their absolute values, or

$$|x + y| = |x| + |y|.$$

2. If x and y have different signs, the absolute value of their sum is the absolute value of the larger less that of the smaller. That is, $|x + y| =$ either $|x| - |y|$ or $|y| - |x|$, depending on which is larger. In either case, the difference of the absolute values is less than their sum, or

$$|x + y| < |x| + |y|.$$

If we now combine 1 and 2, we have $|x + y| \leq |x| + |y|$ for all x and y.

Theorem 3. *For any real x and y, $|x - y| \geq |x| - |y|$.*

Proof: By Theorem 2, $|x + y| \leq |x| + |y|$ for any real x and y. Replace x by $x - y$ wherever it occurs. Then

$$|(x - y) + y| \leq |x - y| + |y|, \quad \text{or} \quad |x| \leq |x - y| + |y|,$$
$$\text{or} \quad |x - y| \geq |x| - |y|.$$

6.17   AN ALTERNATIVE

It is frequently useful to discuss the set of real numbers x satisfying the relation $|x| < k$ for some real number k. An alternate statement, not using the absolute value function, is that the relation is satisfied by any x lying between $-k$ and k. That is, $-k < x < k$ is equivalent to $|x| < k$.

Example 1. Consider a real number line like the x-axis of analytic geometry.

(a) What set of points corresponds to the relation $|x| < 2$? The desired set is the interval from -2 to 2, exclusive.

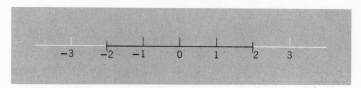

(b) What change is there if the relation is changed to $|x| \leq 2$? In this case the endpoints of the interval are included.

(c) What change is there if the relation is changed to $|x| > 2$? In this case we get all of the points *not* included in case (b).

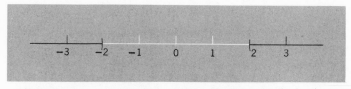

(d) What change is there if the relation is changed to $|x - 2| < 3$? Now, using the alternate statement, we have $-3 < x - 2 < 3$. If 2 is added to each of the three members of the inequality, the inequality is preserved, and $-1 < x < 5$. Our solution set is the interval from -1 to 5, not including the endpoints. In general, if $|x - a| < b$, then

$$-b < x - a < b, \quad \text{or} \quad a - b < x < a + b.$$

6.18   ABSOLUTE VALUE AS A DISTANCE

Let us again consider a real number line. Let x_1 and x_2 be any two points on the line. What is the distance between the points? With the usual orientation, and with the customary identification of real numbers with points on the line, if the number x_1 is greater than the number x_2, the distance between the points is $x_1 - x_2$. If x_2 is greater than x_1, then the distance is $x_2 - x_1$. We can combine these two cases into one by observing that in either event the distance between the points is $|x_1 - x_2|$.

Example 1.   The distance between -3 and 2 is

$$|-3 - 2| = |2 - (-3)| = 5.$$

Example 2.   The distance between -3 and -5 is

$$|-3 - (-5)| = |-3 + 5| = 2.$$

Example 3.   The distance between 7 and 10 is $|7 - 10| = |10 - 7| = 3$.

6.19   EXERCISES

1. Evaluating the following:

   *(a) $[2.718]$ (b) $[-2.718]$ *(c) $[5/3]$
   (d) $[-21/4]$ *(e) $[1.0001]$ (f) $[1.9999]$
   *(g) $[123/(-6)]$ (h) $[-117/39]$

In Exercises 2–18 graph the given relation or function.

   2. $\{(x, y): y = [x] \text{ for } |x| \leq 4\}$ *3. $\{(x, y): y = [x] \text{ for } |x - 2| < 4\}$
   4. $\{(x, y): y = [2x] \text{ for } |x| < 2\}$ *5. $\{(x, y): y = [-x] \text{ for } |x| \leq 2\}$
   6. $\{(x, y): y = [-2x] \text{ for } |x - 2| \leq 3\}$ *7. $\{(x, y): y = [-2x] \text{ for } |x + 2| \leq 3\}$
   8. $\{(x, y): |x| + |y| = 1\}$ *9. $\{(x, y): |x| + |y| < 2\}$
   10. $\{(x, y): |y| \leq 1\}$ *11. $\{(x, y): 1 \leq |y| \leq 2\}$
   12. $\{(x, y): |x - 2| \leq 2\}$ *13. $\{(x, y): |x| < 1 \text{ and } |y| < 2\}$
   14. $\{(x, y): |x| < 2 \text{ and } |y| > 1\}$ *15. $\{(x, y): y = |x|/x\}$
   16. $\{(x, y): y = (x + |x|)/2\}$ *17. $\{(x, y): y = (|x| - x)/2\}$
   18. $\{(x, y): y = x|x|\}$

*19. Graph the postage function of Section 6.15.

20. A test is scored on the basis of 100 possible points with no fractional scores. Five grades are to be given, 0, 1, 2, 3, or 4, according to the following scale:

Score	Grade
89 to 100	4
77 to 88	3
65 to 76	2
53 to 64	1
0 to 52	0

Write the grade g as a function of the score s so that each paper will be assigned the correct grade provided no score is lower than 41. (This last proviso is added to make the problem easier.)

7

The universe, describable only by poets—and calculus.

7.1 INTRODUCTION

The goal of this work is to give the reader a brief introduction to the mathematician, his work, and his methods. So far we have taken a brief glance at the beginnings of mathematics; we have surveyed the development and properties of natural, integral, rational, and real numbers; we have seen how the mathematician develops, explores, and uses the structure of an abstract, formal mathematical system; and we have been introduced briefly to residue classes and congruences, analytic geometry, and the concept and notation of functions and relations. No purported description of the nature of mathematics can possibly avoid another concept that underlies the scientific explosion of the modern age. This is the concept of the limit. In this chapter we shall explore the consequences of the limit concept in an intuitive way, showing how certain limits lead to the vast realm called "calculus," and attempting to show why calculus does play such an important role in modern science. Since our development will be descriptive, rather than rigorous, we must remember that this is not a text in calculus. Instead, our goal is to give the reader an idea of what calculus is.

In Chapters 5 and 6 we have encountered functions and their graphs. We have had some indication that functional relationships are common in the physical world and in the abstraction of the physical world that is examined in mathematics. In many physical situations certain variables such as distance, area, and volume are functions of time. In such situations it is natural to ask questions concerning the rate at which things happen. Calculus provides the language and techniques for discussing such questions. The rate of change of one variable with respect to another will be of basic interest to us.

We know that if a car travels 100 miles in two hours its average speed is 50 miles per hour. We obtain this figure for average speed by dividing the distance traversed by the time required for the trip. But what is meant by the speed of a car at a given instant? During an instant, which is a point in time, the car travels no distance and takes no time to do it. We can no longer employ the procedure used to find average speed. Instead we shall approach the problem by considering average speed over a smaller and smaller interval of time. Then, if the average speed gets close to some fixed value as the time interval decreases, we shall call this fixed value the "instantaneous speed" of the car.

For example, suppose a car travels east along a straight road. We shall let t in hours represent the time elapsed since the car passed through town A. Further, suppose that for any positive t, the distance s of the car from A in miles is given by $s = 25t^2$. Thus, when $t = 2$ hours, $s = 25 \cdot 2^2 = 100$ miles. We know that the average speed of the car for the two hours is 50 miles per hour. Let B be a signpost along the highway, and suppose that the car passes B exactly 36 minutes after leaving A. What is the speed of the car at the instant it reaches B?

When $t = 1$, $s = 25$ miles, and when $t = 0.6$, $s = 9$ miles. Thus the average speed from the time when $t = 0.6$ until the time when $t = 1$ is $(25 - 9)/0.4 = 40$ miles per hour. Let us make a table of t, x, and the average speed from $t = 0.6$ to the given time t.

t	s	Average speed
0.6	9	
1.0	25	$(25 - 9)/0.4 = 40$
0.8	16	$(16 - 9)/0.2 = 35$
0.7	12.25	$(12.25 - 9)/0.1 = 32.5$
0.65	10.5625	$(10.5625 - 9)/0.05 = 31.25$
0.61	9.3025	$(9.3025 - 9)/0.01 = 30.25$
0.601	9.030025	$(9.030025 - 9)/0.001 = 30.025$

Apparently the average speed over shorter and shorter intervals of time is approaching 30 miles per hour.

When we construct the graph of a function, it is of interest to know how steep the curve is at any point and where the graph has high points or low points. Frequently these questions can be answered if we know the slope of the tangent line at each point. It is a simple matter to find a tangent line to a circle at any point on the circle, but what is meant by a tangent line to other curves? The approach we shall use is to look at the slopes of lines through a fixed point A and other points P on the curve. If, as P is chosen nearer and nearer to A, the slope of the line through A and P gets close to a fixed value, we shall call this fixed value the slope of the tangent line at A.

Let A be the point $(a, f(a))$ on the graph of $y = f(x)$. Let $(p, f(p))$ be a point P distinct from A. Then the slope of the line through A and P is given by

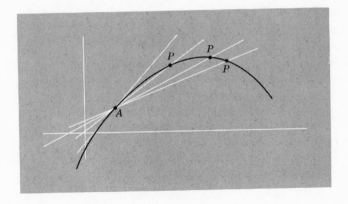

$$m = \frac{f(p) - f(a)}{p - a}.$$

Our suggested procedure is to examine m as p gets closer to a. For example, consider the parabola $y = 25x^2$. Let A be the point $(0.6, 9)$. Let us assign different values to p and form a table of $p, f(p)$, and m for different values of p.

p	$f(p)$	m
0.6	9	
1.0	25	$(25 - 9)/0.4 = 40$
0.8	16	$(16 - 9)/0.2 = 35$
0.7	12.25	$(12.25 - 9)/0.1 = 32.5$
0.65	10.5625	$(10.5625 - 9)/0.05 = 31.25$
0.61	9.3025	$(9.3025 - 9)/0.01 = 30.25$
0.601	9.030025	$(9.030025 - 9)/0.001 = 30.025$

Apparently, the slope of the line through A and P as P gets closer and closer to A is approaching the value 30.

The two examples above show that there is a common process involved. This process is called a "limiting" process, and the rest of our work in this chapter will deal with limits of various kinds. A generalization of the sort of limit discussed in the examples leads to what is called the *derivative*. It is the basis for one part of calculus.

Another class of problems deals with quantities that are being accumulated. When a constant force is applied to an object, the work done is the product of the force by the distance the object is moved. If the force is not constant, however, the problem is more complicated. If the force changes only slightly for a sufficiently small change in distance, we can compute the sum of the small work increments over a succession of small distance increments. This is another facet of the limiting process and calculus. Problems similar to these are finding the work done in pumping air into a tire and finding the area bounded by curves of various sorts.

It is impossible to discuss calculus in any significant way without the introduction of certain new words, symbols, and concepts. The first and most fundamental of these is "limit."

7.2 LIMITS

Let f be a function whose range is a set of real numbers and whose domain we shall suppose to be the set of all real numbers. Then, for every x, $f(x)$ is a real number, and the equation $y = f(x)$ has a graph. We wish to examine the graph of $y = f(x)$ and to establish methods for answering such questions as: "Is the graph unbroken?" "Is the graph smooth?" "Does the graph possess a tangent line at a particular point?" "Are there any points on the graph that are higher or lower than all nearby points?" "Is there an area bounded by the graph and the x-axis between two vertical lines?" "If so, what is it?" It is questions such as these that will be the motivating force behind the rest of this chapter.

Let us begin by examining the question of whether the graph of a function is broken. If it is not broken, we shall say the function is continuous. In the seventeenth century Descartes described a function as being continuous if its graph could be drawn without lifting pencil from paper. This is the idea that we wish to make more meaningful in a mathematical sense. Descartes' description was hardly a useful definition. Let c be some value of x in the domain of the function f. Then the y-value for $x = c$ is $y = f(c)$, and $(c, f(c))$ is a point on the graph. Now, let x be a number different from c, with $(x, f(x))$ the corresponding point on the graph of the function. If, whenever x gets close to c, $f(x)$ gets close to $f(c)$, then we shall say that f is *continuous* at $x = c$. Our entire definition hinges on what we mean by saying that x "gets close to" c and that $f(x)$ "gets close to" $f(c)$. In general, we shall say that $f(x)$ gets close to some number L as x gets close to c if for any positive number, no matter how small, it is true that all values of x sufficiently close to c, but distinct from c, yield values for $f(x)$ that differ from L by less than the small positive number. If this is the case, we say that L is the limit of $f(x)$ as x approaches c, and we write

$$\lim_{x \to c} f(x) = L.$$

We can shorten our definition somewhat by using a couple of symbols. Let ϵ represent an arbitrary positive number. Then, if for *each* ϵ, no matter how

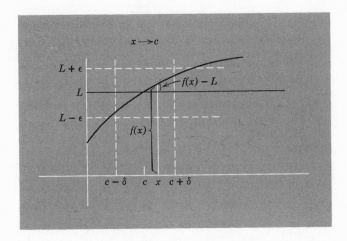

small, there is some positive number δ such that for all x within δ units of c but distinct from c, $f(x)$ differs from L by less than ϵ, then $\lim_{x \to c} f(x) = L$. We can shorten the definition even more by using the absolute value function, which was explored in Chapter 6, Section 6.18, as a distance function. If it is true that for each $\epsilon > 0$ there is some $\delta > 0$ such that $|f(x) - L| < \epsilon$ whenever x satisfies $0 < |x - c| < \delta$, then $\lim_{x \to c} f(x) = L$. In the case of continuity, L is $f(c)$. In short, f is continuous at $x = c$ if and only if $\lim_{x \to c} f(x) = f(c)$. The interpretation of this statement is that when x approaches c, the points on the graph get close to the point $(c, f(c))$. In a way, this says that there is no jump or break in the curve at the point $(c, f(c))$.

Let x_1 and x_2 be two distinct real numbers with $x_1 < x_2$. Then the set of all x such that $x_1 < x < x_2$ is called an *open interval*. The set of x such that $x_1 \leq x \leq x_2$ is called a *closed interval*. If only one of the endpoints is included, the interval is neither open nor closed.

The definition of continuity is clearly a property of a function at a point. However, if f is continuous for every value of x in some open interval, we say that f is continuous on the interval. In this case its graph has no breaks in it on the interval, and we have arrived at the mathematical definition corresponding to Descartes' description of a continuous function. Some functions are continuous everywhere; others are continuous at no point; others fall somewhere between. For example, the graph of $f = \{(x, y): y = x\}$ is a straight line through the origin with slope 1. It is continuous everywhere. But if

$$g = \{(x, y): y = 1 \text{ if } x \text{ is rational and } y = 0 \text{ if } x \text{ is irrational}\},$$

then g is not continuous at any point.

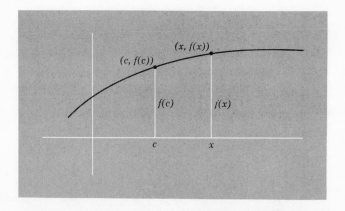

We were careful in our general definition of a limit to insist that x be distinct from c. In the case of continuous functions this restriction is unnecessary. The reason for this is that if we know nothing about a function except that $\lim_{x \to c} f(x) = L$, we do not know if the function is defined at $x = c$ or, if so, whether $f(c) = L$ or not. If f is continuous at c, we know that $f(c)$ exists and that $f(c)$ is the limit approached as x approaches c.

Example 1. Let

$$f = \{(x, y) : y = 2x\}.$$

When x gets close to 1, $2x$ gets close to 2. Thus,

$$\lim_{x \to 1} f(x) = 2.$$

Similarly,

$$\lim_{x \to 0} f(x) = \lim_{x \to 0} 2x = 0, \quad \text{and} \quad \lim_{x \to -3} f(x) = -6.$$

Since $f(1) = 2$, $f(0) = 0$, and $f(-3) = -6$, we see that f is continuous at $x = 1$, 0, and -3. In fact, for any number c and for h not zero, let

$$x = c + h.$$

Then, as $x \to c$, it follows that $h \to 0$. Moreover, since $f(x) = f(c + h) = 2c + 2h$, we have

$$\lim_{x \to c} f(x) = \lim_{h \to 0} (2c + 2h) = 2c = f(c).$$

Thus, f is continuous for all x.

Example 2. Let

$$g = \{(x, y) : y = x^2 + 3\}.$$

Then,

$$\lim_{x \to 1} g(x) = \lim_{x \to 1} (x^2 + 3) = 4, \qquad \lim_{x \to 0} g(x) = 3, \quad \text{and}$$
$$\lim_{x \to 2} g(x) = 7.$$

For any number c,

$$\lim_{x \to c} g(x) = \lim_{h \to 0} g(c + h) = \lim_{h \to 0} (c^2 + 2ch + h^2 + 3)$$
$$= c^2 + 3 = g(c).$$

Thus g is continuous everywhere.

Example 3. Let

$$\phi = \left\{ (x, y) : y = \frac{2x + 3}{x - 1} \right\}.$$

Then,

$$\lim_{x \to 0} \phi(x) = \frac{3}{-1} = -3, \quad \text{and} \quad \lim_{x \to 2} \phi(x) = \frac{4 + 3}{2 - 1} = 7.$$

But what about $\lim_{x \to 1} \phi(x)$? As x gets close to 1, the numerator gets close to 5 but the denominator gets close to 0. When numbers near 5 are divided by numbers closer and closer to 0, the quotient gets large without bound. That is, we can make $\phi(x)$ as large as we please by choosing x sufficiently close to 1. Thus $\lim_{x \to 1} \phi(x)$ does not exist, and as x gets close to 1 $\phi(x)$ does not get close to any real number.

Example 4. Let

$$F = \left\{ (x, y) : y = \frac{x^2 - 4}{x - 2} \right\}.$$

It seems at first that we should have the same difficulty near 2 with F that we had near 1 with ϕ in the last example. A second look shows us that when x approaches 2, *both* numerator and denominator approach 0. Hence we don't know whether the limit exists or not. Let us try to creep up on 2.

$$F(1) = \frac{-3}{-1} = 3$$

$$F(1.5) = \frac{2.25 - 4}{1.5 - 2} = \frac{-1.75}{-0.5} = 3.5$$

$$F(1.6) = \frac{2.56 - 4}{1.6 - 2} = \frac{-1.44}{-0.4} = 3.6$$

$$F(1.9) = \frac{3.61 - 4}{1.9 - 2} = \frac{-0.39}{-0.1} = 3.9$$

$$F(1.99) = \frac{3.9601 - 4}{1.99 - 2} = \frac{-0.0399}{-0.01} = 3.99$$

$$F(2.01) = \frac{4.0401 - 4}{2.01 - 2} = \frac{0.0401}{0.01} = 4.01$$

It appears that $F(x)$ is getting close to 4 as x gets close to 2. Can we show that $\lim_{x \to 2} F(x) = 4$? Let us rewrite $F(x)$ in the form $(x - 2)(x + 2)/(x - 2)$. This is not defined if $x = 2$, but for every other value of x, $(x - 2)/(x - 2) = 1$, so that $F(x)$ reduces to $x + 2$. That is, for all x distinct from 2,

$$F(x) = x + 2.$$

From this,

$$\lim_{x \to 2} F(x) = 2 + 2 = 4.$$

Observe that in this case it was necessary to use that part of the definition of a limit that restricted x from taking on the value c, which is 2 in this example. We shall find that in many of our applications we shall encounter precisely this same problem, the numerator and denominator both approaching 0. When this happens, our limit, if any, is obscured. It is always a sign that we have more work to do. In this example we found that the additional work turned out to be removing a common factor from the numerator and denominator.

Example 5. Let

$$f = \{(x, y) : y = 2x - 4\}.$$

This time, let us suppose that x is some fixed number, and consider

$$\lim_{h \to 0} \frac{f(x + h) - f(x)}{h}.$$

Since $f(x + h) = 2x + 2h - 4$, we find that

$$\frac{f(x + h) - f(x)}{h} = \frac{2x + 2h - 4 - 2x + 4}{h} = \frac{2h}{h}.$$

We are interested in the limit as $h \to 0$ and are thus interested only in values of h different from 0. For all such numbers, $2h/h = 2$. Consequently, our desired limit is 2.

Example 6. Let us try to evaluate the limit of example 5 when $f(x) = x^2$. Now,

$$\frac{f(x + h) - f(x)}{h} = \frac{(x + h)^2 - x^2}{h} = \frac{x^2 + 2hx + h^2 - x^2}{h}$$

$$= \frac{2hx + h^2}{h} = 2x + h$$

if $h \neq 0$. From this we see that

$$\lim_{h \to 0} \frac{f(x + h) - f(x)}{h} = 2x$$

for any x.

7.3 EXERCISES

In Exercises 1–20 evaluate the indicated limits. In each case determine, if you can, whether the function is continuous at the point $(x, f(x))$ in question.

*1. $\lim_{x \to 2} (3x - 5)$
2. $\lim_{x \to 0} (x^2 + 3x + 7)$
*3. $\lim_{x \to -4} (x^3 + 1)$
4. $\lim_{x \to 2} (x^2 + 3)/(x - 5)$
*5. $\lim_{x \to 2} (x^2 + 3)(x - 5)$
6. $\lim_{x \to 3} (2x + 7)(x^2 - 9)$
*7. $\lim_{x \to 1/2} (3x - 5)/(x^2 + 2)$
8. $\lim_{x \to -2} (x^4 + 5x^3 - 3x^2 + 2x + 1)$
*9. $\lim_{x \to 2} (x^{10} - 24)$
10. $\lim_{x \to 2} (x - 5)^3$
*11. $\lim_{x \to 0} (5 + x^2)/x$
12. $\lim_{x \to 0} x^2/x$
*13. $\lim_{x \to -3} (x + 3)/(x - 3)$
14. $\lim_{x \to -3} (x - 3)/(x - 3)$
*15. $\lim_{x \to 3} (x + 3)/(x - 3)$
16. $\lim_{x \to 3} (x - 3)/(x - 3)$
*17. $\lim_{x \to 3} 5$
18. $\lim_{x \to 0} 0$
*19. $\lim_{x \to 2} (x^2 - x - 2)/(x - 2)$
20. $\lim_{x \to -4} (x^2 + x - 12)/(x + 4)$

In Exercises 21–24 evaluate $\lim_{h \to 0} \dfrac{f(x + h) - f(x)}{h}$ for the given functions.

*21. $f(x) = mx + b$
22. $f(x) = ax^2 + bx + c$
*23. $f(x) = \sqrt{x}$
24. $f(x) = 1/x$

7.4 TANGENT LINES

We all know exactly what it means to say that a line is tangent to a circle. It means that the line touches but does not cross the circle, or that the line, passing through a point on the circle, is perpendicular to a radius drawn to the point. Let us consider a more general curve, the graph of a function, f. Let $(a, f(a))$ be a point on the graph. What do we mean when we say that

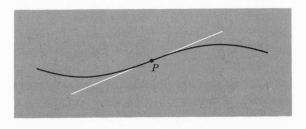

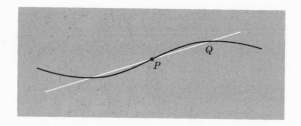

a line through $(a, f(a))$ is tangent to the curve? Does one exist? Can there be more than one? How can we find the tangent if it exists? Our experience with the circle does not help us at all. Obviously, we do not usually have a "center" or "radius" for our general curve, and if the graph has the shape above, we would like the tangent line at P to cross the curve. We have an intuitive idea of what a tangent line should be; our problem is to translate our intuition into an explicit statement. Let us do this by starting with a line through P that is close to what we would like to have as a tangent line, and then, perhaps, we can find out how to come even closer. Draw a line through P and through Q, a nearby point on the curve.

Let us move Q closer to P. As we do so, the line through P and Q becomes closer and closer to what we would like our tangent line to be. In fact, as Q approaches P, we can define the limiting line approached, if it exists, to be the tangent at P.

So far, we have used geometric language. All of our work with limits, however, has been essentially arithmetic, with geometric interpretations. If P is the point $(c, f(c))$ on the graph of a function f, we can let Q be the point $(c + h, f(c + h))$. Then, as $h \to 0$, Q will approach P. So far, so good, but what limit shall we consider as $h \to 0$? As Q approaches P, the slope of the line through P and Q will change, and if we knew the limiting value of the slope of the line, we would be able to specify the tangent line. Let us recall that the slope of a line through (x_1, y_1) and (x_2, y_2) is given by

$$m = \frac{y_2 - y_1}{x_2 - x_1}.$$

Thus the slope of the line through $(c, f(c))$ and $(c + h, f(c + h))$ is given by

$$m(h) = \frac{f(c + h) - f(c)}{(c + h) - c} = \frac{f(c + h) - f(c)}{h}.$$

We write $m(h)$ to indicate that the slope is a function of h. Now we are ready to let Q approach P. If

$$\lim_{h \to 0} \frac{f(c + h) - f(c)}{h}$$

exists, we shall say that this limit is the slope of the tangent line to the graph of f at $(c, f(c))$.

Example 1.   Find the equation of the tangent line to the graph of $y = x^2$ at the point $(2, 4)$.

In this example

$$c = 2 \quad \text{and} \quad f(x) = x^2.$$

Thus

$$m(h) = \frac{f(c + h) - f(c)}{h} = \frac{(2 + h)^2 - 2^2}{h} = \frac{4 + 4h + h^2 - 4}{h} = 4 + h.$$

If m is the slope of the desired tangent line,

$$m = \lim_{h \to 0} m(h) = \lim_{h \to 0} (4 + h) = 4.$$

Thus the desired tangent line has equation

$$y - 4 = 4(x - 2), \quad \text{or} \quad y = 4x - 4.$$

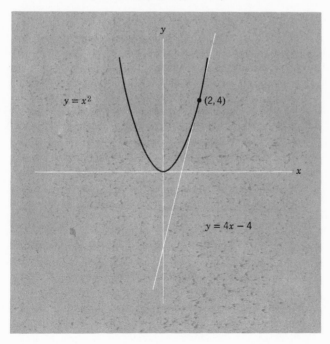

7.5 THE DERIVATIVE

Although it is not yet apparent, the limit defining the slope of the tangent line has a far broader set of meanings, some of which are not particularly connected to the geometry of a graph. For this reason, we shall proceed from the particular to the abstract, as we did in passing from the algebra of sets to Boolean algebra. We shall then be able to return to tangent lines with more information and more tools with which to work.

Let f be a function. Let x_o be any number in the domain of f. If

$$\lim_{h \to 0} \frac{f(x_o + h) - f(x_o)}{h}$$

exists, it is called the *derivative of f with respect to x at $x = x_o$* and is written $f'(x_o)$ or $Df(x_o)$. If the derivative of f with respect to x exists for every x in some set S, then the function $\{(x, f'(x)): x \in S\}$ is called the *derivative of f* and is written f' or Df.

If we let $x + h = t$, then $h = t - x$, and as $h \to 0$, $t \to x$. Thus we can rewrite our limit for the derivative in the form

$$f'(x) = \lim_{t \to x} \frac{f(t) - f(x)}{t - x},$$

if this limit exists. Sometimes this form is a little easier to use than the first. Thus, with each function f for which this limit exists, there is an associated function, the *derivative function*, denoted by f' or Df.

$$f' = Df = \left\{ (x, y): y = \lim_{h \to 0} \frac{f(x + h) - f(x)}{h} \right\}$$

$$= \left\{ (x, y): y = \lim_{t \to x} \frac{f(t) - f(x)}{t - x} \right\}.$$

If we are dealing with an equation of the form $y = f(x)$, for some function f, we can write f' as y' or Dy.

We now see that we can define the tangent line through $(c, f(c))$ on the graph of f as a line through P with slope $f'(c)$. We also see why we picked particular limits to study in Examples 5 and 6 and in Exercises 21–24 of section 7.3. We were finding derivatives. In Example 6 we showed that the function defined by $f(x) = x^2$ has a derivative, $2x$, for any real x. We can now write $D(x^2) = 2x$. In view of our discussion of tangent lines we know that the parabola, the graph of $y = x^2$, has a tangent line at each point and that the slope of the tangent line is $2x$. Thus, at the point $(3, 9)$, the slope of the tangent is 6. At the point $(0, 0)$ the slope is 0, and at $(-2, 4)$ the slope is -4. It is customary to say that the slope of the tangent line to a curve at a point is the *slope of the curve* at the point. Thus, when $x = 3$, the graph of $y = x^2$ has slope 6, and so forth.

Let us investigate the general parabola opening upward or downward. This appeared in Exercise 22 of the last problem set. Its equation is $y = f(x)$, where $f(x) = ax^2 + bx + c$. What is its slope? The slope is given by

$$Df(x) = \lim_{t \to x} \frac{f(t) - f(x)}{t - x}$$

$$= \lim_{t \to x} \frac{(at^2 + bt + c) - (ax^2 + bx + c)}{t - x}$$

$$= \lim_{t \to x} \frac{a(t^2 - x^2) + b(t - x)}{t - x}$$

$$= \lim_{t \to x} \frac{a(t + x)(t - x) + b(t - x)}{t - x}$$

$$= \lim_{t \to x} (a(t + x) + b) = 2ax + b.$$

The vertex of the parabola, whether it opens up or down, is at that point where the tangent line is horizontal. Since a horizontal line has zero slope, we can find where the vertex of the general parabola is by setting the slope, $f'(x)$, equal to zero. Then,

$$2ax + b = 0, \quad \text{or} \quad x = \frac{-b}{2a}.$$

If $a > 0$, the parabola opens upward, and at $x = -b/2a$ the curve reaches its lowest point. If $a < 0$, the curve reaches its highest point where

$$x = \frac{-b}{2a}.$$

The vertex is the point

$$\left(\frac{-b}{2a}, f\left(\frac{-b}{2a} \right) \right).$$

Example 1. Consider the parabola

$$y = 3x^2 + 6x - 5.$$

Then $y' = 6x + 6$, and at the vertex $y' = 0$, or $6x + 6 = 0$, or $x = -1$. At that point

$$y = 3 - 6 - 5 = -8.$$

Thus the vertex is at $(-1, -8)$. Since $3 > 0$, the parabola opens upward from there.

Example 2. Consider

$$y = -2x^2 + 5x + 3.$$

Then

$$y' = -4x + 5.$$

When $y' = 0$,

$$x = \frac{5}{4} \quad \text{and} \quad y = -2\left(\frac{25}{16}\right) + 5\left(\frac{5}{4}\right) + 3 = \frac{49}{8}.$$

The vertex is at $(5/4, 49/8)$.

7.6 EXERCISES

In Exercises 1–10 find y' and the coordinates of the vertex.

*1. $y = 2x^2 + 12x + 3$

2. $y = -x^2 + 2x - 5$

*3. $y = -x^2$

4. $y = 20x^2$

*5. $y = 5x^2 + 3x - 7$

6. $2y = (x + 1)(x + 3)$

*7. $3y = (2 - x)(1 + x)$

8. $2y = 7 - 4x + 3x^2$

*9. $3y = 2x - 6x^2$

10. $5y = 6 - 20x - 10x^2$

*11. If $f(x) = x^3$, find $f'(x)$.

12. If $g(z) = z^{-1}$, find $Dg(z)$.

*13. If $\phi(y) = y^4$, find $\phi'(y)$.

14. A farmer has 120 yards of fencing to enclose three sides of a rectangular field bordering a stream. Find the dimensions of the field that will give the largest area.

$$x \quad A(x) = 120x - 2x^2 \quad x$$

$120 - 2x$

Exercise 14

*15. Prove that of all rectangles with a given perimeter p, the square has maximum area.

$p/2 - x$

$$x \quad A(x) = px/2 - x^2 \quad x$$

$p/2 - x$

Exercise 15

A line is said to be *normal* to a curve at a point on the curve if it is perpendicular to the tangent line at the point. In Exercises 16 to 20 find the equations of the tangent line and the normal line at the given point.

16. $y = x^2$ at $(-2, 4)$

*17. $y = 2x^2 - 4x - 5$ at $(1, -7)$

18. $y = \sqrt{x}$ at $(9, 3)$

*19. $y = 1/x$ at $(2, 1/2)$

20. $y = x^3 + x^2 + x + 1$ at $(-1, 0)$

7.7 DIFFERENTIATION TECHNIQUES

Before proceeding to further interpretation and application of derivatives, let us establish some theorems that will facilitate the process of taking derivatives. This process is called *differentiation*. At present we can differentiate quadratics. We know that

$$D(ax^2 + bx + c) = 2ax + b,$$

regardless of the value of a, b, or c. Thus, if $a = b = 0$, we have $D(c) = 0$. That is, the derivative of any constant is 0. This is hardly surprising, for if we consider the function for which $f(x) = c$, its graph is a horizontal straight line, which has zero slope everywhere. If $a = 0$, the derivative of $bx + c$ is b, which is reasonable since the line whose equation is $y = bx + c$ has slope b. Returning to our quadratics, in the special case where $a = c = 0$ and $b = 1$, we find that $D(x) = 1$. The theorems that follow are not quite so obvious. Their proofs are not difficult, but they contain a confusing mass of symbols if one is not accustomed to such proofs. The student is not expected to master the proofs. In fact, this entire section can be skipped, or the student can merely observe the results obtained. The theorems are here because they provide in a very brief space the tools that will permit the student to carry out with considerable ease a large number of significant problems in differential calculus. It is hoped that the student will find it enjoyable to work so easily a variety of problems quite different from those encountered in previous mathematics.

In the theorems that follow we shall assume without proof that the limit of a sum or product of functions is the sum or product of the limits of the functions. We shall do the same for the limit of a quotient where the denominator does not approach zero. That is, we shall assume that

$$\lim_{x \to c} [f(x) \pm g(x)] = [\lim_{x \to c} f(x)] \pm [\lim_{x \to c} g(x)],$$

$$\lim_{x \to c} [f(x) \cdot g(x)] = [\lim_{x \to c} f(x)] \cdot [\lim_{x \to c} g(x)],$$

and

$$\lim_{x \to c} \frac{f(x)}{g(x)} = \frac{\lim_{x \to c} f(x)}{\lim_{x \to c} g(x)}$$

provided all the limits involved exist and $\lim_{x \to c} g(x) \neq 0$ in the last. In all of these theorems we shall suppose that $f'(x)$ and $g'(x)$ exist.

Theorem 1. $D(f(x) + g(x)) = f'(x) + g'(x)$. *That is, we can find the derivative of a sum by differentiating term by term.*

Proof: $D(f(x) + g(x)) = \lim_{t \to x} \dfrac{(f(t) + g(t)) - (f(x) - g(x))}{t - x}$

$$= \lim_{t \to x} \left[\frac{f(t) - f(x)}{t - x} + \frac{g(t) - g(x)}{t - x} \right]$$

$$= \lim_{t \to x} \left[\frac{f(t) - f(x)}{t - x} \right] + \lim_{t \to x} \left[\frac{g(t) - g(x)}{t - x} \right]$$

$$= f'(x) + g'(x).$$

Theorem 2. $D(kf(x)) = kf'(x)$ *for any constant* k.

Proof:

$$D(kf(x)) = \lim_{h \to 0} \frac{kf(x + h) - kf(x)}{h} = \lim_{h \to 0} k \left[\frac{f(x + h) - f(x)}{h} \right]$$

$$= k \lim_{h \to 0} \frac{f(x + h) - f(x)}{h} = kf'(x).$$

Theorem 3. *For any positive integer* n, $D(x^n) = nx^{n-1}$.

Proof: $\qquad\qquad D(x^n) = \lim_{h \to 0} \dfrac{(x + h)^n - x^n}{h}.$

If we expand $(x + h)^n$ by the binomial theorem, the expansion begins:

$$(x + h)^n = x^n + nx^{n-1}h + \cdots.$$

All we need to know for the present is that all of the remaining terms contain a factor h^2. Thus

$$\frac{(x + h)^n - x^n}{h} = \frac{nx^{n-1}h + h^2(\cdots)}{h} = nx^{n-1} + h(\cdots).$$

Now, when $h \to 0$, we have $D(x^n) = nx^{n-1}$. In particular, $D(x) = 1$, $D(x^2) = 2x$, $D(x^3) = 3x^2$, $D(x^4) = 4x^3$, and $D(5x^{10} + 7x^3 + 2) = 50x^9 + 21x^2$. Our theorems make it easy to differentiate any polynomial.

By Theorem 1, the derivative of a sum is the sum of the derivatives. We might expect, then, that the derivative of a product is probably the product of the derivatives, but the following theorem shows that this is not the case.

Theorem 4. $D(fg) = fg' + gf'$.

Proof:

$$D(f(x)g(x)) = \lim_{t \to x} \frac{f(t)g(t) - f(x)g(x)}{t - x}$$

$$= \lim_{t \to x} \frac{f(t)g(t) - f(t)g(x) + f(t)g(x) - f(x)g(x)}{t - x}$$

$$= \lim_{t \to x} \left[f(t)\left(\frac{g(t) - g(x)}{t - x} \right) + g(x)\left(\frac{f(t) - f(x)}{t - x} \right) \right]$$

$$= f(x)g'(x) + g(x)f'(x).$$

Example 1.

$$D[(x^2 + 2x + 3)(x^2 - 1)] = (x^2 + 2x + 3)(2x) + (x^2 - 1)(2x + 2),$$

which can be simplified to

$$4x^3 + 6x^2 + 4x - 2.$$

The reader can check this result by multiplying first and then differentiating.

Theorem 5. $D(f/g) = (gf' - fg')/g^2$ *for every number in the domain of g for which* $g \neq 0$.

Proof:

$$D\left(\frac{f(x)}{g(x)} \right) = \lim_{t \to x} \frac{f(t)/g(t) - f(x)/g(x)}{t - x}$$

$$= \lim_{t \to x} \frac{g(x)f(t) - f(x)g(t)}{g(t)g(x)(t - x)}$$

$$= \lim_{t \to x} \frac{g(x)f(t) - g(x)f(x) + f(x)g(x) - f(x)g(t)}{g(t)g(x)(t - x)}$$

$$= \lim_{t \to x} \frac{1}{g(t)g(x)} \left[g(x)\left(\frac{f(t) - f(x)}{t - x} \right) - f(x)\left(\frac{g(t) - g(x)}{t - x} \right) \right]$$

$$= \frac{1}{g(x)g(x)} [g(x)f'(x) - f(x)g'(x)].$$

7.8 DIFFERENTIATION OF POLYNOMIALS

The hard work is past. The five theorems of the preceding section permit us to differentiate by inspection all polynomials and all ratios of polynomials. This is a large class of functions, but of course there are many other types.

If we wished to extend our capability of differentiation to such types we would need further theorems. But this is not a calculus text, and the present theorems are adequate to permit us to illustrate the techniques, methods and applications of calculus.

Theorems 1, 2, and 3 permit us to write down immediately the derivative of any polynomial. A polynomial is an expression of the form

$$f(x) = a_0 + a_1 x + a_2 x^2 + a_3 x^3 + \cdots + a_n x^n$$

where the a_i are constants and n is a positive integer. That is, it is a sum of terms, and Theorem 1 permits us to differentiate term by term. Each term is of the form

$$a_i x^i, \quad 0 \le i \le n$$

(note that $a_0 = a_0 x^0$), which is the product of a constant and a power of x. Theorem 2 tells us that

$$D(a_i x^i) = a_i D(x^i).$$

Finally, Theorem 3 tells us that

$$D(x^i) = i x^{i-1}.$$

Putting all of these together, we find that

$$Df(x) = a_1 + 2a_2 x + 3a_3 x^2 + \cdots + n a_n x^{n-1}.$$

Example 1. $D(x^{12} + 10x^{10} - 6.3x^3 + 1000) = 12x^{11} + 100x^9 - 18.9x^2.$

7.9 RATIONAL ALGEBRAIC FUNCTIONS

A rational algebraic function is a ratio of two polynomials. Theorem 5 tells us that the derivative of any ratio of functions is the denominator times the derivative of the numerator, minus the numerator times the derivative of the denominator, divided by the square of the denominator.

Example 1. $D\left(\dfrac{x+1}{x-1}\right) = \dfrac{(x-1)(1) - (x+1)(1)}{(x-1)^2} = \dfrac{-2}{(x-1)^2}.$

Example 2. $D\left(\dfrac{x^2+1}{x^3-1}\right) = \dfrac{(x^3-1)(2x) - (x^2+1)(3x^2)}{(x-1)^2}$

$$= \dfrac{-x^4 - 3x^2 - 2x}{(x-1)^2}$$

Example 3. $D(cx^{-n}) = cD\left(\dfrac{1}{x^n}\right) = c\left[\dfrac{x^n(0) - 1(nx^{n-1})}{x^{2n}}\right] = \dfrac{-cnx^{n-1}}{x^{2n}}$

$$= -cnx^{-n-1}.$$

This example tells us that Theorem 3 holds for negative as well as positive integer exponents.

7.10 EXERCISES

Differentiate the following functions:

*1. $3x^2 + 6x - 1$

2. $x^3 + 3x^2 - x + 7$

*3. $x^5 - 3x^4 + 2x^3 - 6x^2 + 10x - 5$

4. $5x^4 - 12x^3 + 6x^2 - 12x + 10$

*5. $20x^3 - 36x^2 + 12x - 12$

6. $12 - 72x + 60x^2$

*7. $x - x^2 + 2x^3 - 3x^4 + 4x^5 - 5x^6$

8. $6x^6 + 5x^5 - 4x^4 - 3x^3 + 2x^2 + x - 1$

*9. $(x^3 - 4)^2$ (Hint: square first.)

10. $(x^2 + 1)^3$ (Hint: cube first.)

*11. $(x^3 - 4)(x^2 + 1)$

12. $(x^2 + 1)^2(x - 1)^3$

*13. $(2x^2 + 3x - 1)(x^2 + x + 1)$

14. $(x - 1)(x^4 + x^3 + x^2 + x + 1)$

*15. In Exercise 14, multiply before differentiating and compare results.

16. $(x^3 - 4)/(x^2 + 1)$

*17. $x^2 + 3x - 1 - 5/x + 6/x^2$

18. $3x^3 - 5x^2 + 7x - 2 + 3x^{-1} - 5x^{-2} + 3x^{-3}$

*19. $(x^3 + 1)/(x^2 - x + 1)$

20. $(x^4 - 1)/(x^3 + x^2 + x + 1)$

In the following exercises find a function whose derivative is given. Is there more than one such function?

*21. $Df(x) = 0$

22. $Df(x) = 3$

*23. $Df(x) = 2x + 5$

24. $Df(x) = 6x^2 + 4x + 3$

*25. $Df(x) = x^n$ for n a positive integer.

7.11 INCREASING AND DECREASING FUNCTIONS

Consider the graph of $y = f(x)$. We shall say that the function is *increasing* at $x = c$ if

$$\frac{f(x) - f(c)}{x - c} > 0$$

for all x sufficiently near c. This means that for all x in some interval with c as left endpoint, $f(x) > f(c)$, and for all x in some interval with c as right endpoint, $f(x) < f(c)$. It should be intuitively clear that if the graph of $y = f(x)$ has a tangent line with positive slope at a point, then the function is increasing there. That is, f is increasing wherever $f'(x) > 0$. We shall say that the function is *decreasing* at $x = c$ if

$$\frac{f(x) - f(c)}{x - c} < 0$$

for all x sufficiently near c. This means that for all x in some interval with c as left endpoint, $f(x) < f(c)$, and for all x in some interval to the left of c, $f(x) > f(c)$. We conclude that f is decreasing wherever $f'(x) < 0$. Where $f'(x) = 0$ or does not exist, we must apply some other test.

Let us consider

$$f = \{(x, y) : y = x^2 + 2x\}.$$

This function has a derivative for all x, and $f'(x) = 2x + 2$. We find that $f'(-1) = 0$, that $f'(x) > 0$ for $x > -1$, and that $f'(x) < 0$ for $x < -1$. Hence, the function is decreasing to the left of $x = -1$ and increasing to the right of $x = -1$. At $x = -1$, the function is neither increasing nor decreasing.

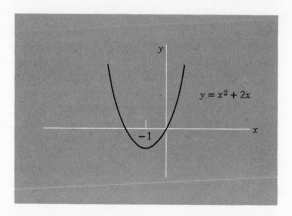

7.12   MAXIMA AND MINIMA

If $y = f(x)$, the largest value assumed by y is called the *maximum* of $f(x)$, and the smallest value assumed by y is called the *minimum* of $f(x)$. If $f(x) = x^2 - 1$, the function has a minimum of -1 where $x = 0$. It has no maximum.

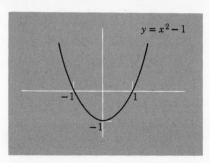

If the function involved is differentiable at a maximum or minimum point, the tangent line will be horizontal, and $f'(x) = 0$. This condition is necessary but not sufficient. For example, if $f(x) = x^3$, then $f'(x) = 3x^2$ and $f'(0) = 0$. However, $f'(x) > 0$ for both $x < 0$ and $x > 0$. Thus the function is increasing both to the left and to the right of $x = 0$. The function has no maximum or minimum.

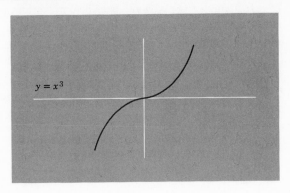

7.13 LOCAL MAXIMA AND MINIMA

A polynomial of degree 4 or higher may have a graph shaped like that shown. There are horizontal tangents ($y' = 0$) at three points, where $x = a$, b, and c. By inspection we see that the minimum occurs at $x = a$ and that

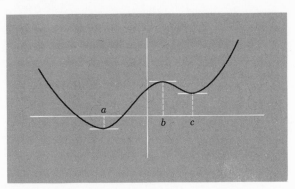

there is no maximum. However, at $x = b$ the function has a larger value than it has anywhere in the immediate vicinity of $x = b$. We shall call such a point a *local maximum* of the function. Similarly, the function has a *local minimum* at $x = c$ because at that point the functional value is less than it is elsewhere in the immediate vicinity. Setting the derivative equal to zero helps us to find the local maxima and minima. We can test to determine whether a given value of x for which $f'(x) = 0$ yields a local maximum or minimum by examining the *sign* of the derivative on either side of the point in question. If the derivative is positive to the left and negative to the right, the point is a local maximum. If the derivative is negative to the left and positive to the right, the function has a local minimum. If the derivative does not change sign, the point is neither a local maximum nor a local minimum.

Example 1. Let

$$f = \{(x, y) : y = x^3 - 6x^2 + 9x\}.$$

We find that

$$f'(x) = 3x^2 - 12x + 9 = 3(x - 1)(x - 3).$$

From this, we see that

$$f'(1) = f'(3) = 0.$$

Since $f(1) = 4$ and $f(3) = 0$, the graph of the function has horizontal tangents at $(1, 4)$ and $(3, 0)$. Moreover, for any $x < 1$, $x - 1 < 0$ and

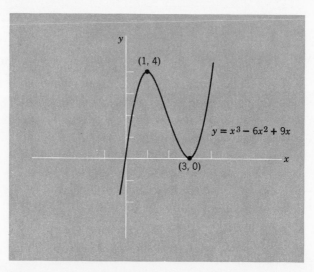

$x - 3 < 0$, so that $f'(x) > 0$, or the function is increasing. For any x between 1 and 3, $x - 1 > 0$ and $x - 3 < 0$, so that $f'(x) < 0$, or the function is decreasing. For any $x > 3$, $f'(x) > 0$, or the function is increasing. Hence, f has a local maximum at $(1, 4)$ and a local minimum at $(3, 0)$.

7.14 GRAPHS

The sign of the derivative can be a great help in graphing a function. Let

$$f = \{(x, y) : y = 2x^3 - 3x^2 - 12x + 6\}.$$

What is the graph of $y = f(x)$? First,

$$f'(x) = 6x^2 - 6x - 12 = 6(x^2 - x - 2) = 6(x + 1)(x - 2).$$

Hence, $f'(x) = 0$ for $x = -1$ and $x = 2$. This is where the horizontal tangents are. Furthermore,

$$f(-1) = -2 - 3 + 12 + 6 = 13, \quad \text{and} \quad f(2) = 16 - 12 - 24 + 6 = -14.$$

To the left of $x = -1$, $x + 1 < 0$ and $x - 2 < 0$. Hence, $f'(x) > 0$, or the curve is rising for all $x < -1$. Between -1 and 2, $f'(x) < 0$, and to the right of 2, $f'(x) > 0$. The curve rises to $(-1, 13)$, which is a local maximum, decreases to $(2, -14)$, which is a local minimum, and rises to the right of $x = 2$. It will help in our graphing if we add a few pertinent points such as $(0, f(0)) = (0, 6)$ and $(1, f(1)) = (1, -7)$. We shall spread out the graph by using different scales on the two axes.

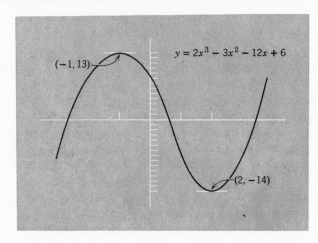

$y = 2x^3 - 3x^2 - 12x + 6$

$(-1, 13)$

$(2, -14)$

Not only does our calculus help us construct a graph, it also permits us to say that $f(x)$ has one root less than -1, one root between 0 and 1, and one root greater than 2.

7.15 ENDPOINTS

In some cases the endpoints must also be examined as potential local maxima or minima, even though $f'(x) \neq 0$ there. Thus for a large class of functions, those that we can differentiate, the maximum of f, if it exists, occurs at an endpoint or at one of the points where $f'(x) = 0$. The same is true of the minimum.

> *Example.* Let us find the maximum and minimum of $y = x^2$ for $1 \leq x \leq 2$. We have $y' = 2x$, so that $y' \neq 0$ for x in the given interval. Nevertheless, the function has a maximum of 4 at the right endpoint and a minimum of 1 at the left endpoint.

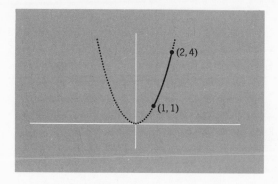

7.16 APPLICATIONS

1. Let us make a tray with maximum volume from a square piece of tin, twelve inches on a side. We shall do this by cutting square pieces out of the corners and then folding up and welding the flaps. If the square removed from each corner is x inches on a side, the resulting volume of the tray is

$$V(x) = x(12 - 2x)^2 = 144x - 48x^2 + 4x^3.$$

For the problem to make sense, x must be restricted to the interval $0 < x < 6$. If $x = 0$ or 6, the resulting tray has zero volume. Thus there should be a maximum somewhere inside this interval.

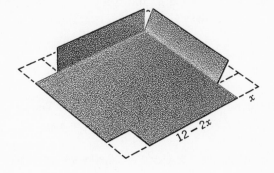

$$V'(x) = 144 - 96x + 12x^2 = 12(x - 2)(x - 6).$$

Thus $V'(x) = 0$ for $x = 2$ and $x = 6$. Since $V(6) = 0$, we know that the maximum volume does not occur for $x = 6$. We conclude that the maximum occurs for $x = 2$. $V(2) = 128$, so the maximum volume for the tray, 128 cubic inches, is obtained by cutting 2-inch squares from the corners. It is helpful to consider the graph of $y = V(x)$. We shall use different scales on the two axes.

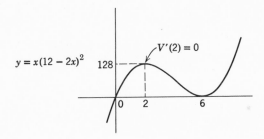

2. Let us assume that the strength of a rectangular wooden beam is proportional to the width and the square of the depth. What are the dimensions of the strongest beam that can be cut from a 3-foot log? Let us draw a picture and label some of its parts. Our assumption is that, for some k, the strength of the beam is given by kxy^2. Since $x^2 + y^2 = 9$, we can reduce the expression for strength to a single variable.

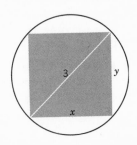

$$S(x) = kx(9 - x^2) = 9kx - kx^3.$$

In this case, $0 < x < 3$, for $S(0) = S(3) = 0$.

If $x = 0$, our beam has no width, and if $x = 3$, the beam has no depth. The next step is to find the value or values of x within the domain that make $S'(x) = 0$. Since

$$S'(x) = 9k - 3kx^2 = 3k(3 - x^2),$$

we find that our condition is satisfied if $x = \pm\sqrt{3}$. The negative root can be discarded because it is not within the given domain. Thus

$$x = \sqrt{3} \quad \text{and} \quad y = \sqrt{9 - x^2} = \sqrt{9 - 3} = \sqrt{6}.$$

We have found the desired dimensions.

3. Let us find the point on the line segment joining $(1, 1)$ and $(4, 4)$ that is closest to $(7, 2)$. The equation of the line through $(1, 1)$ and $(4, 4)$ is $y = x$. Thus we wish to find the point (x, x) that is a minimum distance from $(7, 2)$. The distance is a minimum if and only if its square is also a minimum. Hence let us find an x such that $(x - 7)^2 + (x - 2)^2$ is a minimum. We can write

$$(x - 7)^2 + (x - 2)^2 = x^2 - 14x + 49 + x^2 - 4x + 4 = 2x^2 - 18x + 53.$$

The derivative of this function is $4x - 18$, which is zero only for $x = 9/2$. Since the point $(9/2, 9/2)$ is not on the given line segment, the minimum occurs at an endpoint, in this case at $(4, 4)$.

7.17 EXERCISES

In Exercises 1–10 find and identify all relative maxima and minima, state where each function is increasing or decreasing, and sketch the graph of each.

*1. $y = x^2 + 4x - 10$ 2. $y = 6 - 4x - x^2$

*3. $2y = 3 + 5x - x^2$ 4. $3y = 2x^2 - 7x + 5$

*5. $y = 5x + 1$ 6. $y = 10$

*7. $y = 2x^3 + 3x^2 - 36x + 50$ 8. $y = x^3 - 6x^2 - 15x + 50$

*9. $y = x^5 - 5x + 3$ 10. $y = 3x^5 - 50x^3 + 135x - 100$

*11. A strip of tin 16 inches wide is to be folded to form a rectangular trough, open at the top, with maximum cross-sectional area. Find its dimensions.

12. Find the point on the graph of $y = \sqrt{x}$ that is closest to the point $(2, 0)$.

*13. A cylindrical tin can is to contain 54π cubic inches. Find the dimensions of the can if it is to have minimal surface area.

7.18 RATES OF CHANGE, INSTANTANEOUS VELOCITY

Let us recall our earlier discussion of the speed of an object at an instant. When speed is coupled with direction it is called velocity. For motion along a straight line the direction is indicated by a sign associated with the speed. The distance of the object from some fixed point is a function of time. That is, if s is the distance of the object from the fixed point, then the motion of the object can be described by an expression, $s(t)$, where suitable units are established for time and distance. Let t be a fixed time and h a period of time. Then, between times t and $t + h$ the object moves from the position given by $s(t)$ to that given by $s(t + h)$. Its average velocity over the period from t to $t + h$ is given by the distance divided by the time taken. That is, the average velocity is

$$\frac{s(t + h) - s(t)}{h}.$$

The instantaneous velocity of an object is its velocity at a given instant, not an average over some period of time. The speedometer on a car, for instance, records instantaneous velocity. Mathematically, the instantaneous velocity is obtained by letting the time interval approach zero. To do this, we take a limit

$$v(t) = \lim_{h \to 0} \frac{s(t + h) - s(t)}{h} = s'(t).$$

We are back to our old friend, the derivative; this time it wears a new set of clothes. In Section 7.1 we tried to find the instantaneous velocity when $t = 0.6$ hours of a car whose motion was given by $s = 25t^2$. We found reason to believe that it was 30 miles per hour. A little calculus makes the problem easy.

$$v(t) = D_t(25t^2) = 50t.$$

Thus

$$v(0.6) = 30.$$

A formula says that the distance an object falls in time t when dropped in a vacuum is given by

$$s = \frac{gt^2}{2},$$

where g is the gravitational constant. For purposes of illustration, let us assume $g = 32$. Then $s(t) = 16t^2$. How fast is the object falling at any time t? Its velocity is given by

$$v(t) = s'(t) = 32t.$$

Let us give a slightly more general interpretation to what we have done. Let ϕ be any function of t. Then $\phi'(t)$ is called the rate of change of ϕ with respect to t. What does this generalization mean? It permits us, among other things, to discuss acceleration, the rate of change of velocity with respect to time. Thus, if acceleration is denoted by $a(t)$, $a(t) = v'(t)$. The acceleration of the falling body is then

$$a(t) = D(32t) = 32, \quad \text{or} \quad g.$$

That is, the acceleration of a freely falling body is constant near the surface of the earth. The gravitational constant, g, which is slightly more than 32, is a measure of the gravitational force with which the earth attracts an object. On the moon, which has much smaller mass than the earth, the gravitational constant is much smaller than 32.

> **Example 1.** Suppose that the motion of an object along a straight line is given by the equation
>
> $$s(t) = t^2 - 6t + 8.$$
>
> Then
>
> $$v(t) = 2t - 6 \quad \text{and} \quad a(t) = 2.$$
>
> Let us assume our straight line is vertical with positive distance measured upward and negative distance measured downward from some fixed reference point called the origin. Let the time units be seconds and the distance units feet.
>
> Let us draw the graphs of s, v, and a as functions of time. We are now in a position to draw a number of conclusions about the motion of the object.

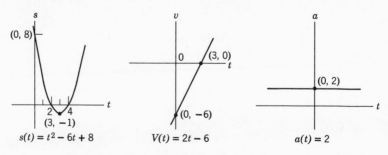

$s(t) = t^2 - 6t + 8 \qquad V(t) = 2t - 6 \qquad a(t) = 2$

1. At time $t = 0$,

$$s(0) = 8,$$

or the object is 8 feet above the origin.

2. At time $t = 0$,

$$v(0) = -6,$$

or the object is moving downward with a speed of 6 feet per second.

3. At all times the acceleration is upward at 2 feet per second per second.

4. Since $v(3) = 0$, the object has come to a momentary halt when $t = 3$.

5. Since $v(t) < 0$ for all $t < 3$, the object is moving downward at all times prior to $t = 3$.

6. Since $v(t) > 0$ for all $t > 3$, the object is moving upward at all times after $t = 3$.

7. When the object comes to a halt, $t = 3$ and $s(3) = -1$. Thus the lowest point reached is 1 foot below the origin.

8. Since $s(t) = (t - 2)(t - 4)$,

$$s(2) = s(4) = 0.$$

Thus the object passes through the origin when $t = 2$ and when $t = 4$.

9. The first time the object passes through the origin its velocity is given by $v(2) = -2$. It is moving downward with a speed of 2 feet per second. Since $v(4) = 2$, it is moving upward at 2 feet per second the second time it passes through the origin.

7.19 EXERCISES

*1. A ball is rolled up an inclined plane from the bottom. The equation of its motion is $s(t) = 8t - t^2$.

(a) How far up the plane does it roll?

(b) What is its velocity when it is released?

(c) What acceleration does it have?

2. A ball was thrown upward at time $t = 0$ from the top of a building. Its distance in feet from the ground is given by $s(t) = 192 + 64t - 16t^2$.

(a) How tall was the building?

(b) With what velocity was the ball thrown upward?

(c) How long was the ball rising?

(d) How high did the ball go?

(e) How long was the ball in the air?

(f) With what speed did the ball strike the ground?

*3. The equation of motion of an object is $s(t) = 2t^3 - 9t^2 + 12t$.

(a) At what times is the object motionless? (Zero velocity.)

(b) What is the acceleration of the object when it is motionless?

(c) What is the minimum distance of the object from the starting point for t between 1 and 5?

(d) What is the maximum distance of the object from the starting point for t between 0 and 2?

(e) What is the maximum distance of the object from the starting point for t between 1 and 5?

(f) Graph s as a function of t for t between 1 and 3.

4. An object moves along a straight path. Its distance in feet from a fixed point P is given by $s(t) = t^3 - 9t^2 + 23t - 15$. Take the positive direction to the right, negative to the left. Describe the motion, including distance from P, velocity, and acceleration, for t between 0 and 6.

*5. If the acceleration of an object at any given time is $a(t) = 2t$, what can you say about its velocity? Would it help if you knew that its velocity is 6 when $t = 0$? In other words, can these problems be worked backward?

7.20 THE ANTIDERIVATIVE

Hopefully, the previous work in this chapter has led the student to some degree of proficiency in differentiating algebraic functions. The reverse process is fully as important. What functions have a given derivative? In particular, what functions have the derivative ax^n, where n is an integer different from -1? In other words, find a solution to the equation

$$y' = ax^n.$$

Since the derivative of x^n is the product of the exponent and x to a power one less, the reverse process leads to the quotient of x to a power one higher divided by the increased exponent. Applied to ax^n, the process leads to

$$\frac{ax^{n+1}}{n+1},$$

which is one solution. But, since the derivative of a constant is 0, the addition of a constant to our function will not change its derivative. In general we have found that a solution to the equation $y' = ax^n$ is given by

$$y = \frac{ax^{n+1}}{n+1} + c$$

for any constant c. It is clear that our solution does not apply if $n = -1$. Our formula requires us to divide by $n + 1$, which in this case is 0, and division by 0 is not meaningful. There is a function of x, the natural logarithm, whose derivative is x^{-1}, but such functions are beyond the scope of this work.

Since the differentiation of a polynomial can be done one term at a time, so also can the reverse be done. For instance, if $y' = x^3 - x^2 + 4x - 7$, our process gives the solution

$$y = \frac{x^4}{4} - \frac{x^3}{3} + 2x^2 - 7x + c.$$

Any solution to the equation $y' = f(x)$ is called an *antiderivative* of $f(x)$. We have found that it is quite simple to write the antiderivative of any polynomial. The problem becomes considerably more complex for other functions, but the polynomials will serve to illustrate the uses of the antiderivative.

A particularly simple example is provided by the linear function. Since the equation of every nonvertical line can be put in the form

$$y = mx + b,$$

we have $y' = m$, or the derivative of y is the slope of the line. Hence, to find a line through $(2, 3)$ with slope -4, we could start with the equation $y' = -4$, whose antiderivative is $y = -4x + c$. This must be the equation of the desired line for some c. To determine c, we use the additional fact that the line passes through the point $(2, 3)$, which must then satisfy the equation of the line. Substituting, we find

$$3 = -4(2) + c, \quad \text{or} \quad c = 11.$$

Thus

$$y = -4x + 11$$

is the desired equation.

7.21   FALLING BODIES

Suppose that a ball is to be thrown upward with a velocity of 40 feet per second from the top of a building 96 feet high. What is the equation of its motion? After its release, the ball is subject to only one force, gravity, which accelerates the ball toward the ground. If we choose to call upward the positive direction, then we can write

$$a(t) = -32.$$

But

$$a(t) = v'(t).$$

Thus

$$v'(t) = -32, \quad \text{or} \quad v(t) = -32t + c.$$

What is c? It is obviously the value of v when t is 0, and we were given that this is 40. Hence,

$$v(t) = -32t + 40.$$

But $v(t) = s'(t)$. Hence

$$s(t) = k + 40t - 16t^2.$$

Again, what is the constant, k? This time it is clear that k is the height, the value of s, when $t = 0$. This was given as 96 feet. Thus

$$s(t) = 96 + 40t - 16t^2.$$

We have found the desired equation of motion. We saw in an earlier section how much information is packed in such an equation.

Notice that three apparently independent equations of physics are really closely related. Let us consider an object dropped in a vacuum. If the single assumption is made that gravity applies an equal accelerative force to any unrestrained object, we have the starting point

$$a(t) = -g.$$

From this it necessarily follows that

$$v(t) = -gt + c.$$

Since the body is given no initial velocity,

$$c = 0, \quad \text{and} \quad v(t) = -gt.$$

From this it necessarily follows that

$$s(t) = \frac{-gt^2}{2}.$$

The constant is omitted since we measure distance from the point where the object is dropped. Perhaps you can see from this example how inseparable mathematics and physics are.

7.22   EXERCISES

In Exercises 1–10 find the general solution to the given equations.

*1. $y' = 2$ 2. $y' = 2x + 3$

*3. $y' = 3x - 5$ 4. $y' = 5 - 8x - 6x^2$

*5. $y' = 3x^2 - 6x + 2$ 6. $y' = x^4 + x^3 + x^2 + x + 1$

*7. $y' = 12x^5 - 7x^3 + 10x$ 8. $y' = 2/x^2 - 6/x^3$

*9. $y' = D(x^2 + 2x - 3)$ 10. $y' = D(2 + x - x^2 - 3x^3)$

*11. Find the equation of the line through $(4, -1)$ with slope 2.

12. Find the equation of the line through $(2, 3)$ with slope -5.

*13. Find the equation of the line through $(2, 3)$ and $(-2, 5)$.

14. Find the equation of the line through $(-2, 4)$ and $(3, -2)$.

*15. A ball is thrown upward from the top of a building 200 feet tall with a velocity of 40 ft/sec.

(a) Find an equation for its velocity and an equation for its distance above ground at any time t.

(b) What is the ball's maximum height above ground?

(c) How long is the ball in the air?

16. The graph of $y = f(x)$ satisfies $y' = 2x + 3$ for all x and passes through the point $(1, 6)$. Find $f(x)$.

*17. The graph of $y = f(x)$ satisfies $y' = 6x^2 - 4x + 8$ for all x and passes through the point $(2, 12)$. Find $f(x)$.

18. For every point on a graph let r be the distance from the point to the origin and let θ be the angle the ray from the origin to the point makes with the positive x-axis. If $D_\theta r = 0$, what can you say about the graph?

*19. Find an antiderivative of each of the following:

(a) $1/(2\sqrt{x})$ (b) $-1/x^2$

20. For each of the following find a function f for which $f(1) = 0$:

(a) $f'(x) = x^2 + 2x - 5$

(b) $f'(x) = 4x^3 - 9x^2 + 6x - 3 + 2/\sqrt{x}$

7.23   AREA

Let us assume that f is a continuous, positive, increasing function for all x in an interval, $a \le x \le b$. We shall assume that the reader has an intuitive idea of what is meant by the *area* bounded by the graph of $y = f(x)$, the x-axis, and the vertical lines $x = a$ and $x = b$.

We shall define area in section 7.26. For now the intuitive ideas we all have will be sufficient. We wish to construct an *area function*, A, in the following way: let x be any point inside the interval from a to b. Let $A(x)$ be the

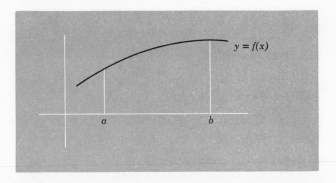

area bounded by the graph, the x-axis, and the vertical lines at a and x. Then A is also a positive, continuous, increasing function. Let h be a small positive number, so that $x + h$ lies between x and b. Then the area of the strip between x and $x + h$ is given by

$$A(x + h) - A(x).$$

Moreover, since the function f is increasing, we have

$$hf(x) < A(x + h) - A(x) < hf(x + h),$$

or

$$f(x) < \frac{A(x + h) - A(x)}{h} < f(x + h).$$

What happens if we shrink h? Since f is continuous,

$$f(x + h) \rightarrow f(x),$$

and

$$\frac{A(x + h) - A(x)}{h}$$

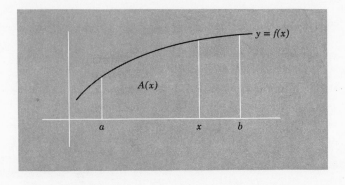

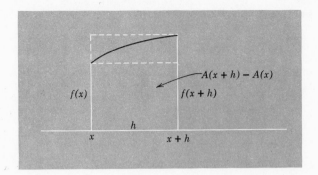

is squeezed between $f(x)$ and something that approaches $f(x)$. As a consequence, we have

$$\lim_{h\to0} \frac{A(x+h) - A(x)}{h} = f(x), \quad \text{or} \quad A'(x) = f(x).$$

This same result would have been obtained if f had been decreasing rather than increasing. In fact, it still holds if we make no assumption at all about whether f is increasing or decreasing as long as it is continuous from a to b. The proof, however, involves too much work to be appropriate here.

We have shown that f is the derivative of A, or, what is more pertinent, that A is an antiderivative of f. But what is the constant? Since $A(a)$ is the area under the curve between $x = a$ and $x = a$, $A(a) = 0$. The constant, then, is chosen to satisfy this condition. Let us try it.

What is the area under the parabola $y = x^2$ from $x = 1$ to $x = 2$? Here, $f(x) = x^2$. Thus

$$A(x) = \frac{x^3}{3} + c.$$

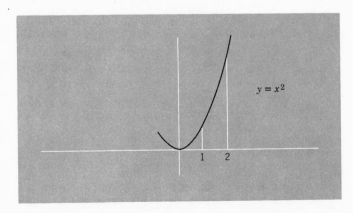

Since we want $A(1) = 0$, we substitute 1 for x and find $c = -1/3$. Hence

$$A(x) = \frac{x^3}{3} - \frac{1}{3} = \frac{x^3 - 1}{3}.$$

In particular, for $x = 2$ we have

$$A(2) = \frac{8 - 1}{3} = \frac{7}{3}.$$

Isn't it strange? With only an intuitive notion of area, we have still come up with a way of measuring it!

7.24 EXERCISES

*1. Find the area under $y = x^2 + 2x + 1$ between $x = 0$ and $x = 2$.
 2. Find the area bounded by $y = x^2 - 4x - 5$ and the x-axis.
*3. Find the area bounded by $y = 3x^2 - 9x$ and the x-axis.
 4. Find the area under $y = x^3$ between $x = 0$ and $x = 2$.
*5. Find the area under $y = -8 - 2x + 5x^2 - x^3$ between $x = 2$ and $x = 4$.
 6. Find the area under $y = x^3 - x$ between 0 and 1. Discuss your negative answer.
*7. Find the area bounded by $y = x^3 - 4x$ and the x-axis.
 8. Can you find a power of x that is the antiderivative of x^{-1}?
*9. Find the area under $y = \sqrt{x}$ between $x = 0$ and $x = 4$.
10. Find the positive number t such that the area under $y = x^2$ between $x = 0$ and $x = t$ is 9.

7.25 THE INTEGRAL

Before going on to area, let us define a more general concept, *the integral of f between a and b*. The integral is a limit of a sum, where the limit concept is used in a way that is somewhat different from that in our earlier work. We shall construct the integral by a series of steps.

1. Let f be a function whose domain includes the interval from

$$x = a \quad \text{to} \quad x = b.$$

2. Partition the interval into n parts by inserting $n - 1$ points between a and b. Let

$$a = x_0, \quad b = x_n,$$

and insert points x_i such that

$$a = x_0 < x_1 < x_2 < \cdots < x_n = b.$$

3. Let the interval from x_{i-1} to x_i be called the ith subinterval, and let its length be denoted by

$$\delta x_i = x_i - x_{i-1}.$$

4. Let $|\delta|$ be the largest of the δx_i.
5. Choose an arbitrary number $\mathbf{x}_i$ in each of the subintervals.
6. Form the sum:

$$f(\mathbf{x}_1)\, \delta x_1 + f(\mathbf{x}_2)\, \delta x_2 + \cdots + f(\mathbf{x}_n)\, \delta x_n.$$

7. Finally, define

$$\int_a^b f(x)\, dx,$$

read "the integral of f between a and b," as the limit, if it exists, of the indicated sum as $|\delta|$ approaches 0.

$$\int_a^b f(x)\, dx = \lim_{|\delta| \to 0} [f(\mathbf{x}_1)\, \delta x_1 + f(\mathbf{x}_2)\, \delta x_2] + \cdots + f(\mathbf{x}_n)\, \delta x_n.$$

One stage in this process is illustrated in the figure below, which shows the graph of $y = f(x)$ from $x = a$ to $x = b$. The terms in the sum of step 6 correspond to the areas of the rectangles in the figure.

This is a limit of a different kind. Notice that $|\delta|$ depends on the way the interval from a to b is partitioned. When we refer to "the limit as $|\delta| \to 0$," we mean that the indicated sum will be arbitrarily close to a fixed number, the integral, for *every* partition for which $|\delta|$ is sufficiently small and for *every* possible way the $\mathbf{x}_i$ of step 5 can be chosen in the subintervals. One way to

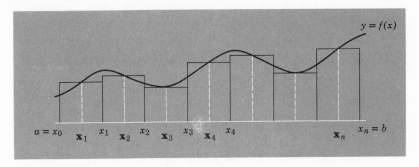

make $|\delta| \to 0$ is to partition the interval into n subintervals of equal length and then to increase n.

As we introduce more and more points into the partitions in such a way that the length of the longest subinterval tends toward zero, it is clear that the sums are approaching what we would like to call the area of the figure.

7.26   AREA

If f is positive and continuous between a and b, the *area* bounded by $y = f(x)$ and the x-axis between vertical lines at a and b is defined to be

$$A = \int_a^b f(x)\, dx.$$

We finally have our definition of area under a curve, but it is not a very nice one to use. It can be used, with considerable difficulty, to evaluate the area under a curve that is the graph of a polynomial of low degree, but in general it is too cumbersome. However, if we replace b by x, then we obtain

$$\int_a^x f(x)\, dx.$$

This expression represents a function of the upper limit of the integral and might be written with less possibility of confusion as

$$\int_a^x f(t)\, dt.$$

A fundamental theorem of calculus is that this function is precisely our old friend $A(x)$. We shall omit the proof. Since we know how to find $A(x)$ for any function for which we can find an antiderivative, the process of finding an integral, called *integration*, is reduced to recognizing derivatives.

Example 1.   Evaluate

$$\int_1^3 (3x^2 + 4x + 10)\, dx.$$

In this example $A(x)$ is a function whose derivative is $3x^2 + 4x + 10$ and that equals zero for $x = 1$. The general antiderivative is

$$x^3 + 2x^2 + 10x + c.$$

Since this is to be 0 for $x = 1$, we have

$$1 + 2 + 10 + c = 0, \quad \text{or} \quad c = -13.$$

Thus for any x,

$$A(x) = x^3 + 2x^2 + 10x - 13.$$

In particular,

$$A(3) = 27 + 18 + 30 - 13 = 62.$$

Hence,

$$\int_1^3 (3x^2 + 4x + 10)\, dx = 62.$$

7.27 COMMENTS

Historically speaking, the integral preceded the derivative. The Greeks of classical antiquity succeeded in integrating a number of elementary functions. Using essentially the methods of integral calculus, Archimedes succeeded in finding correct formulas for the area of a circle, the area under a portion of a parabola, the volume of a sphere, and volumes bounded by a number of surfaces of revolution. The derivative came later and was widely used after Descartes and Fermat had made analytic geometry familiar to the mathematical community. Thus, although Newton and Leibniz are said to be the inventors of calculus, what they actually did was to introduce the notation of calculus and to show the relationship between the integral and the antiderivative. Now, for the first time, integration became reasonably simple. This opened the door for the statement and solution of a vast number of physical problems that can be expressed in terms of integrals and derivatives.

7.28 APPLICATIONS

Loosely, an integral is the limit of a sum of more and more parts, each part becoming smaller and smaller. This is a concept that appears throughout the physical world. For instance, work is the product of a force applied to an object by the distance over which the force is applied. If we slide a block along a level board for ten feet, applying a constant force of five pounds, the work done is $(5)(10) = 50$ foot pounds. However, if a spring is stretched, the force required to stretch the spring depends on the distance the spring has been stretched. It is not constant. Over any very small interval, however, the force does not change much. Thus we can approximate the work done by summing the work done over each of the small intervals, assuming the force to be constant on each interval. Then the work is the limit of this sum as the intervals become smaller. This is precisely the limit of a sum that appears in the definition of an integral. If the force is given by $f(x)$, where

x is the distance the spring is stretched, and the spring is to be stretched from a to b, the work is

$$\text{Work} = \int_a^b f(x)\, dx.$$

For most springs, $f(x) = kx$ for some constant k. The work done in stretching such a spring from $x = 1$ to $x = 5$, for instance, is given by

$$\int_1^5 kx\, dx.$$

If we let $W(x)$ represent the work done in stretching the spring, then $W'(x)$ is kx. Thus $W(x) = kx^2/2 + c$, where c is to be chosen so that $W(1) = 0$. This yields $c = -k/2$ so that $W(x) = k(x^2 - 1)/2$. From this we find that

$$W(5) = \frac{k(25 - 1)}{2} = 12k.$$

If the mass of an iron rod is to be computed, it is no problem if the rod is of uniform density. However, if the rod is not of uniform density, again we approximate the mass by considering it to be made up of many small parts in each of which the density is nearly constant. The limit of the sum is an integral.

Instead of mass, the problem may be that of finding the heat content of a body that is not of uniform temperature. This is abstractly the same problem.

If a body is immersed in a liquid, the pressure varies with the depth of a point on the surface of the body. The total pressure is then a limit of a sum, an integral.

A volume can be computed by taking the limit of a sum of slices. Let us use this technique to find the volume of a sphere. We shall find the volume of a hemisphere and double it. Consider the illustration below, which represents an eighth of the sphere of radius r.

In the drawing we have partitioned the x-axis from 0 to r and constructed a slice on the ith subinterval. We take this slice to be approximately a thin circular cylinder of thickness δx_i and radius $\sqrt{r^2 - x_i^2}$. The volume of such a slice is

$$\pi(r^2 - x_i^2)\, \delta x_i.$$

The limit of the sum of these is

$$\int_0^r \pi(r^2 - x^2)\, dx.$$

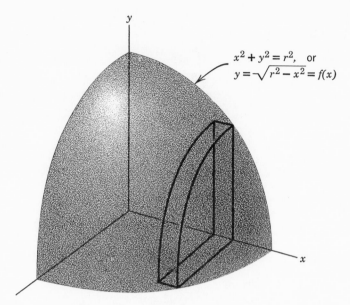

$$x^2 + y^2 = r^2, \quad \text{or}$$
$$y = \sqrt{r^2 - x^2} = f(x)$$

The volume $V(r)$ of the sphere of radius r is twice this integral. Let

$$V(x) = 2\pi \left(r^2 x - \frac{x^3}{3} \right).$$

Then

$$V(0) = 0 \quad \text{and} \quad V'(x) = 2\pi(r^2 - x^2),$$

so that

$$\int_0^r 2\pi(r^2 - x^2) \, dx = \int_0^r V'(x) \, dx.$$

Thus the volume of the sphere is given by $V(x)$ evaluated at $x = r$, or the volume is

$$2\pi \left(r^3 - \frac{r^3}{3} \right) = \frac{4\pi r^3}{3}.$$

This is only a mere handful of the possible applications that lead to integrals. The physical world is filled with such phenomena.

7.29 EXERCISES

In Exercises 1–10 evaluate the given integrals.

*1. $\displaystyle\int_1^3 (2x + 1) \, dx$ 　　　　**2.** $\displaystyle\int_{-1}^3 (3 - 3x) \, dx$

*3. $\int_{-2}^{2} x^2 \, dx$ **4.** $\int_{-2}^{2} x^3 \, dx$

*5. $\int_{-2}^{2} x^4 \, dx$ **6.** $\int_{0}^{1} (6x^5 - 10x^4 + 8x^3 - 9x^2 + 6x - 2) \, dx$

*7. $\int_{-2}^{4} (x^7 - 5) \, dx$ **8.** $\int_{1}^{3} (x^2 + 1)^2 \, dx$

*9. $\int_{-2}^{2} (1 - 2x^2)^2 \, dx$ **10.** $\int_{3}^{3} (x^3 + 5) \, dx$

*11. Prove that if F is any function for which $F' = f$, then

$$\int_{a}^{b} f(x) \, dx = F(b) - F(a).$$

12. Show that the area bounded by $y = x^3 - 4x$ and the x-axis is given by

$$\int_{-2}^{0} y \, dx - \int_{0}^{2} y \, dx.$$

*13. Find the area bounded by $y = x^2$ and $y = 4x$.

14. Find the area bounded by $y = x^3$ and $y = 4x$.

*15. Find the area bounded by $y = x^2$ and $y = x^3$.

16. If $a > b$, how would you define $\int_{a}^{b} f(x) \, dx$?

*17. How would you define $\int_{a}^{a} f(x) \, dx$?

18. What is $D_x \int_{a}^{x} f(x) \, dx$?

*19. Find $\int_{1}^{2} D_x(x^2 + 3x - 2) \, dx$.

20. Suppose it is known that the area of a circle is πr^2. Why does it follow that

$$\int_{0}^{2} \sqrt{4 - x^2} \, dx = \pi?$$

7.30 APPROXIMATIONS

The computation of integrals is simple if we can find the proper anti-derivative. Unfortunately, this is not only often not simple, it is frequently impossible. In such cases we must revert to the definition of the integral and approximate the value by actually making partitions and computing the sums involved. There is an entire branch of mathematics, numerical analysis, devoted to the study of methods of approximation, computing techniques, and error estimates. This branch of mathematics has been spurred into feverish activity by the advent of electronic computers that are capable of doing the messy and extensive arithmetic both rapidly and reliably. Of course, they must be told how to proceed, and such instructions are ultimately the responsibility of the numerical analyst.

7.31 RECOMMENDED READING

Fisher, R. C., and Ziebur, A. D., *Calculus and Analytic Geometry*, Englewood Cliffs, N.J., Prentice-Hall, 1965.

Johnson, R. E., and Kiokemeister, F. L., *Calculus with Analytic Geometry*, Boston, Allyn and Bacon, 1960.

Lang, S., *A First Course in Calculus*, Reading, Mass., Addison-Wesley, 1964.

Milne, W. E., *Introductory College Mathematics*, Boston, Ginn, 1962.

Protter, M. H., and Morrey, C. B., Jr., *College Calculus with Analytic Geometry*, Reading, Mass., Addison-Wesley, 1965.

Young, F. H., *Limits and Limit Concepts*, Boston, Ginn, 1964.

8

A matrix of magnetic cores; a computer's memory.

In Chapter 6 we investigated functions and relations with the emphasis on those relations whose domains were subsets of the real numbers. In several chapters we have encountered ordered pairs of numbers, both in relations and as representations of points in a plane. Let us examine functions that map ordered pairs of numbers into single numbers. The possibilities in this direction are so vast that we shall restrict our attention to some particularly simple cases, the linear functions.

8.1 POINTS TO NUMBERS

First, let us look at a very simple way that we can map ordered pairs of numbers into single numbers. Geometrically, this amounts to finding a function that associates a numerical value with every point in a plane. Let (x, y) represent any point in a plane. Let (a, b) be any ordered pairs of real numbers. Then $ax + by$ is some real number, which we shall call u. Thus (a, b) maps each (x, y) onto some number u by the relation

$$ax + by = u.$$

Let us denote this function by $(a \quad b)$. Then

$$(a \quad b) = \{((x, y), u) : u = ax + by\}.$$

Let us make one more change in notation. This change may appear to be capricious, but its usefulness will appear later. Let us denote $ax + by$ by

$$(a \quad b) \begin{pmatrix} x \\ y \end{pmatrix}.$$

Then

$$(a \quad b) = \left\{((x, y), u) : u = (a \quad b) \begin{pmatrix} x \\ y \end{pmatrix}\right\}.$$

Examples. Let us choose $(a \quad b)$ to be $(3 \quad 4)$. Then $(3 \quad 4)$ maps the point $(2, 1)$ into

$$3(2) + 4(1) = 10.$$

In the notation of the last paragraph

$$(3 \quad 4)\begin{pmatrix} 2 \\ 1 \end{pmatrix} = 10.$$

Similarly,

$$(3 \quad 4)\begin{pmatrix} 1 \\ 0 \end{pmatrix} = 3, \quad (3 \quad 4)\begin{pmatrix} 0 \\ 1 \end{pmatrix} = 4, \quad (3 \quad 4)\begin{pmatrix} 0 \\ 0 \end{pmatrix} = 0,$$

$$(3 \quad 4)\begin{pmatrix} 1 \\ -1 \end{pmatrix} = -1, \quad (3 \quad 4)\begin{pmatrix} -1 \\ 1 \end{pmatrix} = 1.$$

8.2 ORDERED *N*-TUPLES

There is nothing to prevent our extending this functional concept to mappings of ordered *n*-tuples to numbers. For example, if $n = 3$, the ordered triples might represent points in space. The geometric interpretation for higher dimensions becomes somewhat hazy, but the process is straightforward. We can think of an ordered quadruple (x, y, z, w) as representing the scores a student receives on four tests. Then, if a, b, c, and d are some standard weighting factors, $ax + by + cz + dw$ could represent the student's over-all score, S. We can write

$$(a \quad b \quad c \quad d) = \left\{ ((x, y, z, w), S) : S = (a \quad b \quad c \quad d)\begin{pmatrix} x \\ y \\ z \\ w \end{pmatrix} \right\}.$$

Examples.

$$(2 \quad 1 \quad -3)\begin{pmatrix} 1 \\ 1 \\ 1 \end{pmatrix} = 2 + 1 - 3 = 0, \quad (2 \quad 1 \quad -3)\begin{pmatrix} 1 \\ 0 \\ 0 \end{pmatrix} = 2$$

$$(2 \quad 1 \quad -3)\begin{pmatrix} 4 \\ 6 \\ 10 \end{pmatrix} = -16, \quad (2 \quad 1 \quad -3)\begin{pmatrix} 2x \\ 3x \\ 4 \end{pmatrix} = 7x - 12$$

8.3   VECTORS AND VECTOR MULTIPLICATION

We shall call ordered n-tuples n-vectors, or, when it is not necessary to specify the number of components, merely *vectors*. When we write an n-tuple horizontally, we call it a *row vector*, and when we write it vertically, we call it a *column vector*. Our preceding discussion of functions that map ordered n-tuples into numbers can be interpreted as defining implicitly a multiplication of a row vector on the left by a column vector on the right, provided both vectors have the same dimension. For simplicity, most of our examples will use $n = 2$. When $n = 1$, our multiplication of vectors reduces to ordinary multiplication.

Examples. $(2)(3) = 6,$ $(2 \quad 1)\begin{pmatrix} 3 \\ -4 \end{pmatrix} = 2,$

$$(a \quad b \quad c \quad d)\begin{pmatrix} x \\ y \\ z \\ w \end{pmatrix} = ax + by + cz + dw$$

$$(1 \quad 2 \quad 3)\begin{pmatrix} 1 \\ 2 \\ 3 \end{pmatrix} = 14$$

8.4   ALGEBRAIC STRUCTURE OF MULTIPLICATION OF VECTORS

It is clear from the examples above that any two n-vectors can be multiplied to give a real number if we extend our definition of "multiplication" in the natural way. It is understood, of course, that the two vectors have the same number of components. The way that we represent this product is arbitrary to some extent. One method, suggested above, is to write the vector on the left as a row and the one on the right as a column. Another way is to write them both as rows with a dot between them,

$$(a \quad b)\cdot(c \quad d) = ac + bd.$$

This is sometimes called the "dot" product.

If we refer to the section in Chapter 2 concerning the algebraic structure of the real numbers, we find five laws, M1 through M5. The only one of these that is satisfied at this point by vector multiplication is M2, the commutative law. This is true because

$$(a \quad b)\cdot(c \quad d) = ac + bd = (c \quad d)\cdot(a \quad b).$$

Later we shall develop a system of objects called matrices that have more satisfactory multiplicative properties. Also, we shall find that the addition of vectors can be defined in a natural way so that the algebraic properties of numerical addition are preserved.

8.5 SCALAR MULTIPLICATION

Let us call a real number a *scalar*, in contrast to vectors. Thus we shall call 2 a scalar but (2) a one- or 1-vector. Our present concern is to find out how we can define the product of a scalar and a vector. For instance, what should $c(a \quad b)$ mean? If $(a \quad b)$ maps (x, y) into u, then $c(a \quad b)$ should map (x, y) into cu. We know that

$$u = (a \quad b) \begin{pmatrix} x \\ y \end{pmatrix} = ax + by.$$

Thus

$$cu = c(ax + by) = cax + cby = (ca \quad cb) \begin{pmatrix} x \\ y \end{pmatrix}.$$

It is natural, then, to define $c(a \quad b)$ to be $(ca \quad cb)$. The extension to vectors with more components is obvious. To multiply a vector by a scalar, we multiply each component of the vector by the scalar. Also, we want $(a \quad b)c$ to map (x, y) into uc or, since u and c are real numbers and hence commutative, into cu. That is, we shall define

$$(a \quad b)c = c(a \quad b) = (ca \quad cb).$$

Finally, if c and d are any two scalars, how should we define $(c + d)(a \quad b)$ where $(c + d)$ is a scalar? If $(a \quad b)$ maps (x, y) into $ax + by$, then we shall define $(c + d)(a \quad b)$ so that it maps (x, y) into $(c + d)(ax + by)$. But, by the distributive law for real numbers,

$$(c + d)(ax + by) = c(ax + by) + d(ax + by).$$

Since

$$ax + by = (a \quad b) \begin{pmatrix} x \\ y \end{pmatrix},$$

we are led to define

$$(c + d)(a \quad b) = c(a \quad b) + d(a \quad b).$$

Then multiplication by a vector distributes over addition of real numbers.

Examples. $3(2 \quad 4) = (6 \quad 12)$, $-2(1 \quad 2 \quad 3) = (-2 \quad -4 \quad -6)$,
$(2 + 5)(a \quad b) = 2(a \quad b) + 5(a \quad b) = (2a \quad 2b) + (5a \quad 5b)$.

8.6 ADDITION OF VECTORS

In the last paragraph and in the last example there appear indicated sums of vectors. What is the "natural" way to define such a sum? Suppose that $(a \quad b)$ maps (x, y) into u, and $(c \quad d)$ maps (x, y) into v. Then

$$(a \quad b)\begin{pmatrix} x \\ y \end{pmatrix} + (c \quad d)\begin{pmatrix} x \\ y \end{pmatrix} = (ax + by) + (cx + dy)$$

$$= (a + c)x + (b + d)y$$

$$= (a + c \quad b + d)\begin{pmatrix} x \\ y \end{pmatrix}.$$

We are led, then, to define the sum of any two n-vectors to be that vector whose components are the sum of the corresponding components of the two vectors. For example,

$$(a \quad b \quad c) + (d \quad e \quad f) = (a + d \quad b + e \quad c + f).$$

Since the components are real numbers, and addition of real numbers is commutative, it follows that addition of vectors is also commutative. Furthermore, it doesn't matter whether the vectors are written as rows or columns; the sum is obtained in the same way.

We shall define subtraction of vectors as a component by component subtraction. Thus

$$(a \quad b) - (c \quad d) = (a - c \quad b - d).$$

Examples. $(1 \quad 2) + (5 \quad -3) = (6 \quad -1)$,

$(1 \quad 2 \quad 3) + (4 \quad -2 \quad -3) = (5 \quad 0 \quad 0)$, $\begin{pmatrix} 2 \\ 5 \end{pmatrix} + \begin{pmatrix} 3 \\ 6 \end{pmatrix} = \begin{pmatrix} 5 \\ 11 \end{pmatrix}$,

$(3 \quad 7) - (3 \quad 6) = (0 \quad 1)$, $\begin{pmatrix} -3 \\ 7 \end{pmatrix} - \begin{pmatrix} 3 \\ -7 \end{pmatrix} = \begin{pmatrix} 0 \\ 0 \end{pmatrix}$

8.7 EXERCISES

*1. Let $(a \quad b) = (2 \quad -3)$. Into what does $(a \quad b)$ map each of the following?
$(1 \quad 0)$, $(0 \quad 1)$, $(-3 \quad 2)$, $(h \quad k)$, $(x + 2 \quad y - 1)$, $(x \quad x)$,
$(x \quad -x)$, $(b \quad -a)$, $(x + b \quad x - a)$, $(a \quad b)$.

2. Let $(a \quad b \quad c) = (-3 \quad 1 \quad 2)$. Into what does $(a \quad b \quad c)$ map each of the following? $(1 \quad 0 \quad 0)$, $(0 \quad 1 \quad 0)$, $(0 \quad 0 \quad 1)$, $(2 \quad -4 \quad 5)$,
$(1 \quad -3 \quad 3)$, $(x + 1 \quad y - 1 \quad z + 1)$, $(0 \quad 0 \quad 0)$, $(1 \quad 1 \quad 1)$,
$(x + y \quad x - y \quad x)$, $2(4 \quad -3 \quad 2)$.

*3. Evaluate the following vector products:

$(2 \quad 1) \begin{pmatrix} 3 \\ 7 \end{pmatrix}$, $(4 \quad -1) \begin{pmatrix} 2 \\ -3 \end{pmatrix}$, $(6 \quad 12) \begin{pmatrix} 1/2 \\ 2/3 \end{pmatrix}$, $(2 \quad 1 \quad 3) \begin{pmatrix} 2 \\ 1 \\ 3 \end{pmatrix}$,

$(-3 \quad -1 \quad 2) \begin{pmatrix} 4 \\ 1 \\ 7 \end{pmatrix}$

4. Evaluate the following vector products:
$(7 \quad -6) \cdot (2 \quad 1)$, $(-2 \quad -1) \cdot (0 \quad 1)$, $(3 \quad 2 \quad -1) \cdot (0 \quad 1 \quad 0)$,
$(1 \quad -1 \quad 1) \cdot (-1 \quad 1 \quad 0)$, $(a \quad b \quad c) \cdot (c \quad b \quad a)$.

5. Evaluate each of the following:

  *(a) $(1 \quad 2) + (3 \quad 4)$ **(b)** $(-3 \quad 7) + (2 \quad -5)$

  *(c) $(3 \quad 4 \quad 6) + (2 \quad -5 \quad 7)$ **(d)** $(2 \quad -1 \quad 5) - (2 \quad 1 \quad 5)$

  *(e) $(16 \quad 1/2 \quad 3) - (12 \quad 5/2 \quad 2/3)$

  (f) $(1 \quad 3 \quad 5 \quad 7) + (2 \quad 4 \quad 6 \quad 8)$

  *(g) $(a \quad b \quad c \quad d) + (3 \quad 0 \quad 0 \quad 2)$ **(h)** $(a \quad a \quad b \quad b) - (a \quad b \quad b \quad a)$

  *(i) $(2x \quad x \quad 3x \quad 5x) - (x + 1 \quad x + 2 \quad x + 3 \quad x + 4)$

  (j) $(x \quad x \quad x \quad x) + (1 - x \quad 2 - x \quad 3 - x \quad 4 - x)$

6. Evaluate each of the following:

  (a) $2(4 \quad -7)$ **(b)** $3(2 \quad 1 \quad 2)$

  (c) $-4(3 \quad -1 \quad 4)$ **(d)** $0.5(3 \quad -1 \quad 4)$

  (e) $6(2 \quad -1 \quad 12 \quad 7 \quad 3)$ **(f)** $3(a \quad b) + 4(c \quad d)$

  (g) $2(-5 \quad 7) + 3(4 \quad 6)$ **(h)** $3(1 \quad 2 \quad 3) - 4(2 \quad 7 \quad -8)$

  (i) $4(x \quad y \quad z) + 3(a \quad b \quad c)$

  (j) $0.6(2.1 \quad -3.4 \quad -1.2) - 0(3 \quad -2 \quad 5)$

*7. Find a vector $(x \quad y \quad z)$ such that $2(3 \quad -5 \quad 4) + (x \quad y \quad z) = (0 \quad 0 \quad 0)$.

8. Find a vector $(x \quad y \quad z \quad w)$ such that $2(x \quad y \quad z \quad w) - 3(1 \quad 2 \quad 3 \quad 4) = (0 \quad 0 \quad 0 \quad 0)$.

*9. Find a vector $(x \quad y)$ such that $2(x \quad y) + 3(4 \quad -6) = (12 \quad 16)$.

10. Find a vector $(x \quad y)$ such that $3(x \quad y) - 4(6 \quad 9) = (0 \quad 0)$.

*11. Find a vector $(x \quad y \quad z)$ such that $5(x \quad y \quad z) + 4(-5 \quad 2 \quad 1) = (2 \quad 3 \quad 7)$.

12. Find a vector $(x \quad y \quad z \quad w)$ such that $4(x \quad y \quad z \quad w) - 2(4 \quad 1 \quad 2 \quad 0) = (0 \quad 0 \quad 0 \quad 0)$.

8.8   ALGEBRAIC STRUCTURE OF ADDITION OF VECTORS

Let us denote row vectors by letters in bold face. For instance, a vector $(a \ \ b \ \ c)$ might be denoted by **a**. When it is written as a column vector, we shall write $\mathbf{a}^T$. Let us consider the set of all n-vectors whose elements are real numbers. We shall think of n as being fixed for this discussion. By our definition of vector addition, the sum of any two such vectors is an n-vector. That is, we have:

A1. Closure.   The set of n-vectors are *closed under addition.*
We have already shown that:

A2. Commutative Law.   Addition of n-vectors is *commutative.*
Let

$$\mathbf{a} = (a \ \ b), \quad \mathbf{b} = (r \ \ s), \quad \text{and} \quad \mathbf{c} = (x \ \ y).$$

Then, from our definition of vector addition we find that

$$(\mathbf{a} + \mathbf{b}) + \mathbf{c} = ((a + r) + x \ (b + s) + y)$$
$$= (a + (r + x) \ b + (s + y)) = \mathbf{a} + (\mathbf{b} + \mathbf{c}).$$

Since this clearly extends to an arbitrary number of components, we have:

A3. Associative Law.   Addition of n-vectors is *associative.*
Let **0** be the n-vector which has 0 for each component. Then, by the definition of addition of n-vectors,

$$\mathbf{a} + \mathbf{0} = \mathbf{0} + \mathbf{a} = \mathbf{a}.$$

Thus we have:

A4. Identity.   **0** is the *identity* for addition in the set of n-vectors. If any confusion can arise, we shall use a subscript n to denote the number of 0 components of **0**.
Finally, for any vector **a**, let $-\mathbf{a}$ be the vector whose components are the negatives of the corresponding components of a. Then

$$\mathbf{a} + (-\mathbf{a}) = \mathbf{0}.$$

For example,

$$(3 \ \ -2) + (-3 \ \ 2) = (0 \ \ 0) = \mathbf{0}.$$

Thus we have:

A5. Inverses. Every n-vector has an *additive inverse*.

We have shown that the algebraic properties of addition of real numbers that were discussed in Chapter 2 hold for the set of n-vectors. Since the 1-vectors are essentially the numbers themselves, we can consider vectors to be a generalization of real numbers, as far as addition is concerned. But vector multiplication, since it satisfies only M2, gives us a very limited system. Let us try to enlarge it.

8.9 MATRICES

Earlier, we saw that a linear equation like $ax + by = c$ could be interpreted as a function $(a \quad b)$ mapping (x, y) into c. Suppose that we have two such equations:

$$a_1 x + b_1 y = c_1$$
$$a_2 x + b_2 y = c_2.$$

Then these two equations can be interpreted as mapping the vector $(x \quad y)$ into the vector $(c_1 \quad c_2)$. Let us write this transformation in the form

$$\begin{pmatrix} a_1 & b_1 \\ a_2 & b_2 \end{pmatrix} \begin{pmatrix} x \\ y \end{pmatrix} = \begin{pmatrix} c_1 \\ c_2 \end{pmatrix}.$$

This is a way of putting together two of the mappings previously considered,

$$(a_1 \quad b_1) \begin{pmatrix} x \\ y \end{pmatrix} = c_1, \qquad (a_2 \quad b_2) \begin{pmatrix} x \\ y \end{pmatrix} = c_2.$$

More generally, consider any system of m equations in n unknowns. Since it is rather difficult to keep track of the letters involved, let us use a single letter, a, for the coefficients, with two subscripts. The first will represent the number of the equation, and the second will represent the number of the variable. Similarly, let us use x_i, where i takes on the values from 1 to n, to represent each of the n variables. Further, let c_i, where i runs from 1 to m, represent the m constants on the right. For two equations in three unknowns we have

$$a_{11} x_1 + a_{12} x_2 + a_{13} x_3 = c_1$$
$$a_{21} x_1 + a_{22} x_2 + a_{23} x_3 = c_2$$

which we can now write as

$$\begin{pmatrix} a_{11} & a_{12} & a_{13} \\ a_{21} & a_{22} & a_{23} \end{pmatrix} \begin{pmatrix} x_1 \\ x_2 \\ x_3 \end{pmatrix} = \begin{pmatrix} c_1 \\ c_2 \end{pmatrix}.$$

A rectangular array similar to that above is called a *matrix* (plural: *matrices*). In general, a matrix consists of an array of m rows where each row is an n-vector. Such a matrix is said to be of *order* m *by* n.

Examples.

$$\begin{pmatrix} 1 & 2 \\ 3 & 4 \end{pmatrix} \begin{pmatrix} x \\ y \end{pmatrix} = \begin{pmatrix} x + 2y \\ 3x + 4y \end{pmatrix}, \qquad \begin{pmatrix} 1 & 2 \\ 3 & 4 \end{pmatrix} \begin{pmatrix} 1 \\ 2 \end{pmatrix} = \begin{pmatrix} 5 \\ 11 \end{pmatrix},$$

$$\begin{pmatrix} 1 & 0 \\ 0 & 1 \end{pmatrix} \begin{pmatrix} 4 \\ 7 \end{pmatrix} = \begin{pmatrix} 4 \\ 7 \end{pmatrix},$$

$$\begin{pmatrix} 1 & 2 & 3 \\ -4 & -5 & -6 \end{pmatrix} \begin{pmatrix} 2 \\ 2 \\ 2 \end{pmatrix} = \begin{pmatrix} 2 + 4 + 6 \\ -8 - 10 - 12 \end{pmatrix} = \begin{pmatrix} 12 \\ -30 \end{pmatrix},$$

$$\begin{pmatrix} 1 & -4 \\ 2 & -5 \\ 3 & -6 \end{pmatrix} \begin{pmatrix} 2 \\ 2 \end{pmatrix} = \begin{pmatrix} 2 - 8 \\ 4 - 10 \\ 6 - 12 \end{pmatrix} = \begin{pmatrix} -6 \\ -6 \\ -6 \end{pmatrix} = -6 \begin{pmatrix} 1 \\ 1 \\ 1 \end{pmatrix}.$$

8.10   NOTATION

Let us shorten our notation still further. Let us interpret $A = (a_{ij})_{m,n}$ to mean that A is the name of a matrix, that the element in the ith row and the jth column is a_{ij}, and that there are m rows and n columns.

Example 1.   Let

$$A = (a_{ij})_{2,3}, \quad \text{where} \quad a_{ij} = i + j.$$

What is A? We know that A has 2 rows and 3 columns. The element in the ith row and jth column is $i + j$. Thus

$$A = \begin{pmatrix} 1 + 1 & 1 + 2 & 1 + 3 \\ 2 + 1 & 2 + 2 & 2 + 3 \end{pmatrix} = \begin{pmatrix} 2 & 3 & 4 \\ 3 & 4 & 5 \end{pmatrix}.$$

Example 2.   Let

$$M = (m_{ij})_{2,2}, \quad \text{where} \quad m_{ij} = 2i - j.$$

Then

$$M = \begin{pmatrix} 2 \cdot 1 - 1 & 2 \cdot 1 - 2 \\ 2 \cdot 2 - 1 & 2 \cdot 2 - 2 \end{pmatrix} = \begin{pmatrix} 1 & 0 \\ 3 & 2 \end{pmatrix}.$$

8.11 EXERCISES

1. Verify that the cancellation law is valid for addition of 3-vectors. That is, show that if $\mathbf{a}$, $\mathbf{b}$, and $\mathbf{c}$ are 3-vectors and $\mathbf{a} + \mathbf{c} = \mathbf{b} + \mathbf{c}$, then $\mathbf{a} = \mathbf{b}$.

In Exercises 2–10 let $\mathbf{a} = (2 \quad 1 \quad -3)$, $\mathbf{b} = (3 \quad 4 \quad 2)$, and $\mathbf{c} = (-3 \quad -2 \quad 1)$.

2. Verify that $\mathbf{a} + \mathbf{b} = \mathbf{b} + \mathbf{a}$.

*3. Verify that $(\mathbf{a} + \mathbf{b}) + \mathbf{c} = \mathbf{a} + (\mathbf{b} + \mathbf{c})$.

4. Verify that $\mathbf{a} + \mathbf{0}_3 = \mathbf{a}$.

*5. Write $-\mathbf{a}$, $-\mathbf{b}$, and $-\mathbf{c}$.

6. Find $2\mathbf{a} - 3\mathbf{b}$.

*7. Find $3\mathbf{a} - 2\mathbf{b}$.

8. Find $\mathbf{a} + 4\mathbf{b} - 2\mathbf{c}$.

*9. Find $3\mathbf{a} - 2\mathbf{b} + 4\mathbf{c}$.

10. Find $2(\mathbf{a} + \mathbf{b}) - 3(\mathbf{b} + \mathbf{c})$.

*11. Let $A = \begin{pmatrix} 2 & 1 \\ -3 & 4 \end{pmatrix}$, and let $\mathbf{x} = (x \quad y)$. Find $A\mathbf{x}^T$ if

    (a) $\mathbf{x} = (1 \quad 0)$ (b) $\mathbf{x} = (0 \quad 1)$ (c) $\mathbf{x} = (1 \quad 1)$
    (d) $\mathbf{x} = (2 \quad -5)$ (e) $\mathbf{x} = (4 \quad -2)$

12. Let $A = \begin{pmatrix} a & b \\ c & d \end{pmatrix}$, and let $\mathbf{x} = (x \quad y)$. Find $A\mathbf{x}^T$ if

    (a) $\mathbf{x} = (1 \quad 0)$ (b) $\mathbf{x} = (0 \quad 1)$ (c) $\mathbf{x} = (1 \quad -1)$
    (d) $\mathbf{x} = (-1 \quad 1)$ (e) $\mathbf{x} = (h \quad k)$

*13. Let
    $A = \begin{pmatrix} 1 & 2 & 3 \\ -2 & 1 & 2 \\ 1 & 3 & 1 \end{pmatrix}$, and let $\mathbf{x} = (x \quad y \quad z)$. Find $A\mathbf{x}^T$ if

    (a) $\mathbf{x} = (1 \quad 0 \quad 0)$ (b) $\mathbf{x} = (0 \quad 1 \quad 0)$ (c) $\mathbf{x} = (0 \quad 0 \quad 1)$
    (d) $\mathbf{x} = (1 \quad -1 \quad 0)$ (e) $\mathbf{x} = (2 \quad -3 \quad 1)$

14. Let $A = \begin{pmatrix} 2 & 1 \\ 3 & -1 \end{pmatrix}$, let $\mathbf{x} = (x \quad y)$, and let $A\mathbf{x}^T = \mathbf{c}^T$. Find $\mathbf{x}$ if

    (a) $\mathbf{c} = (1 \quad 0)$ (b) $\mathbf{c} = (0 \quad 1)$ (c) $\mathbf{c} = (1 \quad 1)$
    (d) $\mathbf{c} = (-5 \quad 10)$ (e) $\mathbf{c} = (15 \quad -25)$

    (Hint: write $A\mathbf{x}^T = \mathbf{c}^T$ as a pair of simultaneous equations and solve them.)

*15. Let $A = \begin{pmatrix} 1 & 2 \\ 2 & -1 \end{pmatrix}$, let $\mathbf{x} = (x \quad y)$, and let $A\mathbf{x}^T = \mathbf{c}^T$. Find $\mathbf{x}$ if

    (a) $\mathbf{c} = (3 \quad 0)$ (b) $\mathbf{c} = (0 \quad -3)$ (c) $\mathbf{c} = (6 \quad 12)$
    (d) $\mathbf{c} = (-9 \quad 24)$ (e) $\mathbf{c} = (5 \quad 7)$

16. Write out $A = (a_{ij})_{2,2}$ if $a_{ij} = 2i + 3j$.

*17. Write out $B = (b_{ij})_{2,2}$ if $b_{ij} = 3i - 2j$.

18. Write out $C = (c_{ij})_{2,3}$ if $c_{ij} = i$.

***19.** Write out $D = (d_{ij})_{3,3}$ if $d_{ij} = 2i - 3j$.

20. Write out $P = (p_{rs})_{3,3}$ if $p_{rs} = r^2 + s^2$.

8.12 SQUARE MATRICES

Among all matrices, those that have the same number of rows as columns are of particular importance. We shall say that an n by n matrix is of *order n*. We shall denote a square matrix of order n by a capital letter with a subscript denoting the order unless it is understood. For example, if $B = (b_{ij})_3$, then we understand that B has 3 rows and 3 columns.

A square matrix of order n can be used to map any n-vector into another n-vector.

8.13 SIMULTANEOUS EQUATIONS

In Problems 14 and 15 of the last section you were asked to find a vector that was mapped by a given matrix into a given vector. Since the equation $A\mathbf{x}^T = \mathbf{c}^T$ is equivalent to n simultaneous equations in n unknowns whenever A is of order n, one way to solve the problems is to solve the set of equations. For instance, if

$$A = \begin{pmatrix} 3 & 2 \\ 4 & 3 \end{pmatrix} \quad \text{and} \quad c = (-2 \quad 1),$$

then $A\mathbf{x}^T = \mathbf{c}^T$ is equivalent to the pair of equations

$$3x + 2y = -2$$
$$4x + 3y = 1.$$

If we multiply the first equation by 3 and the second by 2, we have

$$9x + 6y = -6$$
$$8x + 6y = 2.$$

Then, subtracting, we find $x = -8$. Upon substitution in either of the original equations, we find $y = 11$. Thus our desired vector is $\mathbf{x} = (-8 \quad 11)$.

In general, if $A = (a_{ij})_n$, $\mathbf{x}$ is the vector $(x_1 \quad x_2 \quad \cdots \quad x_n)$, and $\mathbf{c}$ is $(c_1 \quad c_2 \quad \cdots \quad c_n)$, then the equation $A\mathbf{x}^T = \mathbf{c}^T$ is equivalent to n simultaneous linear equations in n unknowns. Many problems of mathematics can be reduced to the solution of such systems of equations. The problem of solving

$ax = c$ for real numbers is simple. If $a \neq 0$, we multiply both sides by the inverse of a to get

$$a^{-1}ax = a^{-1}c, \quad \text{or} \quad x = a^{-1}c.$$

We have written $a^{-1}c$ rather than c/a so that we can solve the equation $A\mathbf{x}^T = \mathbf{c}^T$ by precisely the same technique. This will come later. First we must find a way to multiply matrices. Then we shall find out what A^{-1} means, when it exists, and how to compute it.

8.14 MATRIX MULTIPLICATION

Let us restrict our attention to matrices of order 2. The generalization to higher orders will be simple. If $A = (a_{ij})_2$, then A maps each $\mathbf{x} = (x \quad y)$ into a vector which we shall call $\mathbf{c} = (c_1 \quad c_2)$. This mapping is indicated by the equation $A\mathbf{x}^T = \mathbf{c}^T$. Suppose that $\mathbf{u} = (u \quad v)$ is mapped into $(x \quad y)$ by a matrix $B = (b_{ij})_2$. Then $B\mathbf{u}^T = \mathbf{x}^T$. If we substitute $B\mathbf{u}^T$ for $\mathbf{x}^T$ in the equation $A\mathbf{x}^T = \mathbf{c}^T$, we obtain $A(B\mathbf{u}^T) = \mathbf{c}^T$. Our task is to define a multiplication of matrices in such a way, if possible, that the product is a matrix AB that maps $\mathbf{u}^T$ onto $\mathbf{c}^T$. If we can do this, so that $(AB)\mathbf{u}^T = \mathbf{c}^T$, then we shall have $A(B\mathbf{u}^T) = (AB)\mathbf{u}^T$. Procedures of this sort are common in mathematics. We want to define something new. We observe that the new object should have certain properties. In this way we are led to make what may be termed a "natural" definition for matrix multiplication. Let us carry out the substitution indicated above.

$$B\mathbf{u}^T = \begin{pmatrix} b_{11} & b_{12} \\ b_{21} & b_{22} \end{pmatrix} \begin{pmatrix} u \\ v \end{pmatrix} = \begin{pmatrix} b_{11}u + b_{12}v \\ b_{21}u + b_{22}v \end{pmatrix}.$$

Then

$$A(B\mathbf{u}^T) = \begin{pmatrix} a_{11} & a_{12} \\ a_{21} & a_{22} \end{pmatrix} \begin{pmatrix} b_{11}u + b_{12}v \\ b_{21}u + b_{22}v \end{pmatrix} = \begin{pmatrix} a_{11}(b_{11}u + b_{12}v) + a_{12}(b_{21}u + b_{22}v) \\ a_{21}(b_{11}u + b_{12}v) + a_{22}(b_{21}u + b_{22}v) \end{pmatrix}$$

$$= \begin{pmatrix} (a_{11}b_{11} + a_{12}b_{21})u + (a_{11}b_{12} + a_{12}b_{22})v \\ (a_{21}b_{11} + a_{22}b_{21})u + (a_{21}b_{12} + a_{22}b_{22})v \end{pmatrix}$$

$$= \begin{pmatrix} (a_{11}b_{11} + a_{12}b_{21}) & (a_{11}b_{12} + a_{12}b_{22}) \\ (a_{21}b_{11} + a_{22}b_{21}) & (a_{21}b_{12} + a_{22}b_{22}) \end{pmatrix} \begin{pmatrix} u \\ v \end{pmatrix}.$$

Thus we are led to define

$$AB = \begin{pmatrix} a_{11} & a_{12} \\ a_{21} & a_{22} \end{pmatrix} \begin{pmatrix} b_{11} & b_{12} \\ b_{21} & b_{22} \end{pmatrix} = \begin{pmatrix} a_{11}b_{11} + a_{12}b_{21} & a_{11}b_{12} + a_{12}b_{22} \\ a_{21}b_{11} + a_{22}b_{21} & a_{21}b_{12} + a_{22}b_{22} \end{pmatrix}.$$

We find the elements of AB are vector products given in the table below.

Location	Vector Product
1st row, 1st column of AB	1st row of A with 1st column of B
1st row, 2nd column of AB	1st row of A with 2nd column of B
2nd row, 1st column of AB	2nd row of A with 1st column of B
2nd row, 2nd column of AB	2nd row of A with 2nd column of B

If we had carried out our substitution on transformations of n-vectors for any larger value of n, our work would be greater, but our result would be in the same pattern. We would be led to define AB as follows:

Definition of Multiplication of Square Matrices. If $A = (a_{ij})_n$ and $B = (b_{ij})_n$, then

$$AB = C = (c_{ij})_n,$$

where c_{ij} is the vector product of the ith row of A with the jth column of B.

Actually, it isn't necessary that A and B be square. It *is* necessary, however, that the corresponding vector products be meaningful. For this to be true, the row vectors of A must be of the same dimension as the column vectors of B. That is, if A is an m by n matrix (has n columns), then B must be n by k (have n rows). Then the product will be an m by k matrix.

General Definition of Matrix Multiplication. If $A = (a_{ij})_{m,n}$ and $B = (b_{ij})_{n,k}$, then

$$AB = C = (c_{ij})_{m,k},$$

where c_{ij} is the vector product of the ith row of A by the jth column of B.

Examples.

$$\begin{pmatrix} 1 & 2 \\ 3 & 1 \end{pmatrix}\begin{pmatrix} -2 & -1 \\ 1 & 2 \end{pmatrix} = \begin{pmatrix} -2+2 & -1+4 \\ -6+1 & -3+2 \end{pmatrix} = \begin{pmatrix} 0 & 3 \\ -5 & -1 \end{pmatrix}$$

$$\begin{pmatrix} -2 & -1 \\ 1 & 2 \end{pmatrix}\begin{pmatrix} 1 & 2 \\ 3 & 1 \end{pmatrix} = \begin{pmatrix} -2-3 & -4-1 \\ 1+6 & 2+2 \end{pmatrix} = \begin{pmatrix} -5 & -5 \\ 7 & 4 \end{pmatrix}$$

$$\begin{pmatrix} 1 & 2 & 3 \\ 2 & 1 & 3 \\ -1 & -1 & 2 \end{pmatrix}\begin{pmatrix} 1 & 2 \\ 3 & 4 \\ -1 & -2 \end{pmatrix} = \begin{pmatrix} 1+6-3 & 2+8-6 \\ 2+3-3 & 4+4-6 \\ -1-3-2 & -2-4-4 \end{pmatrix}$$

$$= \begin{pmatrix} 4 & 4 \\ 2 & 2 \\ -6 & -10 \end{pmatrix}$$

$$\begin{pmatrix} 2 & 1 & 3 \\ 1 & 2 & 1 \end{pmatrix}\begin{pmatrix} -2 & 1 \\ 1 & 2 \\ 3 & 4 \end{pmatrix} = \begin{pmatrix} -4+1+9 & 2+2+12 \\ -2+2+3 & 1+4+4 \end{pmatrix}$$

$$= \begin{pmatrix} 6 & 16 \\ 3 & 9 \end{pmatrix}$$

$$\begin{pmatrix} 1 & 0 & 0 \\ 0 & 1 & 0 \\ 0 & 0 & 1 \end{pmatrix} \begin{pmatrix} a & b & c \\ d & e & f \\ g & h & i \end{pmatrix} = \begin{pmatrix} a & b & c \\ d & e & f \\ g & h & i \end{pmatrix}$$

$$\begin{pmatrix} 0 & 1 & 0 \\ 1 & 0 & 0 \\ 0 & 0 & 1 \end{pmatrix} \begin{pmatrix} a & b & c \\ d & e & f \\ g & h & i \end{pmatrix} = \begin{pmatrix} d & e & f \\ a & b & c \\ g & h & i \end{pmatrix}$$

We have defined matrix multiplication in a general way to demonstrate the power of our approach. As the matrices increase in size, the amount of arithmetic involved in matrix operations also gets large. To multiply two square matrices of order 10, we must form 100 vector products, each the sum of 10 products of numbers. Thus 1000 multiplications must be performed to obtain the product matrix. In general, the multiplication of two square matrices of order n requires n^3 arithmetic multiplications. We have not included the additions. We shall leave such prodigious feats of arithmetic to those devices designed to do them, the digital computers. We shall be satisfied for the most part in illustrating matrix algebra with matrices of order 2 or 3.

8.15 EXERCISES

In Exercises 1–10 find the indicated products.

*1. $\begin{pmatrix} 2 & 1 \\ 7 & -3 \end{pmatrix} \begin{pmatrix} 3 & -1 \\ -2 & 4 \end{pmatrix}$
2. $\begin{pmatrix} -5 & 6 \\ 2 & 3 \end{pmatrix} \begin{pmatrix} 10 & 2 \\ -7 & 4 \end{pmatrix}$

*3. $\begin{pmatrix} 3 & -1 \\ -2 & 4 \end{pmatrix} \begin{pmatrix} 2 & 1 \\ 7 & -3 \end{pmatrix}$
4. $\begin{pmatrix} 10 & 2 \\ -7 & 4 \end{pmatrix} \begin{pmatrix} -5 & 6 \\ 2 & 3 \end{pmatrix}$

*5. $\begin{pmatrix} 3 & -4 \\ 4 & 3 \end{pmatrix} \begin{pmatrix} 2 & 1 \\ -1 & 2 \end{pmatrix}$
6. $\begin{pmatrix} 1 & 0 \\ 0 & 1 \end{pmatrix} \begin{pmatrix} a & b \\ c & d \end{pmatrix}$

*7. $\begin{pmatrix} 2 & 1 \\ -1 & 2 \end{pmatrix} \begin{pmatrix} 3 & -4 \\ 4 & 3 \end{pmatrix}$
8. $\begin{pmatrix} a & b \\ c & d \end{pmatrix} \begin{pmatrix} 1 & 0 \\ 0 & 1 \end{pmatrix}$

*9. $\begin{pmatrix} a & b \\ -b & a \end{pmatrix} \begin{pmatrix} c & d \\ -d & c \end{pmatrix}$
10. $\begin{pmatrix} a & b \\ c & d \end{pmatrix} \begin{pmatrix} d & -b \\ -c & a \end{pmatrix}$

In Exercises 11–16 write each pair of simultaneous equations in matrix form.

*11. $2x + 3y = 7$
     $x - 2y = 3$
12. $4x - y = 2$
    $2x + 3y = 5$

*13. $7x - 7y = 10$
     $2x + 3y = 2$
14. $px + qy = a$
    $rx + sy = b$

*15. $x = 3$
     $y = 5$
16. $x = y$
    $y = 3$

In Exercises 17–22 write the matrix equation as a pair of simultaneous equations.

*17. $\begin{pmatrix} 1 & 2 \\ 5 & 3 \end{pmatrix} \begin{pmatrix} x \\ y \end{pmatrix} = \begin{pmatrix} 2 \\ -3 \end{pmatrix}$
18. $\begin{pmatrix} -3 & 5 \\ 2 & 2 \end{pmatrix} \begin{pmatrix} x \\ y \end{pmatrix} = \begin{pmatrix} 1 \\ 0 \end{pmatrix}$

*19. $\begin{pmatrix} 3 & -5 \\ 1 & 2 \end{pmatrix} \begin{pmatrix} x \\ y \end{pmatrix} = \begin{pmatrix} 6 \\ -6 \end{pmatrix}$ 20. $\begin{pmatrix} m & n \\ p & q \end{pmatrix} \begin{pmatrix} x \\ y \end{pmatrix} = \begin{pmatrix} u \\ v \end{pmatrix}$

*21. $\begin{pmatrix} 1 & 0 \\ 0 & 1 \end{pmatrix} \begin{pmatrix} x \\ y \end{pmatrix} = \begin{pmatrix} 2 \\ 3 \end{pmatrix}$ 22. $\begin{pmatrix} 1 & 0 \\ 0 & 0 \end{pmatrix} \begin{pmatrix} x \\ y \end{pmatrix} = \begin{pmatrix} 3 \\ 1 \end{pmatrix}$

8.16   MULTIPLICATIVE IDENTITY

Let A be a square matrix of order n. Does there exist a square matrix, I, with the property that $AI = IA = A$? It is simple to verify that there is indeed such a matrix. Its elements are m_{ij} where $m_{ij} = 1$ if $i = j$ and 0 if $i \neq j$. That is, the elements are all zero except those on the diagonal from the upper left to lower right, which are all ones. The diagonal that has been described is usually called the "main diagonal" of the matrix.

Examples.

$$\begin{pmatrix} 1 & 0 \\ 0 & 1 \end{pmatrix} \begin{pmatrix} a & b \\ c & d \end{pmatrix} = \begin{pmatrix} a & b \\ c & d \end{pmatrix} = \begin{pmatrix} a & b \\ c & d \end{pmatrix} \begin{pmatrix} 1 & 0 \\ 0 & 1 \end{pmatrix}$$

$$\begin{pmatrix} 1 & 0 & 0 \\ 0 & 1 & 0 \\ 0 & 0 & 1 \end{pmatrix} \begin{pmatrix} a & b & c \\ d & e & f \\ g & h & i \end{pmatrix} = \begin{pmatrix} a & b & c \\ d & e & f \\ g & h & i \end{pmatrix} = \begin{pmatrix} a & b & c \\ d & e & f \\ g & h & i \end{pmatrix} \begin{pmatrix} 1 & 0 & 0 \\ 0 & 1 & 0 \\ 0 & 0 & 1 \end{pmatrix}$$

8.17   OTHER MULTIPLICATIVE PROPERTIES OF MATRICES

From our definition of matrix multiplication, the product of two square matrices of the same order is always a matrix of that order. Thus, although the set of all matrices is not closed under multiplication, a subset consisting of all square matrices of a given order is closed under the operation. It is apparent that if we wish to investigate the algebraic structure of a set of matrices, it will be wise to limit our attention to such sets. Hereafter, let us denote by $\mathfrak{M}_n$ the set of all square matrices of order n. Then $\mathfrak{M}_n$ is closed under multiplication for any n.

Is multiplication commutative in $\mathfrak{M}_n$? Exercises 1 and 3 and exercises 5 and 7 of the last set demonstrate that the answer is negative. Some matrices, such as I, do commute with others, but in general multiplication is not commutative. To illustrate further,

$$\begin{pmatrix} 1 & 1 \\ 2 & 2 \end{pmatrix} \begin{pmatrix} 1 & 2 \\ 1 & 2 \end{pmatrix} = \begin{pmatrix} 2 & 4 \\ 4 & 8 \end{pmatrix} \quad \text{but} \quad \begin{pmatrix} 1 & 2 \\ 1 & 2 \end{pmatrix} \begin{pmatrix} 1 & 1 \\ 2 & 2 \end{pmatrix} = \begin{pmatrix} 5 & 5 \\ 5 & 5 \end{pmatrix}.$$

Is multiplication associative in $\mathfrak{M}_n$? Let A map $\mathbf{v}$ into $\mathbf{w}$, let B map $\mathbf{u}$ into $\mathbf{v}$, and let C map $\mathbf{x}$ into $\mathbf{u}$. In symbols,

$$A\mathbf{v}^T = \mathbf{w}^T, \qquad B\mathbf{u}^T = \mathbf{v}^T, \qquad C\mathbf{x}^T = \mathbf{u}^T.$$

We have defined multiplication in precisely such a way that

$$(BC)\mathbf{x}^T = B(C\mathbf{x}^T) = B\mathbf{u}^T = \mathbf{v}^T.$$

Since A maps $\mathbf{v}$ into $\mathbf{w}$, A maps $(BC\mathbf{x}^T)$ into $\mathbf{w}$, or $A(BC\mathbf{x}^T) = \mathbf{w}^T$. Similarly, since

$$(AB)\mathbf{u}^T = A(B\mathbf{u}^T) = A\mathbf{v}^T = \mathbf{w}^T,$$

(AB) maps $\mathbf{u}$ into $\mathbf{w}$. Since $\mathbf{u}^T = C\mathbf{x}^T$,

$$(AB)(C\mathbf{x}^T) = \mathbf{w}^T.$$

Thus for every A, B, and C, $A(BC)$ and $(AB)C$ map $\mathbf{x}$ into $\mathbf{w}$. This says that $A(BC)$ and $(AB)C$ are the same functions, or multiplication is associative in $\mathfrak{M}_n$.

8.18 INVERSES

If A belongs to $\mathfrak{M}_n$, does A have a multiplicative inverse? If A has an inverse A^{-1}, and if $A\mathbf{x}^T = \mathbf{u}^T$, then we define A^{-1} to be the matrix that maps $\mathbf{u}$ into $\mathbf{x}$;

$$A^{-1}\mathbf{u}^T = A^{-1}(A\mathbf{x}^T) = \mathbf{x}^T.$$

But what matrix maps $\mathbf{x}$ into itself, no matter what vector $\mathbf{x}$ is? It can be shown that there is exactly one matrix in $\mathfrak{M}_n$ that leaves *every* n-vector unchanged. This is the identity I. Let us illustrate in $\mathfrak{M}_2$. Let

$$A = \begin{pmatrix} a & b \\ c & d \end{pmatrix} \quad \text{and} \quad \mathbf{x}^T = \begin{pmatrix} x \\ y \end{pmatrix}.$$

Suppose

$$A\mathbf{x}^T = \begin{pmatrix} ax + by \\ cx + dy \end{pmatrix} = \begin{pmatrix} x \\ y \end{pmatrix}, \quad \text{or} \quad \begin{cases} ax + by = x \\ cx + dy = y \end{cases}.$$

If $A\mathbf{x}^T = \mathbf{x}^T$ for every $\mathbf{x}^T$, then it is true when $\mathbf{x} = (1 \quad 0)$. But then $ax + by = x$ becomes $a = 1$, and $cx + dy = y$ becomes $c = 0$. If $\mathbf{x} = (0 \quad 1)$, then we find that $b = 0$ and $d = 1$. Since this procedure can be extended to any value of n, it follows that if any matrix in $\mathfrak{M}_n$ satisfies $A\mathbf{x}^T = \mathbf{x}^T$ for every $\mathbf{x}$, then $A = I$. On the other hand, it is clear that $I\mathbf{x}^T = \mathbf{x}^T$. For example,

$$\begin{pmatrix} 1 & 0 \\ 0 & 1 \end{pmatrix} \begin{pmatrix} x \\ y \end{pmatrix} = \begin{pmatrix} x \\ y \end{pmatrix}.$$

Hence,

$$A^{-1}(A\mathbf{x}^T) = (A^{-1}A)\mathbf{x}^T = I\mathbf{x}^T$$

holds for all $\mathbf{x}$. Thus A^{-1}, if it exists, must be a matrix such that

$$A^{-1}A = I.$$

In order to find such a matrix let us return to our simultaneous equations. Let

$$A = \begin{pmatrix} a & b \\ c & d \end{pmatrix}, \quad \mathbf{x} = (x \quad y), \text{ and } \mathbf{u} = (u \quad v).$$

Then $A\mathbf{x}^T = \mathbf{u}^T$ can be written as

(1) $ax + by = u$
  $cx + dy = v.$

If $u = v = 0$, then a common solution of the pair of equations is given by $x = y = 0$. Let us suppose that either u or v is different from zero. If we can solve these equations for x and y in terms of u and v, we shall have found A^{-1}. It will be the matrix of the coefficients in the resulting equations.

Let us multiply the first equation by d and the second by b. Then

$$adx + bdy = du$$
$$bcx + bdy = bv.$$

Subtracting the second from the first, we obtain

(2) $(ad - bc)x = du - bv.$

Similarly, if we multiply the first of equations (1) by c and the second by a, we obtain

$$acx + bcy = cu$$
$$acx + ady = av.$$

Then, subtracting the first of these equations from the second, we obtain

(3) $(ad - bc)y = av - cu.$

To complete the problem of solving for x and y, we must divide (2) and (3) by $(ad - bc)$. Is this always permissible? Yes, *unless $ad - bc = 0$*. In that case we can't solve for x and y; that is, A^{-1} doesn't exist.

Let us denote $ad - bc$ by $|A|$. Then $|A|$ is called the *determinant* of A. We shall discuss determinants in greater detail later. We can now complete our solution and obtain

$$x = (d/|A|)u - (b/|A|)v$$
$$y = (-c/|A|)u + (a/|A|)v$$

Thus,

$$A^{-1} = \begin{pmatrix} d/|A| & -b/|A| \\ -c/|A| & a/|A| \end{pmatrix}.$$

We have shown that any matrix of order 2 has an inverse if and only if its determinant is not zero. We could extend precisely the same method to matrices of higher order to define a determinant for each, but there is an easier way that we shall find later. In the meantime we shall say that a square matrix is *singular* if its determinant is zero and *nonsingular* if its determinant is not zero. We have proved, for matrices of order 2, that every nonsingular matrix has a multiplicative inverse.

We have found that $A^{-1}A = I$, when A^{-1} exists. Then

$$A(A^{-1}A) = AI, \quad \text{or} \quad (AA^{-1})A = A,$$

so that $AA^{-1} = I$ also. In other words, even though matrix multiplication is not in general commutative, each matrix commutes with its inverse.

8.19 ALGEBRAIC PROPERTIES OF MULTIPLICATION OF MATRICES

Let us summarize what we have found within the framework of the field properties of multiplication in Chapter 2. We have found that

M1. $\mathfrak{M}_n$ is closed under multiplication.

M3. Multiplication is associative in $\mathfrak{M}_n$.

M4. There is a unique identity I for multiplication in $\mathfrak{M}_n$.

M5. Every *nonsingular* matrix has a unique multiplicative inverse in $\mathfrak{M}_n$.

We have also found that M2, the commutative law, does not hold.

8.20 A COMMENT ON THE SOLUTION OF SIMULTANEOUS EQUATIONS

We have found that a pair of simultaneous linear equations in two variables can be written in the form $A\mathbf{x}^T = \mathbf{c}^T$. Next, we have shown that if

$$A = \begin{pmatrix} a & b \\ c & d \end{pmatrix},$$

then, if $|A| \neq 0$

$$A^{-1} = \begin{pmatrix} d/|A| & -b/|A| \\ -c/|A| & a/|A| \end{pmatrix},$$

and

$$\mathbf{x}^T = A^{-1}\mathbf{c}^T.$$

This is easy to remember. For any nonsingular matrix A of order 2, we obtain A^{-1} by interchanging the two elements on the main diagonal, changing the sign of the other two, and dividing each element by $|A|$.

Example 1. Let us solve

$$3x + 4y = 2$$
$$5x + 7y = 3.$$

Here,

$$A = \begin{pmatrix} 3 & 4 \\ 5 & 7 \end{pmatrix}$$

and the problem is particularly easy because $|A| = 21 - 20 = 1$. Thus

$$A^{-1} = \begin{pmatrix} 7 & -4 \\ -5 & 3 \end{pmatrix}.$$

Hence

$$\begin{pmatrix} x \\ y \end{pmatrix} = \begin{pmatrix} 7 & -4 \\ -5 & 3 \end{pmatrix}\begin{pmatrix} 2 \\ 3 \end{pmatrix} = \begin{pmatrix} 2 \\ -1 \end{pmatrix}, \quad \text{or} \quad \begin{matrix} x = 2 \\ y = -1 \end{matrix}.$$

Example 2. Solve

$$2x - 5y = 3$$
$$3x + 4y = 8.$$

Here, the determinant of the matrix of the coefficients is $8 + 15 = 23$, so that

$$A^{-1} = \begin{pmatrix} 4/23 & 5/23 \\ -3/23 & 2/23 \end{pmatrix},$$

and

$$\begin{pmatrix} x \\ y \end{pmatrix} = \begin{pmatrix} 4/23 & 5/23 \\ -3/23 & 2/23 \end{pmatrix} \begin{pmatrix} 3 \\ 8 \end{pmatrix} = \begin{pmatrix} 52/23 \\ 7/23 \end{pmatrix}, \quad \text{or} \quad \begin{matrix} x = 52/23 \\ y = 7/23 \end{matrix}.$$

8.21 EXERCISES

*1. Find the determinant of each of the following matrices:

(a) $\begin{pmatrix} 2 & 3 \\ 5 & 8 \end{pmatrix}$ (b) $\begin{pmatrix} 9 & -5 \\ 7 & -4 \end{pmatrix}$

(c) $\begin{pmatrix} 4 & -2 \\ -3 & 7 \end{pmatrix}$ (d) $\begin{pmatrix} x & y \\ -y & x \end{pmatrix}$

(e) $\begin{pmatrix} h & k \\ k & h \end{pmatrix}$

2. Find the determinant of each of the following matrices:

(a) $\begin{pmatrix} 5 & -17 \\ -3 & 10 \end{pmatrix}$ (b) $\begin{pmatrix} 4 & -2 \\ 2 & 4 \end{pmatrix}$

(c) $\begin{pmatrix} 5 & 5 \\ 5 & 5 \end{pmatrix}$ (d) $\begin{pmatrix} 1 & 0 \\ 0 & 1 \end{pmatrix}$

(e) $\begin{pmatrix} 3 & 0 \\ 0 & 3 \end{pmatrix}$

*3. Find the inverse of each of the matrices of Exercise 1.

4. Find the inverse of each of the matrices of Exercise 2.

*5. Solve each of the following pairs of simultaneous equations using matrix inverses:

(a) $2x + 3y = 9$ (b) $9x - 5y = 31$
  $5x + 8y = -7$ $7x - 4y = 12$

(c) $4x - 2y = 44$ (d) $3x + 4y = 50$
  $-3x + 7y = -66$ $-4x + 3y = -25$

(e) $5x - 4y = -27$
  $-4x + 5y = 18$

6. Solve each of the following pairs of simultaneous equations by the matrix method:

(a) $5x - 17y = -2$ (b) $4x - 2y = 20$
  $-3x + 10y = 0$ $2x + 4y = 60$

(c) $hx + ky = a$ (d) $x + y = 4$
  $kx + hy = b$ $5x - 7y = -16$

(e) $3x - 5y = 14$
  $x - 6y = -7$

*7. Prove that if A and B are matrices of order 2, $|AB| = |A| \cdot |B|$.

8. Let $A = \begin{pmatrix} a & b \\ c & d \end{pmatrix}$. Let B be the matrix obtained from A by adding k times the first row to the second row. Show that $|B| = |A|$.

*9. Show that if A_2 has one row or one column of zeros, then $|A| = 0$.

10. Show that if A_2 has both rows (or both columns) alike, then $|A| = 0$.

*11. Construct a matrix of order 2 with its elements distinct positive integers and with determinant zero.

12. Let S be the set consisting of all matrices of the form $\begin{pmatrix} x & y \\ -y & x \end{pmatrix}$, where x and y are real numbers. Show that S is closed under multiplication and that multiplication is commutative in S.

8.22 ADDITION OF MATRICES

Let A and B be matrices of the same order. What is the "natural" way to define $A + B$? Let us return to our mappings.

$$A\mathbf{x}^T + B\mathbf{y}^T = \begin{pmatrix} a_{11} & a_{12} \\ a_{21} & a_{22} \end{pmatrix} \begin{pmatrix} x \\ y \end{pmatrix} + \begin{pmatrix} b_{11} & b_{12} \\ b_{21} & b_{22} \end{pmatrix} \begin{pmatrix} x \\ y \end{pmatrix}$$

$$= \begin{pmatrix} a_{11}x + a_{12}y \\ a_{21}x + a_{22}y \end{pmatrix} + \begin{pmatrix} b_{11}x + b_{12}y \\ b_{21}x + b_{22}y \end{pmatrix}.$$

Since the right side is a sum of vectors, and we have defined the sum of vectors in an earlier section, we find that

$$A\mathbf{x}^T + B\mathbf{y}^T = \begin{pmatrix} (a_{11} + b_{11})x + (a_{12} + b_{12})y \\ (a_{21} + b_{21})x + (a_{22} + b_{22})y \end{pmatrix} = \begin{pmatrix} a_{11} + b_{11} & a_{12} + b_{12} \\ a_{21} + b_{21} & a_{22} + b_{22} \end{pmatrix} \begin{pmatrix} x \\ y \end{pmatrix}.$$

Hence we define the sum of any two matrices A and B of the same order to be the matrix whose elements are the sum of the corresponding elements of A and B. Our example was for matrices of order 2, but we would have obtained precisely the same rule if A and B had both been m by n matrices for any m and n.

Examples.

$$\begin{pmatrix} 2 & 1 \\ -3 & 4 \end{pmatrix} + \begin{pmatrix} 2 & -1 \\ 7 & 8 \end{pmatrix} = \begin{pmatrix} 4 & 0 \\ 4 & 12 \end{pmatrix}, \quad \begin{pmatrix} 1 & 2 & 3 \\ 4 & 5 & 6 \end{pmatrix} + \begin{pmatrix} -2 & 1 & 3 \\ 6 & -4 & 2 \end{pmatrix}$$

$$= \begin{pmatrix} -1 & 3 & 6 \\ 10 & 1 & 8 \end{pmatrix}.$$

8.23 SCALAR MULTIPLICATION

Let us define nA, for any real number n and any matrix A, to be the matrix obtained from A by multiplying each element of A by n. It follows that for $n = 2$, for instance, we can write $A + A = 2A$.

Examples.

$$3\begin{pmatrix} 1 & -2 \\ 3 & 4 \end{pmatrix} = \begin{pmatrix} 3 & -6 \\ 9 & 12 \end{pmatrix}, \qquad -0.4\begin{pmatrix} 1 & 2 \\ 3 & 4 \\ 5 & 6 \end{pmatrix} = \begin{pmatrix} -0.4 & -0.8 \\ -1.2 & -1.6 \\ -2 & -2.4 \end{pmatrix}.$$

8.24 ALGEBRAIC PROPERTIES OF MATRIX ADDITION

Let us check the properties A1 through A5 for the set of all matrices of a given order. Let us call this set $\mathfrak{M}_{m,n}$.

A1. Closure. $\mathfrak{M}_{m,n}$ is *closed under addition*. This follows from the definition of addition of matrices.

A2. Commutative Law. Addition is *commutative* in $\mathfrak{M}_{m,n}$. This follows from the definition. For example,

$$\begin{pmatrix} a & b \\ c & d \end{pmatrix} + \begin{pmatrix} e & f \\ g & h \end{pmatrix} = \begin{pmatrix} a+e & b+f \\ c+g & d+h \end{pmatrix} = \begin{pmatrix} e+a & f+b \\ g+c & h+d \end{pmatrix}$$
$$= \begin{pmatrix} e & f \\ g & h \end{pmatrix} + \begin{pmatrix} a & b \\ c & d \end{pmatrix}.$$

A3. Associative Law. Addition is *associative* in $\mathfrak{M}_{m,n}$. The reasoning is similar to that used in A2.

A4. Identity. $0_{m,n}$ is the *additive identity* in $\mathfrak{M}_{m,n}$. This is obvious.

A5. Inverse. For any matrix A, its additive inverse is $-A$, the matrix consisting of the negatives of the elements of A.

8.25 SUMMATION NOTATION

It will help in the work that follows to introduce a notation that is of considerable convenience. We have encountered over and over expressions that are sums of a number of terms. This is true for vector products and for products of matrices. Such a sum also occurs in the definition of a determinant. Let us use the Greek capital sigma, Σ, to denote a sum. Its use can be seen most readily from an example.

$$\sum_{k=1}^{5} ka_k = a_1 + 2a_2 + 3a_3 + 4a_4 + 5a_5$$

Here, k is a counting index. We form the sum of the terms obtained by letting

k take on the values from 1 to 5. The index k is called a dummy index because any other letter could have been used in its place. Examine carefully each of the examples below to see how the sum is formed.

Example 1. $\displaystyle\sum_{i=1}^{3} i = 1 + 2 + 3.$

Example 2. $\displaystyle\sum_{i=2}^{5} i^2 = 4 + 9 + 16 + 25.$

Example 3. $\displaystyle\sum_{j=0}^{4} a_{ij} = a_{i0} + a_{i1} + a_{i2} + a_{i3} + a_{i4}.$

Example 4. $\displaystyle\sum_{i=1}^{4} a_{ij}A_{ij} = a_{1j}A_{1j} + a_{2j}A_{2j} + a_{3j}A_{3j} + a_{4j}A_{4j}.$

Example 5. $\displaystyle\sum_{k=1}^{4} a_{ik}b_{kj} = a_{i1}b_{1j} + a_{i2}b_{2j} + a_{i3}b_{3j} + a_{i4}b_{4j}.$

Example 6. $\displaystyle\sum_{i=1}^{5} 2 = 2 + 2 + 2 + 2 + 2 = 10.$

Observe in Example 6 that, for each value of i, the term to be added is merely 2.

Example 7. $\displaystyle\sum_{k=1}^{1} (3k + 5) = 3(1) + 5 = 8.$ (The sum has only one term.)

Example 8. $\displaystyle\sum_{i=1}^{n} u_i = u_1 + u_2 + \cdots + u_n.$

8.26   THE DISTRIBUTIVE LAW

In the set $\mathfrak{M}_n$ of square matrices of order n, both addition and multiplication are possible. Thus it is reasonable to consider the expression $A(B + C)$ for A, B, and C in $\mathfrak{M}_n$. This time we shall be quite general and let n be any positive integer. Let

$$A = (a_{ij}), \qquad B = (b_{jk}), \quad \text{and} \quad C = (c_{jk}),$$

where the subscripts run from 1 to n. Then,

$$A(B + C) = (a_{ij})[(b_{jk}) + (c_{jk})] = (a_{ij})(b_{jk} + c_{jk}) = \left(\sum_{j=1}^{n} a_{ij}(b_{jk} + c_{jk})\right)$$

$$= \left(\sum_{j=1}^{n} a_{ij}b_{jk} + \sum_{j=1}^{n} a_{ij}c_{jk}\right) = (a_{ij})(b_{jk}) + (a_{ij})(c_{jk}) = AB + AC.$$

We have shown that it is true that

    D. Multiplication distributes over addition in $\mathfrak{M}_n$.

8.27   RINGS

When mathematicians discover that a variety of systems turn out to have the same structure, they frequently give a name to the abstract system. In Chapters 2 and 3 we discussed two such abstract systems, fields and Boolean algebras. Many systems come close to being fields but fail in some respects. One such system is the *ring*. It satisfies all of the field properties except M2, M4, and M5. That is, multiplication in a ring is not necessarily commutative. If it is, we say that the system is a *commutative ring*. Similarly, the ring may not have a multiplicative identity. If it does have one, we refer to it as a *ring with unity*. A ring with unity does not necessarily contain a multiplicative inverse for every nonzero element. If it does, we call it a *division ring*. These names are not very important for our work, but they permit us to classify many systems in a simple fashion.

    Example 1.   A field is a commutative division ring.

    Example 2.   The set of all integers is a commutative ring with unity.

    Example 3.   The set of all even integers is a commutative ring. (But not with unity. The number 1 is not in the set.)

    Example 4. $\mathfrak{M}_n$, the set of all matrices of order n with real elements, is a ring with unity.

8.28   EXERCISES

  *1. Let $A = (a_{ij})$, $B = (b_{ij})$, and $C = (c_{ij})$ be matrices in the ring $\mathfrak{M}_n$. Write out the proof that property A2 holds in $\mathfrak{M}_n$.

  2. With A, B, and C as in Exercise 1, write out a proof that property A3 holds in $\mathfrak{M}_n$.

  *3. With A as in Exercise 1 and 0_n the matrix in $\mathfrak{M}_n$ whose elements are all zeros, write out a proof that property A4 holds in $\mathfrak{M}_n$.

  4. With A as in Exercise 1, write out a proof that property A5 holds in $\mathfrak{M}_n$.

  *5. Let $A = \begin{pmatrix} 2 & 3 \\ -1 & 5 \end{pmatrix}$, $B = \begin{pmatrix} 2 & 1 \\ 3 & 2 \end{pmatrix}$, and $C = \begin{pmatrix} -4 & 2 \\ 1 & 3 \end{pmatrix}$. Compute $A(B + C)$ and $AB + AC$.

  6. Is it true that $(B + C)A = BA + CA$ in $\mathfrak{M}_n$?

  *7. Is it true that $AB + AC = (B + C)A$ in $\mathfrak{M}_n$?

8. Let P be the set of all polynomials in a variable x with real coefficients. Prove that P is a commutative ring with unity.

*9. Let S be the set of all matrices of the form $\begin{pmatrix} x & y \\ -y & x \end{pmatrix}$. Prove that S is a field.

(Since $\mathfrak{M}_2$ is a ring, you need show only that S is closed under addition and multiplication, that 0_2 and I_2 are in S, that multiplication is commutative in S, and that every matrix in S except 0_2 is nonsingular.)

10. Prove that the set of all even integers is a commutative ring.

*11. Let R be the set of all rings, C the set of all commutative rings, U the set of all rings with unity, and F the set of all fields. Classify each of the following by giving the letter or letters designating sets to which it belongs:
   (a) All integers
   (b) All rational numbers
   (c) The integers modulo 3
   (d) The integers modulo 4
   (e) $\mathfrak{M}_3$

8.29 ELEMENTARY OPERATIONS

How do we go about solving a set of simultaneous equations? Let us consider a set of linear equations in n variables.

$$a_{11}x_1 + a_{12}x_2 + \cdots + a_{1n}x_n = b_1$$
$$a_{21}x_1 + a_{22}x_2 + \cdots + a_{2n}x_n = b_2$$
$$\cdot$$
$$\cdot$$
$$\cdot$$
$$a_{n1}x_1 + a_{n2}x_2 + \cdots + a_{nn}x_n = b_n$$

This set of equations can be written compactly in the form

$$A\mathbf{x}^T = \mathbf{b}^T,$$

where

$$A = (a_{ij})_n, \qquad \mathbf{x} = (x_1, \ldots, x_n), \quad \text{and} \quad \mathbf{b} = (b_1, \ldots, b_n).$$

If A is nonsingular, then A^{-1} exists, and $\mathbf{x}^T = A^{-1}(\mathbf{b}^T)$. How do we find A^{-1} if A is of order greater than two? Our purpose is to answer this question by giving a method based on the ordinary process of elimination used in solving a set of equations. This process is made up of combinations of three basic operations:

1. Multiplying both sides of any equation by a nonzero constant.
2. Adding any multiple (possibly negative) of one equation to another.
3. Interchanging any two equations.

We can now proceed to solve our set of equations as follows:

1. Interchange equations, if necessary, so that the leading coefficient of the first equation is not zero.

2. Multiply both sides of the first equation by $1/a_{11}$.

3. Subtract a_{i1} times the first equation from the ith for each i from $i = 2$ to $i = n$.

After these three steps are executed, the resulting system, with the constants relabeled, appears in the following form:

$$x_1 + c_{12}x_2 + \cdots + c_{1n}x_n = k_1$$
$$c_{22}x_2 + \cdots + c_{2n}x_n = k_2$$
$$\vdots$$
$$c_{n2}x_2 + \cdots + c_{nn}x_n = k_n$$

Now we repeat steps (1) to (3) on the last $n - 1$ equations with one addition. Subtract the proper multiple of the second equation from the first to eliminate the $c_{12}x_2$ term. This will not affect the x_1 term.

$$x_1 \quad + d_{13}x_3 + \cdots + d_{1n}x_n = m_1$$
$$x_2 + d_{23}x_3 + \cdots + d_{2n}x_n = m_2$$
$$d_{33}x_3 + \cdots + d_{3n}x_n = m_3$$
$$\vdots$$
$$d_{n3}x_3 + \cdots + d_{nn}x_n = m_n$$

Repeated application of this technique clearly leads to a solution, if one exists. If no solution exists, we shall arrive finally at an equation in which we have $0 = k$, where k is a nonzero constant. Since this is a false statement, the set of equations has no solution. On the other hand, it is possible that one or more equations are entirely eliminated in this process. In this case the remaining equations can be solved for some of the variables in terms of the remaining ones. Then we shall have a solution for each set of values assigned to those remaining variables. This is illustrated in the following example.

Example 1. Let us solve

$$x + 2y - z = 3$$
$$2x - y + z = 1$$
$$4x + 3y - z = 7$$

The first step, dividing the first equation by the coefficient of x, is unnecessary since it is already 1. We proceed to the second step and subtract twice the first equation from the second and four times it from the third.

$$x + 2y - z = 3$$
$$-5y + 3z = -5$$
$$-5y + 3z = -5$$

Subtracting the second equation from the third eliminates the third equation. Let us move the terms involving z to the right side and divide the resulting second equation by -5. This gives

$$x + 2y = 3 + z$$
$$y = 1 + (3/5)z$$

Subtracting twice the second equation from the first leaves

$$x \quad = 1 - (1/5)z$$
$$y = 1 + (3/5)z$$

For $z = 5$, one solution is given by $x = 0, y = 4, z = 5$. For, $z = -10$, another solution is given by $x = 3, y = -5, z = -10$. When one or more equations are eliminated, then, our solution is not unique. If, however, no equation is eliminated, and none has a finial form of $0 = k$, there is one and only one solution. This is illustrated in the next example.

Example 2.   Let us solve

$$2x - 3y + z = 6$$
$$3x + y - 2z = -2$$
$$-2x - y + 3z = 5.$$

Our first step is to divide the first equation by 2. Then we have

$$x - (3/2)y + (1/2)z = 3$$
$$3x + y - 2z = -2$$
$$-2x - y + 3z = 5.$$

The second step is to subtract three times the first equation from the second and to add two times the first equation to the third. This yields

$$x - (3/2)y + (1/2)z = 3$$
$$(11/2)y - (7/2)z = -11$$
$$-4y + 4z = 11.$$

We now multiply the second equation by 2/11 to get

$$x - (3/2)y + (1/2)z = 3$$
$$y - (7/11)z = -2$$
$$-4y + 4z = 11.$$

Next we add 3/2 times the second equation to the first and 4 times the second equation to the third. This gives

$$x \quad - \quad (5/11)z = 0$$
$$y - \quad (7/11)z = -2$$
$$(16/11)z = 3.$$

We now multiply the third equation by 11/16 to find $z = 33/16$. Our final step is to add 5/11 times this equation to the first and 7/11 times it to the second. Our final form is

$$x \qquad\qquad = 15/16$$
$$y \qquad = -11/16$$
$$z = 33/16.$$

If we substitute these values for x, y, and z in the original equations, we find that the system is satisfied.

8.30 A SHORTCUT

The technique of the preceding section, as is clearly evident from the example, involves a great deal of writing, much of it unnecessary. The great value of the method is that the solution of simultaneous equations has been reduced to a clear, simple algorithm. The clarity and simplicity can be retained and the labor reduced if, instead of writing the equations, we merely write the matrix of coefficients together with an additional column on the right consisting of the constants that appear on the right side of the equations. This is called the *augmented matrix* of the system. Thus, for the equations of the last example, we write

$$\begin{pmatrix} 2 & -3 & 1 & 6 \\ 3 & 1 & -2 & -2 \\ -2 & -1 & 3 & 5 \end{pmatrix}.$$

Our elementary operations on equations now can be translated into elementary row operations on the augmented matrix. In these terms the three elementary operations become:

1. Multiplying any row by a nonzero constant.
2. Adding any multiple of one row to another.
3. Interchanging any two rows.

Our technique of solving equations then becomes a technique for changing the augmented matrix into one that has the following form:

$$\begin{pmatrix} 1 & 0 & 0 & \cdots & 0 & k_1 \\ 0 & 1 & 0 & \cdots & 0 & k_2 \\ 0 & 0 & 1 & \cdots & 0 & k_3 \\ & & & \vdots & & \\ 0 & 0 & 0 & \cdots & 1 & k_n \end{pmatrix}$$

$$\begin{array}{c} x_1 = k_1 \\ x_2 = k_2 \\ \text{, which is equivalent to } x_3 = k_3. \\ \vdots \\ x_n = k_n \end{array}$$

At each stage it is possible to read the rows of the matrix as equations.

Example 1. Let us solve

$$2x + 5y = 7$$
$$3x - 6y = 4.$$

We write the augmented matrix

$$\begin{pmatrix} 2 & 5 & 7 \\ 3 & -6 & 4 \end{pmatrix}.$$

We shall use the symbol $\rightarrow$ to mean that a matrix is obtained from the preceding by elementary row operations. Our goal is to obtain a matrix of the form

$$\begin{pmatrix} 1 & 0 & k_1 \\ 0 & 1 & k_2 \end{pmatrix},$$

from which we can read our solution.

Following the steps of the preceding section, we have

$$\begin{pmatrix} 2 & 5 & 7 \\ 3 & -6 & 4 \end{pmatrix} \rightarrow \begin{pmatrix} 1 & 5/2 & 7/2 \\ 3 & -6 & 4 \end{pmatrix} \rightarrow \begin{pmatrix} 1 & 5/2 & 7/2 \\ 0 & -27/2 & -13/2 \end{pmatrix}$$
$$\rightarrow \begin{pmatrix} 1 & 5/2 & 7/2 \\ 0 & 1 & 13/27 \end{pmatrix} \rightarrow \begin{pmatrix} 1 & 0 & 62/27 \\ 0 & 1 & 13/27 \end{pmatrix}.$$

It is simple to check that $x = 62/27$, $y = 13/27$, is the desired solution.

Not every set of n equations in n unknowns has a solution. Also, when a solution exists, it is not necessarily unique. If a set of equations is represented by $A\mathbf{x}^T = \mathbf{c}^T$ and A has an inverse, then

$$A^{-1}(A\mathbf{x}^T) = A^{-1}\mathbf{c}^T, \quad \text{or} \quad \mathbf{x}^T = A^{-1}\mathbf{c}^T.$$

If A does not have an inverse, this procedure cannot be carried out. However, the methods of this section can still be employed, even if A^{-1} does not exist. When this is the case, one of two things can happen.

1. In the final form of the augmented matrix, one or more of the 1's in the first n columns is missing, but the corresponding element in the last column is not zero. In this case a row in which this occurs represents an equation of the form $0 = c$. If $c \neq 0$, this contradiction implies that there is no solution. We shall illustrate with two equations in two unknowns, but the procedure can be used with any number of equations in any number of unknowns. The matrix of the coefficients, then, need not necessarily be square.

Example 2. Let us try to solve

$$x + 2y = 3$$
$$2x + 4y = 5$$

We find that

$$\begin{pmatrix} 1 & 2 & 3 \\ 2 & 4 & 5 \end{pmatrix} \rightarrow \begin{pmatrix} 1 & 2 & 3 \\ 0 & 0 & -1 \end{pmatrix}.$$

Since the last row represents the equation $0 = -1$, there is no solution.

2. In the final form of the augmented matrix one or more rows may consist entirely of 0's. In this case the original equations are not independent, and infinitely many solutions exist.

Example 3. Let us try to solve

$$x + 2y = 3$$
$$2x + 4y = 6$$

We find that

$$\begin{pmatrix} 1 & 2 & 3 \\ 2 & 4 & 6 \end{pmatrix} \rightarrow \begin{pmatrix} 1 & 2 & 3 \\ 0 & 0 & 0 \end{pmatrix}.$$

The equations are not independent; the second is twice the first. Any x and y for which $x + 2y = 3$ satisfy both equations. Writing this equation in the form $x = 3 - 2y$, we see that for every value of y there is a corresponding value of x such that both equations are satisfied. There are infinitely many solutions.

8.31 EXERCISES

Use the method of Section 8.33 to solve the following sets of equations. Check your solutions.

*1. $2x - 3y = 16$
$3x + 4y = 7$

2. $4x - 6y = 10$
$x + 3y = -11$

*3. $2x + 5y = 7$
   $3x - 2y = 3$

*5. $2x + y - z = -1$
   $3x - 2y + z = 7$
   $-x - y + 2z = 4$

*7. $2x - y + z = 3$
   $x - y + 2z = 4$
   $y - z = 2$

4. $3x - 2y = 7$
   $5x - 2y = -3$

6. $x + y - z = -2$
   $x - y + z = 0$
   $x \quad + z = 2$

8. $x + y = 2$
   $x + z = 3$
   $y + z = 4$

*9. Show that the following set of equations has no solution:

$$x + y - z = 4$$
$$2x - y + z = 1$$
$$4x + y - z = 5$$

10. Show that the following set of equations has infinitely many solutions:

$$x + y - z = 4$$
$$2x - y + z = 1$$
$$4x + y - z = 9$$

*11. Find three sets of solutions of the following pair of equations:

$$x + 2y - 3z = -7$$
$$2x - y + z = 5$$

12. Solve the following set of equations, if possible:

$$2x - 3y = 1$$
$$x + y = 3$$
$$8x - 7y = 9$$

8.32 ELEMENTARY MATRICES

Each of the elementary row operations on an augmented matrix can be accomplished by multiplying the matrix on the left by a suitable matrix. The suitable matrix is merely the matrix that results from performing the elementary row operation on the identity matrix, as we shall illustrate. For example, operation (1) is that of multiplying any row by a nonzero constant. Thus, to multiply the third row of the augmented matrix by c, we multiply as below:

$$\begin{pmatrix} 1 & 0 & 0 \\ 0 & 1 & 0 \\ 0 & 0 & c \end{pmatrix} \begin{pmatrix} a_{11} & a_{12} & a_{13} & b_1 \\ a_{21} & a_{22} & a_{23} & b_2 \\ a_{31} & a_{32} & a_{33} & b_3 \end{pmatrix} = \begin{pmatrix} a_{11} & a_{12} & a_{13} & b_1 \\ a_{21} & a_{22} & a_{23} & b_2 \\ ca_{31} & ca_{32} & ca_{33} & cb_3 \end{pmatrix}$$

The second operation is adding a multiple of one row to another. To add k times the first row to the second, we multiply as below:

$$\begin{pmatrix} 1 & 0 & 0 \\ k & 1 & 0 \\ 0 & 0 & 1 \end{pmatrix} \begin{pmatrix} a_{11} & a_{12} & a_{13} & b_1 \\ a_{21} & a_{22} & a_{23} & b_2 \\ a_{31} & a_{32} & a_{33} & b_3 \end{pmatrix}$$

$$= \begin{pmatrix} a_{11} & a_{12} & a_{13} & b_1 \\ ka_{11}+a_{21} & ka_{12}+a_{22} & ka_{13}+a_{23} & kb_1+b_2 \\ a_{31} & a_{32} & a_{33} & b_3 \end{pmatrix}$$

The third operation is interchanging two rows. To interchange the second and third rows, we multiply as below:

$$\begin{pmatrix} 1 & 0 & 0 \\ 0 & 0 & 1 \\ 0 & 1 & 0 \end{pmatrix} \begin{pmatrix} a_{11} & a_{12} & a_{13} & b_1 \\ a_{21} & a_{22} & a_{23} & b_2 \\ a_{31} & a_{32} & a_{33} & b_3 \end{pmatrix} = \begin{pmatrix} a_{11} & a_{12} & a_{13} & b_1 \\ a_{31} & a_{32} & a_{33} & b_3 \\ a_{21} & a_{22} & a_{23} & b_2 \end{pmatrix}$$

Thus the series of operations that produced the solution matrix in our last example can be accomplished by repeatedly multiplying on the left by the matrix that results from performing the desired operation on the identity. These matrices are called *elementary matrices*.

Example. Let us repeat the example of Section 31, using elementary matrices.

$$\begin{pmatrix} 1/2 & 0 \\ 0 & 1 \end{pmatrix} \begin{pmatrix} 2 & 5 & 7 \\ 3 & -6 & 4 \end{pmatrix} = \begin{pmatrix} 1 & 5/2 & 7/2 \\ 3 & -6 & 4 \end{pmatrix}$$

$$\begin{pmatrix} 1 & 0 \\ -3 & 1 \end{pmatrix} \begin{pmatrix} 1 & 5/2 & 7/2 \\ 3 & -6 & 4 \end{pmatrix} = \begin{pmatrix} 1 & 5/2 & 7/2 \\ 0 & -27/2 & -13/2 \end{pmatrix}$$

$$\begin{pmatrix} 1 & 0 \\ 0 & -2/27 \end{pmatrix} \begin{pmatrix} 1 & 5/2 & 7/2 \\ 0 & -27/2 & -13/2 \end{pmatrix} = \begin{pmatrix} 1 & 5/2 & 7/2 \\ 0 & 1 & 13/27 \end{pmatrix}$$

$$\begin{pmatrix} 1 & -5/2 \\ 0 & 1 \end{pmatrix} \begin{pmatrix} 1 & 5/2 & 7/2 \\ 0 & 1 & 13/27 \end{pmatrix} = \begin{pmatrix} 1 & 0 & 62/27 \\ 0 & 1 & 13/27 \end{pmatrix}.$$

Since multiplication of matrices is associative, we could have written this as

$$\begin{pmatrix} 1 & -5/2 \\ 0 & 1 \end{pmatrix} \begin{pmatrix} 1 & 0 \\ 0 & -2/27 \end{pmatrix} \begin{pmatrix} 1 & 0 \\ -3 & 1 \end{pmatrix} \begin{pmatrix} 1/2 & 0 \\ 0 & 1 \end{pmatrix} \begin{pmatrix} 2 & 5 & 7 \\ 3 & -6 & 4 \end{pmatrix}$$

$$= \begin{pmatrix} 1 & 0 & 62/27 \\ 0 & 1 & 13/27 \end{pmatrix}.$$

8.33   MATRIX INVERSES

In the example above we have

$$\left[\begin{pmatrix} 1 & -5/2 \\ 0 & 1 \end{pmatrix}\begin{pmatrix} 1 & 0 \\ 0 & -2/27 \end{pmatrix}\begin{pmatrix} 1 & 0 \\ -3 & 1 \end{pmatrix}\begin{pmatrix} 1/2 & 0 \\ 0 & 1 \end{pmatrix}\right]\begin{pmatrix} 2 & 5 & \vdots & 7 \\ 3 & -6 & \vdots & 4 \end{pmatrix}$$

$$= \begin{pmatrix} 1 & 0 & \vdots & 62/27 \\ 0 & 1 & \vdots & 13/27 \end{pmatrix}.$$

The indicated product of the four matrices enclosed in brackets is a matrix worthy of note. Let us call it M. We have subdivided the augmented matrices by dotted lines. The matrix lying to the left of the dotted line is the matrix of coefficients of our equations. Let us call it A. Our work shows that $MA = I$. Hence, M is the inverse of A, or $M = A^{-1}$. Further, our vector of solutions is obtained by multiplying the original vector of constants by A^{-1} on the left.

We thus have an algorithm for finding the inverse of any nonsingular matrix, but it is unwieldy. It involves the multiplication of a considerable number of elementary matrices. A somewhat simpler technique is to write the n by $2n$ matrix whose left half is I and whose right half is A. Then perform the elementary row operations that transform A into I. These operations will then transform I into A^{-1} if the matrix has an inverse. However, if the process leads to a row in which every element is 0, the matrix does not have an inverse.

Example.   Let us continue with our last example. We can write

$$\begin{pmatrix} 1 & 0 & \vdots & 2 & 5 \\ 0 & 1 & \vdots & 3 & -6 \end{pmatrix} \rightarrow \begin{pmatrix} 1/2 & 0 & \vdots & 1 & 5/2 \\ 0 & 1 & \vdots & 3 & -6 \end{pmatrix} \rightarrow \begin{pmatrix} 1/2 & 0 & \vdots & 1 & 5/2 \\ -3/2 & 1 & \vdots & 0 & -27/2 \end{pmatrix}$$

$$\rightarrow \begin{pmatrix} 1/2 & 0 & \vdots & 1 & 5/2 \\ 1/9 & -2/27 & \vdots & 0 & 1 \end{pmatrix} \rightarrow \begin{pmatrix} 2/9 & 5/27 & \vdots & 1 & 0 \\ 1/9 & -2/27 & \vdots & 0 & 1 \end{pmatrix}.$$

Thus

$$A^{-1} = \begin{pmatrix} 2/9 & 5/27 \\ 1/9 & -2/27 \end{pmatrix}.$$

It is clear that finding the inverse of a matrix involves more work than does the solution of a system of equations. However, this extra work, which is not excessive, sometimes pays big dividends. We know that a matrix A transforms vectors into vectors. The problem of solving a set of simultaneous equations is equivalent to finding what vectors, if any, are transformed into the vector of constants on the right side of the equations. If we have a number of sets of equations that differ only in the vector of constants on the right, then we must solve the system once for each vector in the set. If, however, we find A^{-1}, then all we need do is to multiply each vector in the set by A^{-1}. This effects a great saving in time and effort. Such problems frequently arise. One such case was seen in Chapter 4, in which a matrix was used to encode a message. If letters and punctuation marks are given numerical values, then a given matrix A will transform a vector of n symbols into n others. For decoding, the message is broken into vectors of length n and multiplied by A^{-1}. The machines capable of doing this are discussed in the next chapter.

8.34 EXERCISES

Find the inverse of each of the following matrices by the method of the last section.

*1. $\begin{pmatrix} 2 & -3 \\ 3 & 4 \end{pmatrix}$

2. $\begin{pmatrix} 4 & -6 \\ 1 & 3 \end{pmatrix}$

*3. $\begin{pmatrix} 2 & 5 \\ 3 & -2 \end{pmatrix}$

4. $\begin{pmatrix} 3 & -2 \\ 5 & -2 \end{pmatrix}$

*5. $\begin{pmatrix} 0 & 3 \\ -2 & 1 \end{pmatrix}$

6. $\begin{pmatrix} 2 & 1 & -1 \\ 3 & -2 & 1 \\ -1 & -1 & 2 \end{pmatrix}$

*7. $\begin{pmatrix} 1 & 1 & -1 \\ 1 & -1 & 1 \\ 1 & 0 & 1 \end{pmatrix}$

8. $\begin{pmatrix} 2 & -1 & 1 \\ 1 & -1 & 2 \\ 0 & 1 & -1 \end{pmatrix}$

*9. $\begin{pmatrix} 1 & 1 & 0 \\ 1 & 0 & 1 \\ 0 & 1 & 1 \end{pmatrix}$

10. $\begin{pmatrix} 1 & 2 & 3 \\ 4 & 5 & 6 \\ -2 & 1 & -2 \end{pmatrix}$

Show that each of the following matrices does not have an inverse.

*11. $\begin{pmatrix} 1 & 1 & -1 \\ 2 & -1 & 1 \\ 4 & 1 & -1 \end{pmatrix}$

12. $\begin{pmatrix} 2 & 3 & -5 \\ 3 & 8 & -11 \\ 1 & -2 & 1 \end{pmatrix}$

8.35 DETERMINANTS

We have defined the determinant of second-order matrices, and we have denoted the determinant of A by $|A|$. This same notation can be extended to the array form when A is written out. That is,

$$\begin{vmatrix} a & b \\ c & d \end{vmatrix} = ad - bc.$$

Our present goal is to define the determinant of matrices of higher order than 2. Let us consider a square matrix of order n, (a_{ij}), where i and j run from 1 to n. We shall form a recursive definition of a determinant. Such a definition will define the determinant of a matrix of order n in terms of determinants of matrices of order $n - 1$. Since we know what the determinant of a matrix of order 2 is, our definition will permit us to find determinants of matrices of order 3. These, in turn, can be used to find determinants of order 4, and so on.

First, let us define the *minor* of any element a_{ij} of a square matrix as the determinant of the matrix obtained by deleting the row and column containing a_{ij}.

Second, let us define the *cofactor* of any term a_{ij} to be the minor of a_{ij} if $i + j$ is even and the negative of the minor if $i + j$ is odd. Further, let us denote the cofactor of a_{ij} by A_{ij}. For example, consider the matrix

$$A = \begin{pmatrix} a_{11} & a_{12} & a_{13} \\ a_{21} & a_{22} & a_{23} \\ a_{31} & a_{32} & a_{33} \end{pmatrix}.$$

The cofactors of the elements of A are

$$A_{11} = \begin{vmatrix} a_{22} & a_{23} \\ a_{32} & a_{33} \end{vmatrix}, \qquad A_{12} = -\begin{vmatrix} a_{21} & a_{23} \\ a_{31} & a_{33} \end{vmatrix}, \qquad A_{13} = \begin{vmatrix} a_{21} & a_{22} \\ a_{31} & a_{32} \end{vmatrix},$$

$$A_{21} = -\begin{vmatrix} a_{12} & a_{13} \\ a_{32} & a_{33} \end{vmatrix}, \qquad A_{22} = \begin{vmatrix} a_{11} & a_{13} \\ a_{31} & a_{33} \end{vmatrix}, \qquad A_{23} = -\begin{vmatrix} a_{11} & a_{12} \\ a_{31} & a_{32} \end{vmatrix},$$

$$A_{31} = \begin{vmatrix} a_{12} & a_{13} \\ a_{22} & a_{23} \end{vmatrix}, \qquad A_{32} = -\begin{vmatrix} a_{11} & a_{13} \\ a_{21} & a_{23} \end{vmatrix}, \qquad A_{33} = \begin{vmatrix} a_{11} & a_{12} \\ a_{21} & a_{22} \end{vmatrix}.$$

We now define the *determinant of* $A = (a_{ij})$ to be the vector product of the first row of A by the vector whose components are the cofactors of the elements of the first row. Thus, for matrices of order 3,

$$\begin{vmatrix} a_{11} & a_{12} & a_{13} \\ a_{21} & a_{22} & a_{23} \\ a_{31} & a_{32} & a_{33} \end{vmatrix} = a_{11}A_{11} + a_{12}A_{12} + a_{13}A_{13}$$

$$= a_{11}\begin{vmatrix} a_{22} & a_{23} \\ a_{32} & a_{33} \end{vmatrix} - a_{12}\begin{vmatrix} a_{21} & a_{23} \\ a_{31} & a_{33} \end{vmatrix} + a_{13}\begin{vmatrix} a_{21} & a_{22} \\ a_{31} & a_{32} \end{vmatrix}$$

$$= a_{11}(a_{22}a_{33} - a_{23}a_{32}) - a_{12}(a_{21}a_{33} - a_{23}a_{31}) + a_{13}(a_{21}a_{32} - a_{22}a_{31})$$

$$= a_{11}a_{22}a_{33} - a_{11}a_{23}a_{32} - a_{12}a_{21}a_{33} + a_{12}a_{23}a_{31}$$
$$+ a_{13}a_{21}a_{32} - a_{13}a_{22}a_{31}.$$

Now that we have the determinant of a third-order matrix, we can use it to find the determinant of a fourth-order matrix, and so on.

The definition given above and the recursive method have a truly formidable appearance. However, although the definition is useful, it is not the technique that we shall use to evaluate numerical determinants. That technique is embodied in a number of theorems that will be given. Some of the theorems will be proved, but others will merely be stated.

8.36   PROPERTIES OF DETERMINANTS

The first theorem will be given without proof. The student should verify it for determinants of second- and third-order matrices.

Theorem 1.   *The determinant of $A = (a_{ij})$ is the vector product of any row or column with the vector whose components are the cofactors of the elements of the row or column chosen. That is,*

$$|A| = \sum_{j=1}^{n} a_{ij}A_{ij}$$

for any i, or

$$|A| = \sum_{i=1}^{n} a_{ij}A_{ij}$$

for any j.

We shall illustrate Theorem 1 by evaluating the determinant of a third-order matrix by selecting the second column. Then

$|A| = a_{12}A_{12} + a_{22}A_{22} + a_{32}A_{32}$

$$= -a_{12}\begin{vmatrix} a_{21} & a_{23} \\ a_{31} & a_{33} \end{vmatrix} + a_{22}\begin{vmatrix} a_{11} & a_{13} \\ a_{31} & a_{33} \end{vmatrix} - a_{32}\begin{vmatrix} a_{11} & a_{13} \\ a_{21} & a_{23} \end{vmatrix}$$

$$= -a_{12}(a_{21}a_{33} - a_{23}a_{31}) + a_{22}(a_{11}a_{33} - a_{13}a_{31}) - a_{32}(a_{11}a_{23} - a_{13}a_{21})$$

$$= -a_{12}a_{21}a_{33} + a_{12}a_{23}a_{31} + a_{11}a_{22}a_{33} - a_{13}a_{22}a_{31} - a_{11}a_{23}a_{32} + a_{13}a_{21}a_{32},$$

which, except for the arrangement of the terms, is the same result we obtained earlier.

Theorem 2.   *If any row or column of a matrix A consists entirely of zeros, then $|A| = 0$.*

Proof: The proof is immediate if we evaluate the determinant using the row or column consisting of zeros as our selected vector in Theorem 1.

Example. $\begin{vmatrix} 2 & 1 & 3 \\ 0 & 0 & 0 \\ 4 & 2 & 5 \end{vmatrix} = -0\begin{vmatrix} 1 & 3 \\ 2 & 5 \end{vmatrix} + 0\begin{vmatrix} 2 & 3 \\ 4 & 5 \end{vmatrix} - 0\begin{vmatrix} 2 & 1 \\ 4 & 2 \end{vmatrix} = 0.$

Theorem 3. *If B is obtained from a matrix A by interchanging two rows or two columns,* $|B| = -|A|$.

Proof: This is easily verified for matrices of order 2. When two rows of a third-order matrix are interchanged, consider the minors of the elements in the row that is unchanged. Each minor, being the determinant of a second-order matrix, is reversed in sign. Thus, when the determinant of the matrix B is computed using the unchanged row, we find that $|B| = -|A|$. Hence the theorem is true for matrices of order 3. The theorem can be proved true for any order by induction.

Example. Let

$$A = \begin{pmatrix} 2 & 1 & 3 \\ 1 & 2 & 1 \\ 4 & 2 & 5 \end{pmatrix} \quad \text{and} \quad B = \begin{pmatrix} 1 & 2 & 3 \\ 2 & 1 & 1 \\ 2 & 4 & 5 \end{pmatrix}.$$

Note that B is obtained from A by interchanging the first two columns. Let us evaluate $|A|$ and $|B|$ by using the third column, which was left unchanged. Then,

$$|A| = 3\begin{vmatrix} 1 & 2 \\ 4 & 2 \end{vmatrix} - \begin{vmatrix} 2 & 1 \\ 4 & 2 \end{vmatrix} + 5\begin{vmatrix} 2 & 1 \\ 1 & 2 \end{vmatrix} = 3(-6) - (0) + 5(3) = -3,$$

and

$$|B| = 3\begin{vmatrix} 2 & 1 \\ 2 & 4 \end{vmatrix} - \begin{vmatrix} 1 & 2 \\ 2 & 4 \end{vmatrix} + 5\begin{vmatrix} 1 & 2 \\ 2 & 1 \end{vmatrix} = 3(6) - (0) + 5(-3) = 3.$$

Theorem 4. *If two rows or two columns of a matrix A are identical,* $|A| = 0$.

Proof: If we interchange two rows or columns that are exactly alike, there is no change in A, but the sign of the determinant is reversed. That is, $|A| = -|A|$. The only number that is equal to its negative is zero.

Example.

$$\begin{vmatrix} 2 & 1 & 3 \\ 1 & 2 & 1 \\ 2 & 1 & 3 \end{vmatrix} = 2\begin{vmatrix} 2 & 1 \\ 1 & 3 \end{vmatrix} - \begin{vmatrix} 1 & 3 \\ 1 & 3 \end{vmatrix} + 2\begin{vmatrix} 1 & 3 \\ 2 & 1 \end{vmatrix} = 2(5) - 0 + 2(-5) = 0.$$

Theorem 5. *The vector product of any row (or column) of a matrix with the vector of cofactors of another row (or column) is zero.*

Proof: Let $A = (a_{ij})$. Let us evaluate $|A|$ by using the rth row. Then,

$$|A| = \sum_{j=1}^{n} a_{rj}A_{rj}.$$

Consider

$$\sum_{j=1}^{n} a_{rj}A_{sj}, \qquad s \neq r.$$

The latter expression is exactly what we should get for $|A|$ if rows r and s were alike. By Theorem 4, the determinant of such a matrix is zero.

Example. Let

$$A = \begin{pmatrix} 2 & 1 & 3 \\ 1 & 2 & 1 \\ 4 & 2 & 5 \end{pmatrix}.$$

Let us form the vector product of the first column of A with the cofactors of the second column. We obtain

$$2\begin{vmatrix} 1 & 1 \\ 4 & 5 \end{vmatrix} - 1\begin{vmatrix} 2 & 3 \\ 4 & 5 \end{vmatrix} + 4\begin{vmatrix} 2 & 3 \\ 1 & 1 \end{vmatrix} = 2(1) - 1(-2) + 4(-1) = 2 + 2 - 4 = 0.$$

If we form the vector product of the second row of A with the cofactors of the third row, we obtain

$$-1\begin{vmatrix} 1 & 3 \\ 2 & 1 \end{vmatrix} + 2\begin{vmatrix} 2 & 3 \\ 1 & 1 \end{vmatrix} - 1\begin{vmatrix} 2 & 1 \\ 1 & 2 \end{vmatrix}$$
$$= -1(-5) + 2(-1) - 1(3) = 5 - 2 - 3 = 0.$$

Theorem 6. *If any row (or column) of A contains a factor k, then $|A| = k|B|$, where B is the matrix that remains after the common factor is removed.*

Proof: Suppose $a_{rj} = kb_{rj}$ for some r, $j = 1$ to n. Let B be the matrix obtained by replacing the rth row of A by $b_{rj}, j = 1$ to n. Then

$$|A| = \sum_{j=1}^{n} a_{rj}A_{rj} = \sum_{j=1}^{n} kb_{rj}A_{rj} = k\sum_{j=1}^{n} b_{rj}A_{rj} = k|B|.$$

Example. Let

$$A = \begin{pmatrix} 1 & -4 & 5 \\ 3 & 12 & 6 \\ 7 & 0 & 3 \end{pmatrix}.$$

We shall make use of the 0 entry in A by using the second column of A to evaluate $|A|$.

$$|A| = 4\begin{vmatrix} 3 & 6 \\ 7 & 3 \end{vmatrix} + 12\begin{vmatrix} 1 & 5 \\ 7 & 3 \end{vmatrix} = 4(-33) + 12(-32) = -132 - 384 = -516.$$

By Theorem 6, there is a common factor of 4 in the second column and a common factor of 3 in the second row. Hence,

$$|A| = 4\begin{vmatrix} 1 & -1 & 5 \\ 3 & 3 & 6 \\ 7 & 0 & 3 \end{vmatrix} = (4)(3)\begin{vmatrix} 1 & -1 & 5 \\ 1 & 1 & 2 \\ 7 & 0 & 3 \end{vmatrix} = 12\left[\begin{vmatrix} 1 & 2 \\ 7 & 3 \end{vmatrix} + \begin{vmatrix} 1 & 5 \\ 7 & 3 \end{vmatrix}\right]$$

$$= 12(-11 - 32) = -516.$$

Theorem 7.   *If k times the sth row (column) of A is added to the rth row (column) of A, the determinant of the altered matrix is the same as $|A|$ if $s \neq r$.*

Proof: Let

$$A = (a_{ij}).$$

Let B be the matrix obtained from A by replacing a_{rj} by $(a_{rj} + ka_{sj}), j = 1$ to n. Then

$$|B| = \sum_{j=1}^{n} (a_{rj} + ka_{sj})A_{rj} = \sum_{j=1}^{n} a_{rj}A_{rj} + \sum_{j=1}^{n} (ka_{sj}A_{rj}).$$

But

$$\sum_{j=1}^{n} ka_{sj}A_{rj} = k \sum_{j=1}^{n} s_{sj}A_{rj} = 0$$

by Theorem 5. Hence,

$$|B| = \sum_{j=1}^{n} a_{rj}A_{rj} = |A|.$$

Example 1.   Let

$$A = \begin{pmatrix} 2 & 1 & 3 \\ 1 & 2 & 1 \\ 4 & 2 & 5 \end{pmatrix}.$$

Let us make use of the fact that $a_{21} = 1$ and that the second row contains the smallest numbers. We shall use a_{21} to obtain zeros above and below it by using Theorem 7. $|A|$ is unchanged if we add -2 times the second row to the first and -4 times the second row to the third. Then,

$$|A| = \begin{vmatrix} 0 & -3 & 1 \\ 1 & 2 & 1 \\ 4 & 2 & 5 \end{vmatrix} = \begin{vmatrix} 0 & -3 & 1 \\ 1 & 2 & 1 \\ 0 & -6 & 1 \end{vmatrix} = -1\begin{vmatrix} -3 & 1 \\ -6 & 1 \end{vmatrix} = -3.$$

The last example made use of the nature of the numbers in the matrix. A more general technique, one that can be mechanized on a computer, is to obtain ones (or zeros) in the first column by factoring out of each row the first element if it is not zero. Then interchange rows, if necessary, so that the first element in the first row is 1, not 0. Then subtract the first row from each row below that does not start with zero. Finally, since the first column now contains all zeros except the first element, evaluate $|A|$ by the elements of the first column. The process can be repeated on the determinant of the resulting reduced matrix. This process is essentially the same as that used in the solution of sets of simultaneous equations in Section 8.30.

Example 2.
$$\begin{vmatrix} 2 & 1 & 3 \\ 1 & 2 & 1 \\ 4 & 2 & 5 \end{vmatrix} = 2\begin{vmatrix} 1 & 1/2 & 3/2 \\ 1 & 2 & 1 \\ 4 & 2 & 5 \end{vmatrix} = 2(4)\begin{vmatrix} 1 & 1/2 & 3/2 \\ 1 & 2 & 1 \\ 1 & 1/2 & 5/4 \end{vmatrix}$$

$$= 8\begin{vmatrix} 1 & 1/2 & 3/2 \\ 0 & 3/2 & -1/2 \\ 0 & 0 & -1/4 \end{vmatrix} = 8\begin{vmatrix} 3/2 & -1/2 \\ 0 & -1/4 \end{vmatrix} = 8\left(\frac{3}{2}\right)\begin{vmatrix} 1 & -1/3 \\ 0 & -1/4 \end{vmatrix}$$

$$= 8\left(\frac{3}{2}\right)\left(\frac{-1}{4}\right) = -3.$$

Theorem 8. *If A and B are both of order n, $|AB| = |A| \cdot |B|$.*

We shall not prove Theorem 8, but we shall illustrate it. Let

$$A = \begin{pmatrix} 2 & 1 \\ -3 & 4 \end{pmatrix}, \qquad B = \begin{pmatrix} 3 & 5 \\ 2 & -4 \end{pmatrix}.$$

Then

$$|A| = 8 + 3 = 11, \quad \text{and} \quad |B| = -12 - 10 = -22.$$

$$AB = \begin{pmatrix} 8 & 6 \\ -1 & -31 \end{pmatrix}, \quad \text{and} \quad |AB| = -248 + 6$$
$$= -242 = (11)(-22) = |A| \cdot |B|.$$

8.37 EXERCISES

In Exercises 1–10 evaluate the given determinants.

*1. $\begin{vmatrix} -2 & 3 \\ 1 & 4 \end{vmatrix}$

2. $\begin{vmatrix} 5 & -7 \\ 8 & -3 \end{vmatrix}$

*3. $\begin{vmatrix} -2 & 3 & 1 \\ 4 & 2 & 6 \\ 6 & 3 & 5 \end{vmatrix}$

4. $\begin{vmatrix} 4 & 0 & 8 \\ 3 & 6 & 9 \\ 12 & 1 & -12 \end{vmatrix}$

*5. $\begin{vmatrix} 1 & 2 & 3 \\ 4 & 5 & 6 \\ 7 & 8 & 9 \end{vmatrix}$

6. $\begin{vmatrix} 1 & 0 & 1 \\ 1 & 1 & 0 \\ 0 & 1 & 1 \end{vmatrix}$

*7. $\begin{vmatrix} 3 & -5 & 7 \\ 2 & 4 & 6 \\ -9 & 15 & -21 \end{vmatrix}$

8. $\begin{vmatrix} a & b & c \\ 0 & d & e \\ 0 & 0 & f \end{vmatrix}$

*9. $\begin{vmatrix} x & y & 1 \\ 4 & 3 & 1 \\ 2 & 6 & 1 \end{vmatrix}$

10. $\begin{vmatrix} x & y & z \\ 1 & 2 & 3 \\ 2 & 1 & 5 \end{vmatrix}$

In Exercises 11–16 explain why the given determinant is zero without working it out.

*11. $\begin{vmatrix} 4 & -1 & 4 \\ 2 & 16 & 2 \\ 3 & 25 & 3 \end{vmatrix}$

12. $\begin{vmatrix} 6 & 2 & -12 \\ 17 & 4 & 13 \\ -3 & -1 & 6 \end{vmatrix}$

*13. $\begin{vmatrix} 1 & 16 & -4 \\ 3 & -8 & 2 \\ 7 & 12 & -3 \end{vmatrix}$

14. $\begin{vmatrix} x & y & 1 \\ 13 & -4 & 2 \\ 2x & 2y & 2 \end{vmatrix}$

*15. $\begin{vmatrix} 2 & -1 & 3 \\ 1 & 1 & 1 \\ 3 & 0 & 4 \end{vmatrix}$

16. $\begin{vmatrix} 5 & 2 & 3 \\ 3 & 1 & 2 \\ 5 & 4 & 1 \end{vmatrix}$

In Exercises 17–20 verify that $|AB| = |A| \cdot |B|$.

*17. $A = \begin{pmatrix} 4 & 2 \\ -1 & 3 \end{pmatrix}$ $B = \begin{pmatrix} 2 & -1 \\ 4 & 10 \end{pmatrix}$ 18. $A = \begin{pmatrix} 3 & 1 \\ 4 & 2 \end{pmatrix}$ $B = \begin{pmatrix} 6 & -3 \\ -2 & 1 \end{pmatrix}$

*19. $A = \begin{pmatrix} -2 & 3 & 1 \\ 4 & 2 & 6 \\ 6 & 3 & 5 \end{pmatrix}$ $B = \begin{pmatrix} 1 & 0 & 1 \\ -1 & 1 & 0 \\ 1 & 1 & 1 \end{pmatrix}$

20. $A = \begin{pmatrix} 2 & 1 & 2 \\ 0 & 3 & -1 \\ 1 & 2 & 1 \end{pmatrix}$ $B = A$

8.38   APPLICATIONS OF DETERMINANTS

Determinants are of use in mathematics in many rather surprising ways. In this section we shall examine some areas in which determinants can be applied.

First, let us consider a triangle in a plane with vertices $P_1(x_1, y_1)$, $P_2(x_2, y_2)$, and $P_3(x_3, y_3)$. We shall suppose that the vertices are numbered in such a way that, as we go around the triangle from P_1 to P_2 to P_3, we go in a counter-

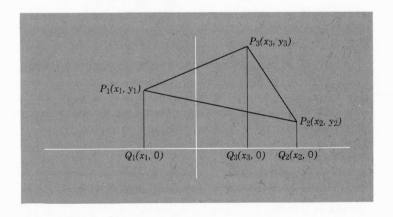

clockwise direction; that is, as we go around the triangle, the interior of the triangle always lies to the left. What is the area of such a triangle?

In the figure, perpendiculars have been dropped from each vertex to the x-axis. The foot of the perpendicular from P_i is labeled Q_i, $i = 1, 2, 3$. The area of the triangle, which we shall denote by K, can be obtained by adding together the areas of the trapezoids $P_1Q_1Q_3P_3$ and $P_3Q_3Q_2P_2$ and subtracting from this sum the area of $P_1Q_1Q_2P_2$. Since the area of a trapezoid is one half the sum of the parallel bases times the altitude, we have

$$K = (1/2)[(y_1 + y_3)(x_3 - x_1) + (y_3 + y_2)(x_2 - x_3) - (y_2 + y_1)(x_2 - x_1)]$$

$$= (1/2)(x_3y_1 + \cancel{x_3y_3} - \cancel{x_1y_1} - x_1y_3 + x_2y_3 + \cancel{x_2y_2} - \cancel{x_3y_3} - x_3y_2$$
$$- \cancel{x_2y_2} - x_2y_1 + x_1y_2 + \cancel{x_1y_1})$$

$$= (1/2)[(x_2y_3 - x_3y_2) - (x_1y_3 - x_3y_1) + (x_1y_2 - x_2y_1)].$$

We have written the result in a rather peculiar way because the quantity in brackets is precisely the determinant

$$\begin{vmatrix} x_1 & y_1 & 1 \\ x_2 & y_2 & 1 \\ x_3 & y_3 & 1 \end{vmatrix}$$

evaluated by using the elements of the third column. Thus

$$K = \frac{1}{2}\begin{vmatrix} x_1 & y_1 & 1 \\ x_2 & y_2 & 1 \\ x_3 & y_3 & 1 \end{vmatrix},$$

and it can be proved that, when P_1, P_2, and P_3 are not on the same straight line and are in counterclockwise order, K is necessarily positive.

In our figure we have chosen P_3 in such a way that x_3 lies between x_1 and x_2. It is simple to show that the result is valid for any other position of P_3. If the vertices are labeled in such a way that we go around the triangle in the opposite (clockwise) direction, the result is the same as if we interchanged two rows. By Theorem 3, our computation will give us $-K$.

Example 1. Let us find the area of the triangle whose vertices are $(-1, 3)$, $(2, -1)$, and $(1, 5)$.

$$K = \frac{1}{2}\begin{vmatrix} -1 & 3 & 1 \\ 2 & -1 & 1 \\ 1 & 5 & 1 \end{vmatrix} = \frac{1}{2}\begin{vmatrix} -1 & 3 & 1 \\ 3 & -4 & 0 \\ 2 & 2 & 0 \end{vmatrix} = \frac{1}{2}\begin{vmatrix} 3 & -4 \\ 2 & 2 \end{vmatrix} = \frac{1}{2}(6 + 8) = 7$$

In this example we have used Theorem 7 to help us evaluate the determinant. We subtracted the first row from the second and the third rows.

For our second application, let (x_1, y_1) and (x_2, y_2) be any two distinct points in a plane. Where are all the points (x, y) in the plane such that

$$\begin{vmatrix} x & y & 1 \\ x_1 & y_1 & 1 \\ x_2 & y_2 & 1 \end{vmatrix} = 0?$$

If we evaluate the determinant by using the elements of the first row, we have

$$ax + by + c = 0,$$

where

$$a = y_1 - y_2, \quad b = x_2 - x_1, \quad \text{and} \quad c = x_1 y_2 - x_2 y_1.$$

Since this is a linear equation, we know that all of the points that satisfy the given equation lie on a line. Our job is to identify the line. If we substitute x_1 for x and y_1 for y, the determinant will have two rows alike. Since Theorem 4 says that any determinant with two rows alike is zero, our equation is satisfied, or the line passes through (x_1, y_1). By the same reasoning, it also passes through (x_2, y_2).

The last result can also be attained by returning to the preceding illustration. The given determinant is zero for those points and only those points (x, y) such that the triangle with vertices (x, y), (x_1, y_1), and (x_2, y_2) has zero area. This is true if and only if the three points lie on the same line.

Example 2. The equation of the line through $(-1, 3)$ and $(2, -1)$ is

$$\begin{vmatrix} x & y & 1 \\ -1 & 3 & 1 \\ 2 & -1 & 1 \end{vmatrix} = 0,$$

$$\text{or} \quad x \begin{vmatrix} 3 & 1 \\ -1 & 1 \end{vmatrix} - y \begin{vmatrix} -1 & 1 \\ 2 & 1 \end{vmatrix} + \begin{vmatrix} -1 & 3 \\ 2 & -1 \end{vmatrix} = 0,$$

$$\text{or} \quad 4x + 3y - 5 = 0.$$

Let us extend the idea of the last application to an equation of higher degree. We know that an equation of the form

$$a(x^2 + y^2) + bx + cy + d = 0$$

has a circle for its graph. Then what is the graph of the equation

$$\begin{vmatrix} x^2 + y^2 & x & y & 1 \\ x_1^2 + y_1^2 & x_1 & y_1 & 1 \\ x_2^2 + y_2^2 & x_2 & y_2 & 1 \\ x_3^2 + y_3^2 & x_3 & y_3 & 1 \end{vmatrix} = 0,$$

where x_i and y_i are real numbers, $i = 1, 2, 3$?

If we evaluate the determinant by the elements of the first row of the matrix, we find that we have the equation of a circle. By the reasoning of the preceding illustration, the circle passes through the three points (x_1, y_1), (x_2, y_2), and (x_3, y_3).

In Section 8.18 we found that the system

$$ax + by = u$$
$$cx + dy = v$$

has the solution

$$x = \frac{du - bv}{ad - bc}, \qquad y = \frac{av - cu}{ad - bc}.$$

We can write these in determinant form,

$$x = \frac{\begin{vmatrix} u & b \\ v & d \end{vmatrix}}{\begin{vmatrix} a & b \\ c & d \end{vmatrix}}, \qquad y = \frac{\begin{vmatrix} a & u \\ c & v \end{vmatrix}}{\begin{vmatrix} a & b \\ c & d \end{vmatrix}}.$$

This form is not hard to remember. In each case the denominator is the determinant of the matrix of coefficients, and in each case the numerator is the determinant of the matrix that differs from the coefficient matrix only in that the column of coefficients of the variable sought is replaced by the column of constants. This method can be extended to systems of more than two equations, but no computational advantage is gained. The method of Section 8.30 involves less work for the larger systems and for two equations it is almost as simple. For two equations, however, the simplicity of the method permits us, with a little practice, to write down the solution immediately, provided a unique solution exists. A significant drawback of the determinant method is that it fails to distinguish between the cases in which there is no solution and those in which there are many solutions. In both cases the determinant appearing in the denominator is zero.

Example 3. Solve

$$3x - 2y = 5$$
$$-4x + 6y = -3.$$

$$x = \frac{\begin{vmatrix} 5 & -2 \\ -3 & 6 \end{vmatrix}}{\begin{vmatrix} 3 & -2 \\ -4 & 6 \end{vmatrix}} = \frac{24}{10} = \frac{12}{5}, \qquad y = \frac{\begin{vmatrix} 3 & 5 \\ -4 & -3 \end{vmatrix}}{10} = \frac{11}{10}.$$

8.39 EXERCISES

*1. Find the area of the triangle with vertices $(1, 3)$, $(7, 2)$, and $(5, 6)$.

2. Find the area of the triangle with vertices $(1, 3)$, $(-3, 2)$, and $(-5, -6)$.

*3. Find the area of the triangle with vertices $(1, 4)$, $(5, -1)$, and $(-5, -3)$.

4. Find the area of the triangle with vertices $(-3, 4)$, $(6, 2)$, and $(3, -3)$.

*5. Find the area of the quadrilateral with vertices $(-1, 1)$, $(3, 4)$, $(2, -3)$, and $(-2, -4)$. (Hint: break the quadrilateral into two triangles.)

6. Three vertices of a parallelogram are $(-2, 1)$, $(3, 3)$, and $(1, -2)$.

   (a) There are three possible locations for the fourth vertex. What are they?

   (b) What is the area of each of these parallelograms?

*7. A triangle with area 8 has two vertices at $(1, 2)$ and $(-3, 1)$. The third vertex must lie on one of two lines. What are their equations?

8. Use the method of the last section to find the equation of the line through

   (a) $(2, -1)$ and $(3, 4)$

   (b) $(4, 3)$ and $(-5, -6)$

   (c) $(0, b)$ and $(1, m + b)$

   (d) (a, b) and (c, d)

   (e) $(a, 0)$ and $(0, b)$.

9. Use the determinant method to solve the following sets of equations:

   *(a) $2x - y = 3$
   $3x + 2y = 5$

   (b) $-x + 2y = -3$
   $2x - 3y = 4$

   *(c) $2x + y = 5$
   $2x + 3y = 7$

   (d) $0.5x - 3.1y = 2.7$
   $1.3x + 2.7y = 1.9$

   *(e) $162x - 353y = 1074$
   $212x + 153y = -863$

10. Use the determinant method to solve

$$3x - 2y + z = 11$$
$$-x - 3y + 2z = 7 \ .$$
$$5x + y + z = 12$$

8.40 RECOMMENDED READING

Beaumont, R. A., and Ball, R. W., *Introduction to Modern Algebra and Matrix Theory*, Rinehart, New York, 1954.

Birkhoff, G., and MacLane, S., *A Brief Survey of Modern Algebra*, Macmillan, New York, 1953.

Mal'cev, A. I., *Foundations of Linear Algebra*, Freeman, San Francisco, 1963.

McCoy, N. H., *Introduction to Modern Algebra*, Allyn and Bacon, Boston, 1960.

Murdoch, D. C., *Linear Algebra for Undergraduates*, Wiley, New York, 1957.

9

The digital computer; one of man's newest and most powerful tools.

9.1 THE EARLY HISTORY OF MECHANICAL AIDS TO COMPUTATION

The performance of arithmetic computation is perhaps the simplest and yet the most obnoxious aspect of mathematics. Perhaps it is not quite correct to call such computation "mathematics." It is a skill that can be developed by persons entirely ignorant of basic mathematical concepts. In fact, there are persons whom psychologists call "idiots savants" who have very low intelligence and yet are capable of truly remarkable feats of computation. Such exceptional ability, of course, is not limited to low intellects. Some of the greatest mathematicians have also had this ability, but it is rare. Most of us find arithmetic computation an onerous chore and we are not very good at it. We find that prolonged arithmetic operations lead to weariness, headaches, and errors. Thus it is not surprising that man has long sought aid with this activity. In early times the tally stick was used. Later came sandboxes, pebbles on marked boards, and eventually the abacus.

The seventeenth century saw two great advances in aids to computation. The first of these was the invention of logarithms in 1614 by the Scottish mathematician John Napier. Three years later he introduced marked rods of ivory or bone that could be manipulated in such a way as to facilitate multiplication and division. This device, called "Napier's rods," was the basis for our modern slide rule. It should be mentioned that Henry Briggs, an English mathematician, worked with Napier in developing the theory of logarithms.

Not long after, about 1640, the French philosopher and mathematician Blaise Pascal invented an arithmetical machine that performed additions and subtractions with cogwheels. This device was improved by Gottfried Leibniz, the great German mathematician, near the end of the century. The machine of Pascal and Leibniz, although still in use in essentially the same form as it had in Leibniz' day, was the forerunner of our present adding machines and desk calculators.

The next giant stride came in the first half of the nineteenth century. In 1822 a most remarkable professor of mathematics at Cambridge University, Charles Babbage, proposed an intricate mechanical device he termed a "difference engine." According to his plans, the machine would perform complicated mathematical computations by working with small differences of the variables. Although Babbage received government support, eight years of effort failed to produce the machine. Abandoning his earlier device, he then planned a much more complicated computer, which he called an "analytic engine." This machine, like its predecessor, was never built. Babbage was a century ahead of his time. What he had done was to invent the modern digital computer. Unfortunately, the technology of his day was totally inadequate to construct it. Today we use electronic circuits where Babbage envisioned mechanical linkages, but the logical design of his analytical engine is essentially that on which modern computers are based. Babbage even foresaw our modern punched-card equipment. In 1801 the French inventor Joseph Jacquard had exhibited his famous loom, which wove intricate patterns under the control of holes punched in cards. It was cards similar to these that Babbage proposed to use for input and output for his analytic engine.

9.2 THE DIGITAL COMPUTER

In the twentieth century, before World War II, there was rapid development of a wide variety of calculating devices. The electric relay and the vacuum tube provided the raw material for thousands of machines that were aids to computation. None of these, however, can boast of being a true digital computer by the present definition of the term. Today, it is commonly accepted that a digital computer is a mechanism with the following capabilities:

1. It can carry out all arithmetic operations.
2. It can store data and instructions internally.
3. It can modify its own program.

The statement of these three criteria involves words that must be clarified. For instance, how can a computer store a number? What do we mean when we say that a device, mechanical or electronic, can carry our arithmetic operations? What is an "instruction" to a computer? How can a computer store such instructions? How can it "modify" these instructions, whatever that means? These are the questions we shall try to answer. Babbage first conceived of a mechanism to accomplish these things, but it was not until the 1940's that one was actually constructed. Now there are scores of thousands of them, ranging from rather simple devices to multimillion-dollar giants. Some are small enough to fit in a matchbox. Others take large rooms with special power lines and air conditioning.

9.3 STORING NUMBERS

One way to store a number is to write it on a piece of paper. The number 257 has been stored in this sentence. In order to "store" it in this way, we must agree as to what 2, 5, and 7 mean, and we must understand the positional notation of our numeration system. Otherwise, the stored information cannot be retrieved. It is lost. It is retrieved by the reader through a marvelous mechanism, the human nervous system with its sensory organs. The computer is a much cruder, simpler device. It is essentially based on the idea of a switch. An ordinary switch, such as is used to turn on your hall light, has two positions, off and on. A switch, then, can store two numbers, 0 and 1, if we agree that the "off" position represents 0 and the "on" position represents 1. The switch is the basic storage element of all computers today, but switches take on a great variety of forms.

The fact that a simple switch has only two positions means that we must examine a numeration system based on 2 rather than 10. We recall that the decimal system uses ten digits, 0 to 9, and that if a, b, and c are digits, then the number $abc.ca$ means $a(10^2) + b(10) + c + c(10^{-1}) + a(10^{-2})$. The binary numeration system is based on 2; thus only two symbols are needed, 0 and 1. If a, b, and c are binary digits, the number $abc.ca$ means $a(2^2) + b(2) + c + c(2^{-1}) + a(2^{-2})$. Below is a count from 0 to 16 in the binary system. To the right of each number we have written its equivalent in the decimal system.

Binary	Decimal
0	0
1	1
10	2
11	3
100	4
101	5
110	6
111	7
1000	8
1001	9
1010	10
1011	11
1100	12
1101	13
1110	14
1111	15
10000	16

In the following examples we shall convert numbers expressed in the binary system into their decimal equivalents.

Example 1.
$$110.101 = 1(2^2) + 1(2) + 0 + 1(2^{-1}) + 0(2^{-2}) + 1(2^{-3})$$
$$= 4 + 2 + 0 + \frac{1}{2} + 0 + \frac{1}{8}$$
$$= 4 + 2 + 0.5 + 0.125 = 6.625.$$

Example 2.
$$1011.0101 = 1(2^3) + 0(2^2) + 1(2) + 1 + 0(2^{-1}) + 1(2^{-2}) + 0(2^{-3}) + 1(2^{-4})$$
$$= 8 + 0 + 2 + 1 + 0 + \frac{1}{4} + 0 + \frac{1}{16}$$
$$= 8 + 2 + 1 + 0.25 + 0.0625 = 11.3125.$$

Example 3.
$$1111111 = 2^6 + 2^5 + 2^4 + 2^3 + 2^2 + 2 + 1$$
$$= 64 + 32 + 16 + 8 + 4 + 2 + 1 = 127.$$

Example 4. $0.00001 = 2^{-5} = \dfrac{1}{32} = 0.03125.$

9.4 BINARY ARITHMETIC, NUMBER CONVERSION

It will help in our understanding of computers if we have some facility in binary arithmetic. Basically, since there are only two symbols, 0 and 1, arithmetic in base 2 is much simpler than in base 10. The price we pay for this simplicity is that we require a longer string of digits to represent a number. For instance, two digits suffice in base 10 to represent all numbers from 0 to 99. In base 2, the largest number that can be written with only two binary digits is 3, whose binary representation is 11. In order to write 99 in binary form, we look for the highest power of 2 that is equal to or less than 99. This is 64, or 2^6. Then, $99 = 64 + 35$. We repeat our process on 35. The highest power of 2 not exceeding 35 is 32, or 2^5. Now, $99 = 64 + 32 + 3$. In full, we have

$$99 = 1 \cdot 2^6 + 1 \cdot 2^5 + 0 \cdot 2^4 + 0 \cdot 2^3 + 0 \cdot 2^2 + 1 \cdot 2 + 1.$$

Thus the binary representation of 99 is 1100011. It requires seven binary digits to represent a number that requires only two decimal digits. Incidentally, the words "binary digit" are used so often in discussing computers that a shorter form has been coined. It is "bit." In computer jargon the binary representation of 99 is a seven-bit number.

Let us try another example. This time let us convert 53 to base 2.

The highest power of 2 in 53 is $32 = 2^5$. Thus $53 = 2^5 + 21$.
The highest power of 2 in 21 is $16 = 2^4$. Thus $53 = 2^5 + 2^4 + 5$.
The highest power of 2 in 5 is $4 = 2^2$. Thus $53 = 2^5 + 2^4 + 2^2 + 1$.

We are done. 53 = 110101.

This method requires that we know or have available the powers of 2. There is another way that does not require this. For example, suppose that

$$n = a(2^5) + b(2^4) + c(2^3) + d(2^2) + e(2) + f,$$

where a, b, c, d, e, and f are each either 0 or 1. If n is odd, then $f = 1$, for otherwise 2 would be a factor of the right side, hence a factor of n. If n is even, then $f = 0$. In either case, f is the least significant bit in the binary representation of n. Let us subtract f from n and divide by 2. Let us set $(n - f)/2 = n_1$. Then

$$n_1 = a(2^4) + b(2^3) + c(2^2) + d(2) + e.$$

By a repetition of our argument, e is the least significant bit of n_1, and is also the next least significant bit of n. Then let

$$n_2 = \frac{n_1 - e}{2} = a(2^3) + b(2^2) + c(2) + d,$$

and so forth. It may not be clear at this point, but we have obtained a neat algorithm for converting decimal integers to binary. To see that this is true, let us apply it to 53.

First, 53 is odd. Thus the least significant bit is 1. Since $(53 - 1)/2 = 26$, and 26 is even, the next least significant bit is 0. Since $(26 - 0)/2 = 13$, and 13 is odd, the next least significant bit is 1. Since $(13 - 1)/2 = 6$, and 6 is even, the next bit is 0. Since $(6 - 0)/2 = 3$, and 3 is odd, the next bit is 1. Since $(3 - 1)/2 = 1$, our most significant bit is 1. Writing our result in reverse order yields 53 = 110101.

Let us shorten this process still more. You may have noticed that our process of subtracting the last bit at each step is equivalent to throwing away the remainder after each division by 2. Observe! We shall divide by 2 and throw away remainders.

$2\underline{|53}$ is odd; thus the last bit is 1.
$2\underline{|26}$ is even; thus the next bit is 0.
$2\underline{|13}$ is odd; thus the next bit is 1.
$2\underline{|6}$ is even; thus the next bit is 0.
$2\underline{|3}$ is odd; thus the next bit is 1.
1 is odd; thus the next bit is 1.   53 = 110101.

Observe in the algorithm above that if, instead of discarding the remainders, we retain them, they form the consecutive binary digits of the desired number in reverse order.

$$\begin{array}{r|l} & \quad\quad\quad \textit{Remainder} \\ 2\overline{)53} & \\ 2\overline{)26} & \quad 1 \\ 2\overline{)13} & \quad 0 \\ 2\overline{)6} & \quad 1 \\ 2\overline{)3} & \quad 0 \\ 2\overline{)1} & \quad 1 \\ 0 & \quad 1 \end{array}$$

We can use much the same method in reverse to convert decimal fractions to binary fractions. Let us consider 0.625. If we multiply by 2, we get 1.25. This is one method of showing that the original number was equal to or greater than one half, which is 0.1 in binary form. Thus the binary representation of 0.625 starts 0.1 . . . . Let us repeat the process on the fractional part of 1.25. Since 2(0.25) = 0.5, which is less than 1, our next bit is 0. So far, 0.625 = 0.10 . . . . Another repetition gives 2(0.5) = 1.0, which tells us that the third bit is 1, and we are through. The decimal fraction 0.625 is the binary fraction 0.101. This is easy to check. The binary number 0.101 is 1/2 + 1/8 = 5/8 = 0.625. Notice that in this case our binary fraction has no more bits than our original number has digits. This is accidental. In general we shall have more bits in our binary form. In fact many numbers that can be expressed as finite decimals turn out to require infinitely many bits. For example, 1/5 = 0.2 in decimal form, but its binary form is the repeating binary expression 0.00110011 . . . . With a different number base, we should not be surprised at this.

Observe that there is a very simple algorithm for the process given above. When we multiply each fraction by 2, let the carry past the decimal point to the left be called the "overflow." Then the overflow bits form the consecutive bits of the binary expression.

Examples.

$$\begin{array}{c} 0.9375 \\ \underline{\quad 2 \quad} \\ \rightarrow 1.8750 \\ \underline{\quad 2 \quad} \\ \rightarrow 1.7500 \\ \underline{\quad 2 \quad} \\ \rightarrow 1.5000 \\ \underline{\quad 2 \quad} \\ \rightarrow 1.0000 \\ \text{Thus, } 0.9375 = 0.1111. \end{array} \qquad \begin{array}{c} 0.3 \\ \underline{\quad 2 \quad} \\ \rightarrow 0.6 \leftarrow \\ \underline{\quad 2 \quad} \\ \rightarrow 1.2 \\ \underline{\quad 2 \quad} \\ \rightarrow 0.4 \\ \underline{\quad 2 \quad} \\ \rightarrow 0.8 \\ \underline{\quad 2 \quad} \\ \rightarrow 1.6 \end{array}$$

Since our process repeats from the indicated point on, 0.3 = 0.01001100110011001···.

9.5 EXERCISES

*1. Express 2^n in both binary and decimal form for $n = 0$ through 10. (Remember that $2^0 = 1$.)

2. Express 2^n in both binary and decimal form for $n = -1$ through -6.

In Exercises 3–10 express the given binary number in decimal form.

*3. 1010   4. 10001
*5. 11111   6. 110110110
*7. 101101   8. 111000111
*9. $100000 - 1$ 10. $111111 + 1$

In Exercises 11–18 express the given binary number in both decimal and rational fraction form.

*11. 0.11   12. 0.111
*13. 0.101   14. 0.0101
*15. 0.00101   16. 0.00011
*17. $1 - 0.001$ 18. $0.0111 + 0.0001$

In Exercises 19–28 express the given decimal number in binary form.

*19. 25   20. 43
*21. 63   22. 65
*23. 511   24. 0.5
*25. 0.125   26. 6.3125
*27. 1.5625   28. 0.4

9.6 SERIAL BINARY ADDITION

With base 2 as with base 10, addition and subtraction involve carrying and borrowing. In adding two bits we observe that $0 + 0 = 0$, $0 + 1 = 1$, and $1 + 1 = 10$. Thus we get a carry whenever we add two 1's. Let us try an addition problem. We shall add A and B, where $A = 10101$ and $B = 10110$. Let us check our work. A is 10101, which in decimal form is

$$2^4 + 2^2 + 1 = 21,$$

Carry	1	0	1	0	0	
A		1	0	1	0	1
B		1	0	1	1	0
Sum	1	0	1	0	1	1

and B is 10110, which in decimal form is

$$2^4 + 2^2 + 2 = 22.$$

Our sum is 101011, which in decimal form is

$$2^5 + 2^3 + 2 + 1 = 43.$$

Since $21 + 22 = 43$, our work is correct.

An interesting thing about binary addition is that there is an easy way to compute the carries without doing the addition. Let us set up an addition problem like the one above with four lines: Carry, *A*, *B*, and Sum. What we are actually doing is adding the first three lines without carrying. To make the first line complete, let us introduce a 0 in the least significant bit position of the carry. This is permissible, for there is never a carry at the beginning. Now, let us work our way from right to left. We shall not get a carry bit of 1 until we have first encountered a bit place where *A* and *B* are both 1's. Then, after the carry occurs, it will stay until we find a bit place where *A* and *B* are both 0's.

Example.	Carry	1	0	0	0	1	1	1	0	0	0
	A	0	1	0	1	0	1	0	1	0	1
	B	0	1	1	0	0	0	1	1	1	0
	Sum	1	0	1	1	1	0	0	0	1	1

For the addition itself, we find that the sum bit can be formed according to the following rules:

$$\text{Sum bit} = \begin{cases} 1 \text{ if} \begin{cases} \text{bits in } A \text{ and } B \text{ are different and carry is 0.} \\ \text{bits in } A \text{ and } B \text{ are alike and carry is 1.} \end{cases} \\ 0 \text{ if} \begin{cases} \text{bits in } A \text{ and } B \text{ are different and carry is 1.} \\ \text{bits in } A \text{ and } B \text{ are alike and carry is 0.} \end{cases} \end{cases}$$

The reasons for putting the rules in such explicit form are twofold. One is that we have a complete algorithm defined for the addition of any two positive numbers. The second is that once such an algorithm is given, it becomes clear precisely what is required to mechanize the process. Later we shall refer to this algorithm when we examine one way a digital computer can add two numbers.

The process we have given above is called *serial addition* because it is a way of adding two numbers bit by bit, from right to left. This is the usual method of addition. There is another way, which we may describe as a "kerchunk" method, in which the numbers are examined in their entirety and the sum bits are all formed at the same time. This is called *parallel addition*. The difference is the same as that between typing a number and stamping it with a stamp. The logic for parallel addition is considerably more complex than it is for serial addition. For this reason we shall restrict our attention to serial operations.

9.7 SERIAL BINARY SUBTRACTION

Let us find an algorithm for subtraction that is similar to that for addition. We have two tasks to accomplish. One is to determine a rule for the borrow; the other is to determine a rule for the difference bits. To avoid complication at this stage, we shall consider only differences of the form $A - B$ where A and B are nonnegative numbers and $A > B$. For example, let us subtract 101 from 11011.

$$
\begin{array}{cccccc}
 & \overset{1}{} & & & & \\
1 & 1 & 0 & 1 & 1 \\
 & & 1 & 0 & 1 \\
\hline
1 & 0 & 1 & 1 & 0 \\
\end{array}
$$

The mark above the second bit indicates that the subtraction in the previous stage, where the subtraction of 1 from 0 is indicated, requires a borrow.

First, let us write down the possible cases. From these we shall assemble our algorithm. We shall write our cases in the form of a table. In the first two columns we shall list the possible bits in a given place of A and B. In the third column a 1 will indicate that the subtraction in the previous stage required a borrow, and a 0 will indicate no borrow. In the fourth column is the difference bit, and in the last column a 1 will indicate a borrow in the next stage; a 0 will indicate no borrow. See Table 1.

Table 1

A	B	Borrow	Difference	Borrow
0	0	0	0	0
0	1	0	1	1
1	0	0	1	0
1	1	0	0	0
0	0	1	1	1
0	1	1	0	1
1	0	1	0	0
1	1	1	1	1

When we start subtracting from right to left, we find that a borrow is first required when we must subtract a 1 in B from a 0 in A. Once a borrow occurs, there will be a borrow at every stage until a 0 in B is to be subtracted from a 1 in A. The situation is similar to the carry in addition. A certain combination, 0 in A and 1 in B, creates a borrow in the next stage. There will continue to be a borrow until another condition, 1 in A and 0 in B, removes it.

A careful examination of the eight cases above shows that the rule for the difference is:

$$\text{Difference bit} = \begin{cases} 1 \text{ if} \begin{cases} \text{bits in } A \text{ and } B \text{ are different and borrow is 0.} \\ \text{bits in } A \text{ and } B \text{ are alike and borrow is 1.} \end{cases} \\ 0 \text{ if} \begin{cases} \text{bits in } A \text{ and } B \text{ are different and borrow is 1.} \\ \text{bits in } A \text{ and } B \text{ are alike and borrow is 0.} \end{cases} \end{cases}$$

What is remarkable about this rule is that it is precisely the same as the rule for addition if the borrow bit replaces the carry bit.

The importance of this remarkable result is that a mechanism designed to carry out serial binary addition requires only a minor change to permit it to subtract. All that is necessary is to make a slight change in the carry rule.

Example.

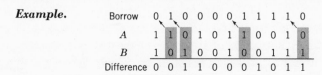

Borrow	0 1 0 0 0 0 1 1 1 1 0
A	1 1 0 1 0 1 1 0 0 1 0
B	1 0 1 0 0 1 0 0 1 1 1
Difference	0 0 1 1 0 0 0 1 0 1 1

9.8 EXERCISES

In Exercises 1–10 carry out the indicated additions.

*1. 101101 + 010110
*3. 11111 + 11111
*5. 10101 + 10101
*7. 10101 + 1010 + 1
*9. 11.011 + 1.1101

2. 11111 + 1
4. 10000 + 11111
6. 11101110 + 10101010
8. 10111 + 11011 + 11101
10. 101.1011 + 10.011 + 1.1111

In Exercises 11–20 carry out the indicated subtractions.

*11. 101101 − 10110
*13. 11110 − 11101
*15. 101010 − 1111
*17. 110101 − 1101 − 110
*19. 11.011 − 1.1101

12. 100000 − 1
14. 11011 − 101010
16. 11101110 − 10101010
18. 111011 − 1001 − 1001
20. 101.1011 − 10.011 − 1.1111

9.9 LIMITED NUMBER LENGTH

There is no upper bound to the number of digits that may be required to write a number. On the other hand, the largest number ever written required only a finite number of digits. We might feel ourselves to be restricted if, in our writing of numbers, we were limited to strings of digits of a fixed length. This restriction is not too severe, however. We do not feel overly hampered by the fact that desk calculators have registers ten or twelve digits in length. This is enough for most needs. Furthermore, if we need to handle very large or very small numbers, we can express them in so-called "scientific notation." With this convention a number is written in two parts: a number between 1 and 10 times a power of 10. For example, $763,000,000,000 = 7.63(10^{11})$, and $0.000000763 = 7.63(10^{-7})$. This notation permits us to express enormously large and extremely small numbers with a reasonably small number of digits. The restriction on the "length" of a number then becomes a restriction on precision rather than size.

Let us see what the consequences are of using finite registers to store binary numbers. If we consider only integers, a binary register of n places can store the integers from 0 to $2^n - 1$. A 30-bit register, for example, can hold all the integers from 0 to $2^{30} - 1 = 1,073,742,823$.

9.10   REPRESENTATION OF NEGATIVE NUMBERS

There are two ways to handle the sign of a number held in a register. One is the familiar method of providing an extra bit and letting either 0 or 1 represent $+$ and the other represent $-$. There is another method that is not only possible but is frequently used in computers that store numbers in a strictly binary form. Because of its novelty, we shall investigate this method. For purposes of illustration we shall show how registers of length $n = 4$ can be used to store the integers from -7 to $+7$. We shall think of these registers as consisting of rows of four switches, each of which has two positions denoted by 0 and 1. We shall use the customary binary form to represent the positive integers. That is, 6 is represented by 0110.

Now, let us consider what number $x = 1010$ should represent. Let us add x and 6.

$$
\begin{array}{rl}
x = & 1010 \\
6 = & \underline{0110} \\
\text{sum} = & 10000
\end{array}
$$

If our register has only four places it can store only the last four bits, which are 0000. Thus x is the number which, added to 6, yields 0. Hence we shall let 1010 represent -6. For each of the numbers 1 through 7 we can do the same thing to find a representation for the negative integers. A binary number system in which the negative numbers are represented in this way is called a "two's complement" number system. Table 2 is a list of the two's complements of the integers from 0 to 7. Notice that one combination, 1000, is omitted. It can be used, but we shall simplify our present discussion by considering it to be meaningless.

Table 2

Integer	Binary Form	Two's Complement	Integer
0	0000	0000	-0
1	0001	1111	-1
2	0010	1110	-2
3	0011	1101	-3
4	0100	1100	-4
5	0101	1011	-5
6	0110	1010	-6
7	0111	1001	-7

There is a simple rule for forming the two's complement of any number. Start at the right end and proceed to the left. Copy all successive 0's and the first 1 bit. After that reverse every bit to the left. If this is done and a number is added to its complement, the sum will consist of 0's until we come to the first 1. By the method of formation, the rightmost 1's in the two numbers occur in the same position. The sum of two 1's is 0 with a carry. In all positions to the left there will be a 0, a 1, and a carry, so that the sum bits are all 0's. The final carry is propagated off the left end of the finite register.

In the two's complement number system the leftmost bit indicates the sign of a number. If it is 0, the number is positive. If it is 1, the number is negative.

Example 1. The two's complement of 011011010 is 100100110.

Example 2. The two's complement of 110110110 is 001001010.

Since 2^n has a binary representation of 1 followed by n 0's, it appears in a register of length n as zero. Thus we may think of zero as being represented by 2^n. Then, if x is any number less than 2^n in absolute value, its negative has a two's complement representation that can be interpreted as $2^n - x$. This representation is not unique. However, in the n rightmost digits we find that $2^m - x$ has the same appearance as $2^n - x$ for any $m > n$. Thus, if x and y are two negative numbers that are contained in a register of length n, and if their sum can also be contained in the register, then their sum is

$$(2^n - x) + (2^n - y) = 2(2^n) - x - y = 2^{n+1} - (x + y).$$

That is, the ordinary sum of two negative numbers represented in the two's complement number system has the correct representation.

9.11 BINARY FRACTIONS

Suppose we desire a register of length n to contain numbers between -1 and 1, not inclusive. Where should the binary point be? If we want to use the two's complement number system, let us place our binary point after the first bit on the left. Then $5/8 = 0.101$, $-5/8 = 1.011$, $1/2 = 0.1$, and $-1/2 = 1.1$. When this is done, the leftmost bit indicates the sign of a number. Also, if $5/8$ and $-5/8$ are added, the sum is 10.000. If a register does not hold the leftmost bit, the number appearing in the register will be 0.000, which is the desired sum. In an n-bit register the largest fraction that we can store is $0.11 \cdots 1 = 1 - 2^{-(n-1)}$, and the smallest number is $1.11 \cdots 1 = -1 + 2^{-(n-1)}$. We can store all numbers between these two values. Hence, in a five-bit register we can store all numbers between $-1 + 2^{-4} = -1 + 1/16 = -15/16$ and $1 - 2^{-4} = 1 - 1/16 = 15/16$.

As in a desk calculator, the binary point does not appear in the register itself. It must be remembered by the person using the computer. Actually the binary point can be any place we want it to be, but it is usually convenient to treat our numbers as either integers or fractions. Otherwise serious problems arise whenever we wish to add or subtract two numbers whose binary points are in different locations. This problem is solved by "scaling," the process of shifting numbers right or left, and it is one reason for using the number representation we shall discuss in Section 9.13.

9.12 EXERCISES

In Exercises 1–10 give the two's complement representation of the given number in a register of seven bits.

*1. -12　　　　　　　2. -63　　　　　　　*3. -1

4. -33　　　　　　　*5. -45　　　　　　　6. $\dfrac{-5}{32}$

*7. $\dfrac{-1}{64}$　　　　　　　8. $\dfrac{-33}{64}$　　　　　　　*9. $\dfrac{-45}{64}$

10. $\dfrac{-42}{64}$

In Exercises 11–20 carry out the indicated operations as they would appear in a register of seven bits.

*11. $20 - 13$　　　　　　　12. $13 - 20$　　　　　　　*13. $33 - 45$

14. $-17 + (-25)$　　　　*15. $-23 + 48$　　　　16. $\dfrac{20}{64} - \dfrac{13}{64}$

*17. $\dfrac{13}{64} - \dfrac{20}{64}$　　　　　18. $\dfrac{5}{8} - \dfrac{15}{32}$　　　　　*19. $\dfrac{-7}{8} + \dfrac{-52}{64}$

20. $\dfrac{-50}{64} + \dfrac{63}{64}$

In Exercises 21–25 carry out the indicated operations in two ways, as an addition and as a subtraction. Assume the register has seven bits.

*21. $45 + (-52)$ and $45 - 52$ 22. $-19 + 32$ and $-19 - (-32)$

*23. $-50 + 23$ and $-50 - (-23)$ 24. $\frac{14}{64} + \left(\frac{-52}{64}\right)$ and $\frac{14}{64} - \frac{52}{64}$

*25. $\frac{-37}{64} + \left(\frac{-13}{64}\right)$ and $\frac{-37}{64} - \frac{13}{64}$

9.13 FLOATING POINT

If we wish to add 011.1010 and 0011.101, where the two numbers are held in seven-bit registers in two's complement form, it is necessary to shift one of the numbers to the left or the other to the right one bit before the operation can be performed. What is worse, since the location of the binary point does not appear internally in the computer's register, the programmer must keep track of where each binary point is at each stage of a problem. This is difficult and can easily lead to errors. Also, with finite registers it is quite possible that a series of additions or multiplications can lead to a number that cannot be contained in a register. For instance, if we wish to find the average of, say, 1000 numbers, where each number can be held in a register, we must add the numbers and divide by 1000. The sum may be too large to be held in a register. For these reasons it has become commonplace to represent numbers in a "floating-point" format. In this format a number is expressed as a number between -1 and 1 times a power of 2. Then two numbers are stored in the computer: the fraction (F) and the exponent (E).

> **Examples.** Let us suppose that a number is held in a seven-bit register with the binary point as indicated. Let us store the fractional part (F) and the exponent (E) in two registers of the same length.
>
> 1. $0110.101 = 0.110101(2^3); F = 0110101, E = 0000011$
> 2. $0.000011 = 0.110000(2^{-4}); F = 0110000, E = 1111100$
> 3. $-01011.10 = 1010.010 = 1.010010(2^4); F = 1010010, E = 0000100$
> 4. $-0.000011 = 1.111101 = 1.010000(2^{-4}); F = 1010000, E = 1111100$

In the examples above we have followed the common custom of representing F as a fraction whose magnitude lies between $1/2$ and 1. This is indicated by the fact that the bits preceding and following the binary point of F are different if the number is not $0 = 0.0$ or $-1/2 = 1.1$. If the fractional part obeys this rule, the number is said to be "normalized." Most machines are so built that only normalized floating-point representations are possible, but a few experimental computers permit fractions outside this range. It is possible with such computers to have some indication of how many bits in the result of an operation are meaningful. Since this is a rather complicated area, we shall restrict our attention to the normalized floating point.

We have given examples indicating that the registers storing F and E for a number are the same length. This is not ordinarily the case. A typical length for F would be about 24 to 36 bits, whereas registers for E are usually 7 to 9 bits long.

9.14 EXERCISES

In Exercises 1–10 show how the given numbers would be stored in normalized floating-point form in F and E registers, where F is seven bits and E is five bits.

*1. 43	2. 4.25	*3. −3.125
4. −17.5	*5. 13.25	6. −0.125
*7. 2.625	8. 63	*9. 1
10. −16		

*11. Find a rule for multiplying two numbers in floating-point form.

12. Find a rule for dividing two numbers in floating-point form.

9.15 FLIP-FLOPS

We have seen that numbers can be stored in a binary form in registers of switches. It is now time to investigate the sophisticated types of switches used

in modern digital computers. The most common is an electronic circuit called a "flip-flop." It is beyond the scope of this work to examine the electronics of these devices. Instead, we shall look at their logical operation—what they do. There are various kinds of flip-flops, but we shall single out one common type as an example, one that is called an "RS flip-flop." It is a device with two

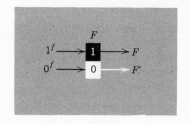

input wires and two output wires. We shall call the flip-flop F and label the input and output wires as in the figure.

We have used the symbol F to be both the name of the flip-flop and the name of one of its outputs, but this will cause no confusion. Since we shall sometimes wish to use subscripts on capital letters to denote different flip-flops, we shall use prescripts before small letters to designate the inputs.

Let us suppose that there are two voltages that can appear in the computer. For simplicity, we shall denote these by 0 and 1. F is a two-state device. That is, at any given time the voltages on the outputs F and F' are opposite. We can write $F = 1$ and $F' = 0$ or $F = 0$ and $F' = 1$. In the first case, when $F = 1$ and $F' = 0$, we say that F is "true" or F is "on." In the other case, when $F = 0$ and $F' = 1$, we say that F is "false" or F is "off." Since F must be in one state or the other, it suffices to say that $F = 1$ when it is on or $F = 0$ when it is off.

We are going to restrict our attention to a large class of computers called "synchronous." In these computers there is a regularly recurring pulse of electricity, called a "clock." All flip-flops retain their states until a clock pulse comes along. When this happens each flip-flop may or may not change its state according to the voltages appearing on the input wires. For RS flip-flops we shall summarize in Table 3 the action that occurs. We assume that the inputs, $_0f$ and $_1f$, must each have the value 0 or 1.

Table 3

$_1f$	$_0f$	F(old)	F(new)	
0	0	1	1	no change
0	0	0	0	
1	0	1	1	$F \to 1$ when $_1f = 1, {_0f} = 0$
1	0	0	1	
0	1	1	0	$F \to 0$ when $_1f = 0, {_0f} = 1$
0	1	0	0	
1	1	1	?	unpredictable when $_1f = 1, {_0f} = 1$
1	1	0	?	

It is clear that we wish to avoid having both inputs equal to 1 at the same time if we care about the state of F. Aside from this case, $_1f$ has the effect of turning F on, $_0f$ has the effect of turning F off, and if both inputs are 0 F does not change state.

Another type of flip-flop, termed JK, does not have the unpredictability of the RS type. Whenever both inputs are 1, a JK flip-flop reverses its state. The JK flip-flop is somewhat more complicated to construct than is an RS type.

9.16 GATES

There are many electronic circuits called "logical gates." We shall look at only two, the "AND-gate" and the "OR-gate." The AND-gate is a device with several inputs and one output. The output is 1 if and only if all the inputs

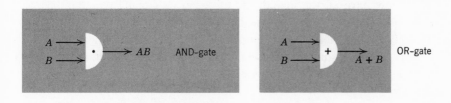

are 1. The inputs are normally either the outputs of flip-flops or the outputs of other gates. If A and B are inputs to an AND-gate, then we shall designate the output by AB. That is, $AB = 1$ if and only if $A = 1$ and $B = 1$. We shall use the diagram shown to represent such an AND-gate.

An OR-gate is a device with several inputs and one output and with the property that the output is 1 if and only if one or more of the inputs is 1. If A and B are inputs to an OR-gate, we shall represent the output by $A + B$. Thus $A + B = 1$ if and only if $A = 1$, $B = 1$, or both. We shall use the diagram shown to represent such an OR-gate.

In summary, we have two voltages, 0 and 1, appearing in the computer. These voltages, when they appear on wires, can be combined by gates to form products and sums according to Tables 4 and 5.

Table 4(·)

	0	1
0	0	0
1	0	1

Table 5 (+)

	0	1
0	0	1
1	1	1

Do these tables look familiar? They are precisely the tables for multiplication and addition in the two-valued Boolean algebra of Chapter 3. Moreover, if A is any signal (output of a flip-flop or gate), then if $A = 1$ we shall let $A' = 0$, and if $A = 0$ we shall let $A' = 1$. This is in accord with our definition of flip-flops. We are now justified in calling the set of symbols $A, B, C, \ldots,$ $F, \ldots,$ together with the operations of AND(·) and OR(+) as performed by the gates, a Boolean algebra. Thus all of the theorems and techniques of Chapter 3 can be used.

9.17   LOGICAL CIRCUITS

We now have all the ingredients to construct circuits that simulate any Boolean expression. For instance, let us consider the expression $A(B' + C)$. We shall let A, B, and C serve a dual purpose. The letters will serve both to identify flip-flops and to represent their outputs. The circuit below shows how we can form the given expression.

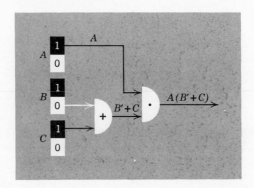

As another example, let us construct a circuit that is always true. Since a flip-flop, by definition, always has one output true and the other false, consider the circuit below.

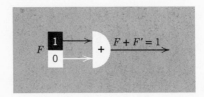

If we had used an AND-gate rather than an OR-gate, the output would be FF', which is always 0.

Let us construct a circuit that will give a true output whenever two flip-flops A and B are in the same state. We can do this by mechanizing the expression $AB + A'B'$.

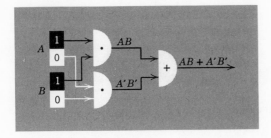

What does the circuit below do?

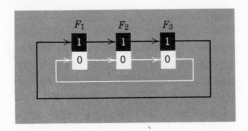

According to our notation for inputs and outputs of flip-flops, $_1f_2 = F_1$, and $_0f_2 = F_1'$. Thus at each clock pulse F_2 is set to the state that F_1 previously had. Similarly, F_3 copies F_2, and F_1 copies F_3. If we think of F_1, F_2, and F_3 as forming a register, and if we think of the states of the flip-flops at any given time as being a binary number stored in the register, then the number shifts one bit to the right and around into the left end each clock pulse. We call such an arrangement a "circulating register." After every third clock pulse the register contains its original number. For instance, if the register originally holds the number 101, after one clock pulse it holds 110. After two clock pulses it holds 011. After three clock pulses it is back to 101 again. Circulating registers of various lengths play an important role in many digital computers.

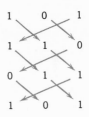

9.18 EXERCISES

1 to 5. Answer the following questions, where F is the flip-flop with the connections shown.

(a) If $F = 1$, what value will it have after the next clock pulse?

(b) If $F = 0$, what value will it have after the next clock pulse?

(c) Describe the action of F as successive clock pulses come along.

340

*Exercise 1   Exercise 2   *Exercise 3   Exercise 4   *Exercise 5

6–10. Express the output of the gate as a Boolean expression in terms of A and B.

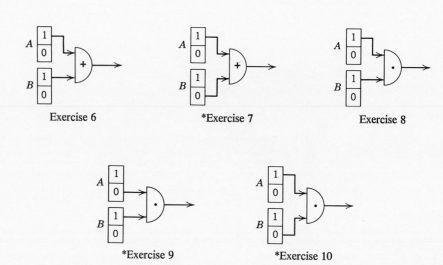

Exercise 6   *Exercise 7   Exercise 8

*Exercise 9   *Exercise 10

11–15. Express the output of each gate as a Boolean expression in terms of the flip-flops involved.

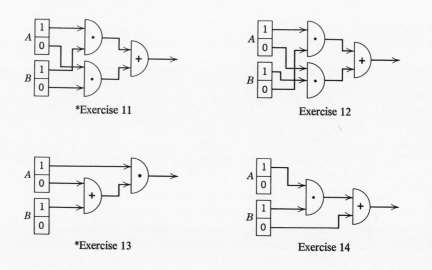

*Exercise 11   Exercise 12

*Exercise 13   Exercise 14

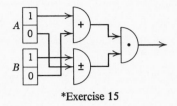

*Exercise 15

16. In the following circuit,

   (a) Express the output of each gate as a Boolean expression in terms of A, B, and C.

   (b) Form a table for the output of the last gate for all possible states of A, B, and C.

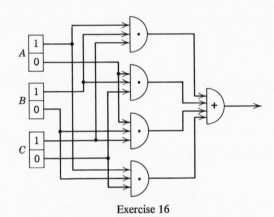

Exercise 16

A	B	C	Output
0	0	0	?
0	0	1	?

. . . .

9.19   A BINARY ADDER

In Section 9.6 we found an algorithm for serial binary addition. In later sections we examined the characteristics of RS flip-flops, AND-gates, and OR-gates. With these components it is possible to design a mechanism to carry out serial binary addition.

Let us suppose that two numbers are stored in two circulating registers of flip-flops. For the purposes of our illustration, let us suppose that these registers are four bits in length. This is hardly a realistic length, but the logic for the device is independent of the length of the registers. The A-register will consist of flip-flops A_1, A_2, A_3, and A_4. The B-register will consist of flip-flops B_1, B_2, B_3, and B_4. The carry flip-flop will be called C. In addition, let E be a flip-flop that controls addition. That is, when E is on we shall add the number in the B-register to that in the A-register, leaving the sum in A. The B-register will remain unchanged. When E is off, both registers merely circulate. That is, A_4 copies A_3, A_3 copies A_2, A_2 copies A_1, and A_1 copies A_4. The B-register does the same. When E is on, the only change is that A_1 copies not A_4 but the sum of A_4 and B_4 with the proper carry.

Since A_2, A_3, A_4, and the B-register always do the same thing, regardless of E, their logical equations are very simple. These equations are given below. We shall include the equations for A_1 when E is off.

$$_1a_1 = A_4E' \qquad _1a_2 = A_1 \qquad _1a_3 = A_2 \qquad _1a_4 = A_3$$
$$_0a_1 = A_4'E' \qquad _0a_2 = A_1' \qquad _0a_3 = A_2' \qquad _0a_4 = A_3'$$

$$_1b_1 = B_4 \qquad _1b_2 = B_1 \qquad _1b_3 = B_2 \qquad _1b_4 = B_3$$
$$_0b_1 = B_4' \qquad _0b_2 = B_1' \qquad _0b_3 = B_2' \qquad _0b_4 = B_3'$$

So far our equations indicate that the flip-flops are to be connected as in the figure.

When E is on, we wish to add A and B. For this we refer to the algorithm found in Section 9.6. We shall suppose that the carry is off when the addition

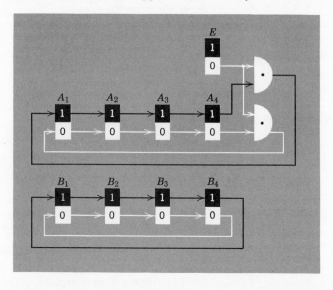

starts. That is, when E is turned on, C is off. According to the algorithm, C remains off until both

$$A_4 = 1 \quad \text{and} \quad B_4 = 1.$$

Then C remains on until

$$A_4 = 0 \quad \text{and} \quad B_4 = 0.$$

Moreover, this operation occurs only while E is on. Thus

$$_1c = A_4 B_4 E$$
$$_0c = A_4' B_4' E.$$

The algorithm for the sum bit tells us that when E is on, A_1 is to be set to 1 if A_4 and B_4 are different and the carry is off or A_4 and B_4 are alike and the carry is on. Otherwise A_1 is set to 0.

$$_1a_1 = (A_4 B_4' C' + A_4' B_4 C' + A_4 B_4 C + A_4' B_4' C)E$$
$$_0a_1 = (A_4 B_4' C + A_4' B_4 C + A_4 B_4 C' + A_4' B_4' C')E$$

Since a diagram of the equations above would be rather extensive, we shall not draw the complete circuit. However, in Exercise 16 of the last exercise set you will find the circuit representing the quantity in parentheses that occurs in the equation for $_1a_1$.

9.20 SUBTRACTION

We have used the flip-flop E as a control for addition. Let us extend our control by introducing another flip-flop, D. Further, let us suppose that E and D are used in the following way: if E is on, the A- and B-registers will be either added or subtracted, according to D. If D is on, A and B are to be added. If D is off, B is to be subtracted from A. In both cases the result of the operation is to be placed in the A-register. The reason for making this change in the role of E is that we found in Section 9.7 that the logic for forming the difference bit in subtraction is precisely the same as that for forming the sum bit in addition. If $E = 1$ indicates that addition *or* subtraction is to be performed, we need make no change in our equations for any of the A or B flip-flops. The only change that must be made is that C can be used for both the carry in addition and the borrow in subtraction if we write its equations as below:

$$_1c = (A_4 B_4 D + A_4' B_4 D')E$$
$$_0c = (A_4' B_4' D + A_4 B_4' D')E.$$

If E and D are both on, C acts as the carry in addition. If E is on but D is off, C is turned on when $A_4 = 0$ and $B_4 = 1$, and C is turned off when $A_4 = 1$ and $B_4 = 0$. This is exactly what we found, in Section 9.7, that the operation of the borrow should be.

> **Example 1.** Since it takes four clock pulses for a complete circulation of a four-bit register, let us denote the successive times of a cycle by T_1, T_2, T_3, and T_4. Suppose that at time T_1 the A-register contains the number 6 (0110 in binary form), and the B-register contains 3 (0011). Further, suppose that C is off, E is on, and D is on. Then addition should occur. In the following illustration let us trace the operation of our adder, clock-pulse by clock-pulse.
>
> When the second T_1 time occurs, the A-register holds the number 9, which is the correct sum. The B-register holds the same information as before.

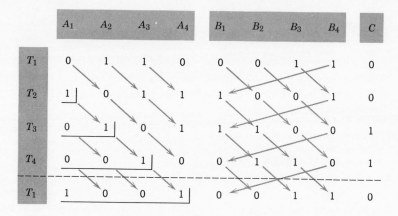

	A_1	A_2	A_3	A_4	B_1	B_2	B_3	B_4	C
T_1	0	1	1	0	0	0	1	1	0
T_2	1	0	1	1	1	0	0	1	0
T_3	0	1	0	1	1	1	0	0	1
T_4	0	0	1	0	0	1	1	0	1
T_1	1	0	0	1	0	0	1	1	0

> **Example 2.** In the next illustration let us trace the operation of our registers if one change is made. Suppose that D is off. Our logic is written in such a way that subtraction should occur.

	A_1	A_2	A_3	A_4	B_1	B_2	B_3	B_4	C
T_1	0	1	1	0	0	0	1	1	0
T_2	1	0	1	1	1	0	0	1	1
T_3	1	1	0	1	1	1	0	0	1
T_4	0	1	1	0	0	1	1	0	0
T_1	0	0	1	1	0	0	1	1	0

When the second T_1 occurs, the A-register holds the number 3, which represents the difference $6 - 3$.

9.21   A BIT COUNTER

In a serial computer it is necessary to be able to distinguish the clock-pulses of a cycle. A cycle, the time from any T_1 until the next T_1, must be counted. Otherwise we would have no way of knowing when our answer has appeared in the proper form in the A-register. Also, at the end of the cycle E must be turned off so that the information in the A register will be preserved. If this were not done, the addition or subtraction would continue. Moreover C should be off at the start of the next cycle. Thus we must include logic at time T_4 to turn C off.

Every computer has a number of counters of one sort or another. Let us construct logic that can be mechanized to yield a device that will count in binary fashion from 0 to 3 and repeat indefinitely. We shall need two flip-flops for this, P_1 and P_2. The times T_1 to T_4 will be identified by the following table:

	P_1	P_2
T_1	0	0
T_2	0	1
T_3	1	0
T_4	1	1

By examining the succession of counts we find that P_2 is to be turned on whenever it is off and turned off whenever it is on. P_1 is turned on when $P_1 = 0$ and $P_2 = 1$, and turned off when $P_1 = P_2 = 1$.

$$_1p_1 = P_1'P_2 \qquad _1p_2 = P_2'$$
$$_0p_1 = P_1P_1 \qquad _0p_2 = P_2.$$

Thus, to turn E off at time T_4, we write

$$_0e = P_1P_2.$$

To inhibit a carry past time T_4 we must extend the equations for C so that the carry logic is implemented only during times T_1, T_2, and T_3, which is indicated by the complement of P_1P_2. Our Boolean algebra tells us that

$$(P_1P_2)' = P_1' + P_2'.$$

Hence we have

$$_1c = (A_4B_4D + A_4'B_4D')E(P_1' + P_2')$$
$$_0c = (A_4'B_4'D + A_4B_4'D')E + P_1P_2.$$

With this logic C is turned off at each time T_4. That is, at each T_4 time C receives a signal to go off. This means that we are assured that at each T_1 time C will be 0.

9.22 EXERCISES

*1. Write the equations for a three-bit register, P_1, P_2, P_3, that counts in binary form from 000 to 111 and repeats.

2. Write the equations for a five-bit register, P_1, P_2, P_3, P_4, P_5, that counts in binary form from 00000 to 11111 and repeats.

*3. Let T_{31} be a flip-flop that is on when $P_1 = P_2 = P_3 = P_4 = P_5 = 1$, where the P's are as in Exercise 2 and T_{31} is off for all other counts.

4. Consider two five-bit registers, A_1 to A_5 and B_1 to B_5, with carry C and controls D and E as in the preceding sections. That is, when E is on, B is to be added to or subtracted from A according to whether D is on or off. When E is off, A circulates. B always circulates. Let T be a flip-flop that is on once each 5 clock pulses, during the last bit of each word time.
   (a) Write the logical equations for B_1, B_2, B_3, B_4, and B_5.
   (b) Write the logical equations for C, using A_5, B_5, D, E, and T.
   (c) Write the logical equations for A_1, A_2, A_3, A_4, and A_5.

5. *(a) Write the input equations for three flip-flops, F_1, F_2, and F_3, where F_2 copies F_1, F_3 copies F_2, and F_1 inverts F_3. That is, F_1 is turned on when F_3 is off and turned off when F_3 is on.
   (b) Give the sequence of counts generated by this counter, starting with 000.

6. (a) Write the input equations for three flip-flops, F_1, F_2 and F_3, where F_2 copies F_1, F_3 copies F_2, and F_1 copies F_3 when $F_1 = 1$ and copies the opposite of F_3 when $F_1 = 0$.
   (b) Give the sequence of counts generated, starting with 000.

*7. Write the equations for a three-bit register, P_1, P_2, P_3, that counts down in binary form from 111 to 000 and repeats.

9.23 STORAGE DEVICES

In addition to carrying out arithmetic operations a computer must be capable of storing information, both data and instructions, until this information is needed. We have seen that it is possible to store numbers in flip-flop registers. Such storage is quite expensive when we realize that we want to be able to store thousands of numbers. We shall not examine all the devices that have been used in the past for this purpose. Instead we shall look at only two: revolving magnetic devices and magnetic cores. For the first, we may think of a device something like a record player. Suppose that a record has many concentric channels rather than a single spiral groove. Further, suppose that each channel consists of a chain of spots of magnetic material. It is characteristic of magnetic material that it can be magnetized in either of two polarities. Let us agree that a spot magnetized with one polarity will represent the binary digit 1, and the other polarity will represent 0. The phonograph pickup will resemble that on a tape recorder. When it passes over a spot with a polarity representing 1, a small current is induced in a certain direction. A reversed polarity in the spot induces a current in the opposite direction. Such a device can be reversed in its operation so that a current in the pickup magnetizes with a certain polarity a spot that is passing under the pickup. If our computer now has one register storing the channel where the pickup is located and another counting bits around the channel, we have a device capable of picking up (reading) or storing (writing) digital information. Some computers actually use disks that resemble phonograph records in appearance. Others have the channels arranged in parallel around a cylinder, which is universally called a "drum" in computer jargon. Some computers have a single pickup (called a read-write head) that can be mechanically positioned on any channel specified by a register. Others have one or more heads on each channel. In the latter case the specifying register acts merely to select the desired head.

The magnetic disks and drums store information serially. When a number is to be transferred to or from the device, it is done one bit at a time. Much faster operation can be achieved if all the bits of a number can be transferred at the same time. This is called *parallel* transmission. The most common way of doing this is to use arrays of tiny magnetic coated doughnuts, called *cores*, strung on wires. Each core can be magnetized in either of two polarities, so that each core can store a bit. (If a current is fed through a wire that goes through a core, the current is impeded by a magnetic field with one polarity but not by the reverse.) Although this is a vastly oversimplified picture of the operation, it is possible both to sense and to set a 1 or a 0 in a core. The cores are arranged in such a way that each row in an array represents a stored number. Furthermore, each such row has associated with it a number, called its *address*. When this address is stored in the appropriate register, it is possible to single out a specific number from thousands stored in the arrays and to transfer information between the cores and a flip-flop register.

9.24   COMPUTER INSTRUCTIONS

An instruction to a computer takes a variety of forms. Since it is to be stored in the computer memory, it must be a number. In some computers the number is binary, so that it is a simple sequence of 0's and 1's. In others decimal digits are translated into one of a number of binary codes and stored as decimal digits. All instruction formats must provide for a minimum of two parts to the instruction. One part specifies an operation to be performed. In addition, there are one or more parts that specify addresses. These addresses may specify the location of operands, or they may specify the location of the next instruction to be executed. If only one address is included in an instruction, then it is necessary to have a counter that keeps track of the location of the next instruction to be performed. Such an instruction counter will be advanced each time an instruction is completed. A counter of this sort is not necessary if the instruction format includes the address of the next instruction.

Let us suppose that a program, a list of instructions, is stored in the memory. The program is initiated by setting the instruction counter to the address of the first instruction in the program. When this is done, the specified instruction is fetched from memory. The operation code is stored in an "operation code register," and the address portion in an "address register." We shall suppose that the machine has at least two additional flip-flop registers, which we shall call A and B. A typical instruction may consist of the code for "add" and the address of an operand. First there is an interpretation phase in which the operation code register is examined to determine what to do next. Since the code is "add," the next thing is to fetch the number whose address is in the address register to the B-register. The next step is to add the contents of B to A. While this is going on the instruction counter is counting up by one. When the addition is completed, the cycle is repeated. The next instruction is brought from memory, interpreted, executed, and so on until an instruction is reached that calls a halt to the entire process.

The number of different operations that can be executed varies widely from computer to computer. Some have as few as sixteen. Others have hundreds. In all cases, however, the computer must be capable of transferring information to and from the outside world, whether on cards, punched paper tape, magnetic tape, manual keyboard, or other device. Further, the computer must be capable of performing the basic arithmetic operations either by hardware or by program. Finally, the computer must be capable of making decisions. One way to accomplish this is to have an instruction which we shall call "branch on negative." When this instruction is to be executed, the computer first looks at a number held in some particular location, the A-register, for instance. If the number is zero or positive, the computer does nothing and goes on to the next instruction. If the number is negative, however, the contents of the address register are transferred to the instruction counter. This effectively breaks the sequence of instructions and causes the program to branch to a different sequence. Such an instruction is called a "conditional branch" command. Also, in our hypothetical computer, we need the flexibility to make a jump that is not conditional. That is, there are times when we wish to branch to a new sequence of instructions regardless of any condition. This can be accomplished by a simple command that always transfers the contents of the address register to the instruction counter.

9.25   A PROGRAM

Let us see how a computer such as we have described might add 100 numbers. We shall suppose the numbers are stored in memory locations whose addresses are 201 to 300, and the sum is to be placed in location 100. We shall start our program in location 500. One possible program is given below. We have written the operations in English, but we understand that each operation is specified by a number in the machine.

	Instruction		
Location	Operation	Address	Interpretation
500	Fetch	201	First number (stored in location 201) is brought to the A-register.
501	Add	202	Second number (stored in location 202) is added to the first.
502	Add	203	Third number is added to the partial sum.
.	.	.	
.	.	.	
.	.	.	
599	Add	300	Last number (stored in location 300) is added to the partial sum.
600	Store	100	The sum is placed in location 100.
601	Halt	—	The program stops.

The program occupies 102 locations in memory. If there had been 1000 numbers to add, the program would require 1002 locations. This is extremely wasteful of memory space, as we shall see. The power of digital computers lies in their ability to do repetitive computations with ease. Let us see how this is done. The algorithm to be followed is given by the following steps:

1. Add a number to the contents of location 100.
2. Determine whether the number added was the last in the list.
3. If the number just added was not the last, go back to step 1.
4. If the number just added was the last, halt.

In order to execute this algorithm, we shall assume that 0 is stored in memory location 100, −100 in location 301, and 1 in location 302. We shall add one instruction, called *BAN*, which will branch to the address given if *A* is negative. Our basic step will consist of the single instruction, "Add 201," which will be brought to the *A*-register, increased by 1, so that it reads "Add 202," and put back in place. Then a counter, which starts at −100, will be brought to the *A*-register, increased by 1 so that it is −99, and put back in place. As long as the count is negative the program will branch back to the basic Add instruction. When the count 0 is reached, all 100 numbers will have been added, and the program halts. The program depends upon the fact that, since "Add" is merely a mnemonic device to represent a coded number, the instruction "Add 201" is a single number ending in 201. If we add 1 to this number and replace it in its former location, it will be interpreted as the instruction "Add 202."

	Instruction		
Location	Operation	Address	Interpretation
500	Fetch	100	Bring the partial sum (0 at first) to the *A*-register.
501	Add	201	Form a new partial sum in the *A*-register.
502	Store	100	Replace new partial sum in location 100.
503	Fetch	501	Bring [Add 201] to the *A*-register.
504	Add	302	The *A*-register now contains [Add 202].
505	Store	501	Replace the modified instruction in 501.
506	Fetch	301	Bring the count to the *A*-register.
507	Add	302	Add 1 to the count.
508	Store	301	Replace the modified count in the counter. (Note that it is also still in the *A*-register.)
509	BAN	500	If the count is still negative, go back to the instruction in location 500.)
510	Halt	—	The program stops.

A program like the one above is said to use a "loop." The computer runs through the instructions located from 500 to 509 over and over again until the problem is completed. We should observe two things. One is that the eleven steps of this program are independent of the number of numbers to be added. Simply by changing the count originally in location 301 we can add any number of numbers that we please. The second thing to observe is that this simple program can be used over and over again to add different lists if we merely set certain initial constants. All computers use such universal programs. They are called *subroutines* and can be used by any program.

The problems for which computers are used are those in which a very great amount of computation is involved. The algorithms for the solutions of such problems nearly always involve loops, often loops within loops within loops. It is not surprising, then, that the logical design of digital computers has reflected this requirement. Most modern computers are built with extra registers and extra commands that make the programming of loops easier and that permit the programs to run faster. It is fascinating to investigate more thoroughly the wonderful complexity of modern computers, but it is not within the scope of this book.

9.26   COMPILERS

Each digital computer is built with a certain "machine language." This language is the precise numerical code that represents the operations the computer can execute. At one time all programs were written in the machine language of the particular computer on which the programs were to be run. Since different computers can have radically different machine languages, a program written for one computer might be completely useless even as a basis for a program for another computer. Also, it is not easy to write programs in most machine languages. This is particularly true for the more powerful computers whose languages reflect the complexity and flexibility of sophisticated logical design. Thus there arose the concept of "problem-oriented languages." These are languages that are somewhat closer to English. Most of them are oriented toward problems of a particular nature, as ALGOL is an *algo*rithmically *o*riented *l*anguage, FORTRAN is a *for*mula *trans*lator, COBOL is a *com*mon *b*usiness *o*riented *l*anguage, LISP is a *lis*t *p*rocessor, and so forth. Once such languages are established and there is general agreement about their vocabulary, syntax, and punctuation, it becomes possible to write a program for each computer that will translate problem-oriented language programs into machine language. These translating programs are called "compilers." Most programs are now written in one of these more general languages. As a consequence, such programs are not restricted to particular computers. They can be run on any computer that has the appropriate compiler.

One reason for the increased use of these superlanguages is that computer hardware has advanced rapidly and has increased the power of machines until some are capable of executing millions of program steps per second. This means that they are capable of handling problems of enormous complexity, problems whose programs have hundreds of thousands of instructions. It would be physically impossible to get such programs written if compilers did not permit this use of languages to simplify the task.

Let us return to our problem of adding 100 or 1000 numbers. If we were using a language like FORTRAN, for instance, we would not be required to know where the individual data were located in the memory. When information is read into the memory, it is assigned a name and is thereafter referred to by that name. The compiler keeps track of where it is. A list of numbers is assigned a name with subscripts so that our list of numbers might be called A(I). Here A is the name of the list and I is the subscript that takes on the values from 1 to N, if there are N numbers in the list. If we wished the sum of the N numbers, we could write the following program:

$$\text{SUM} = 0$$
$$\text{DO } 7, \text{I} = 1,\text{N}$$
$$7 \text{ SUM} = \text{SUM} + \text{A(I)}$$

The first line sets a storage location called SUM to zero. The second line says that the line labeled 7 is to be repeated N times with I assuming the successive values from 1 to N. The third line, which carries the label 7, says that for each value of I, A(I) is to be added to the current contents of SUM, forming a new number in SUM.

9.27 EXERCISES

*1. What basic property must a physical device have in order for it to be used to store binary information?

2. What is the length in bits of the shortest binary register capable of holding any of the digits from 0 to 9?

*3. What is the length in bits of the shortest binary register capable of holding any of the letters of the English alphabet?

4. What is the length in bits of the shortest binary register capable of holding any decimal digit *or* letter?

*5. What is the length in bits of the shortest binary register capable of holding any of the notes on a standard piano keyboard? (There are 88 notes.)

6. (a) In the example of Section 9.25, where an eleven-step program was given to add 100 numbers, what changes can be made to form the sum of only those numbers in memory locations with *even* addresses?

(b) What changes can be made to form the sum of only those numbers in memory locations with *odd* addresses?

*7. Let x be stored in location 100 and y in location 101. Using *Fetch, Store, Subtract, BAN,* and *Halt,* write a program that will leave x and y alone if $x > y$ but will interchange the two if $x \leq y$. Start your program at location 1. (The *Subtract* command causes the number at the given address to be subtracted from the number in the A-register.)

9.28 RECOMMENDED READING

Bartee, T. C., Lebow, I. L., and Reed, I. S., *Theory and Design of Digital Machines,* New York, McGraw-Hill, 1962.

Halacy, D. S. Jr., *Computers, the Machines We Think With,* New York, Harper and Row, 1962.

Hohn, F. E., *Applied Boolean Algebra,* New York, Macmillan, 1960.

McCracken, D. D., *Digital Computer Programming,* New York, Wiley, 1957.

Phister, M., Jr., *Logical Design of Digital Computers,* New York, Wiley, 1958.

Richards, R. K., *Arithmetic Operations in Digital Computers,* Princeton, Van Nostrand, 1955.

Stibitz, G. R., and Larrivee, J. A., *Mathematics and Computers,* New York, McGraw-Hill, 1957.

Ulam, S. M., "Computers," *Scientific American,* vol. 211, no. 3, Sept., 1964.

Whitesitt, J. E., *Boolean Algebra and its Applications,* Reading, Mass., Addison-Wesley, 1961.

Young, F. H., *Digital Computers and Related Mathematics,* Boston, Ginn, 1961.

Solutions to Selected Exercises

1.6

5. The formula for the volume of the frustum of a right pyramid:

$$V = \frac{h(a^2 + ab + b^2)}{3}.$$

6.

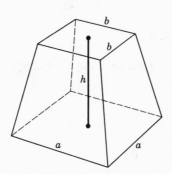

Solution to Exercise 6

7. $\dfrac{768(12)}{14000} = 0.651$, or approximately $\dfrac{2}{3}$ inch.

8. Express a, b, and h in feet: $a = 768$, $b = 12$, $h = 251$. Then

$$V = \frac{251(768^2 + 768 \cdot 12 + 12^2)}{3} = 51,306,408 \text{ cu. ft.}$$

9. $V = \dfrac{251(768^2 + 12^2)}{2} = 49,360,656$ cu. ft.

1.13

2. The area of a square $a + b$ on a side is

$$(a + b)^2 = a^2 + 2ab + b^2.$$

The area of the rearranged square is the sum of the area of a square c on a side and four right triangles, each of area $ab/2$. Thus

$$a^2 + 2ab + b^2 = c^2 + 2ab, \quad \text{or} \quad a^2 + b^2 = c^2.$$

3. The square whose side is of length $a + b$ is made up of two smaller squares, one with area a^2 and the other with area b^2, and two rectangles of area ab. Thus

$$(a + b)^2 = a^2 + 2ab + b^2.$$

5. If $a = 7$ and $b = 24$, then

$$c^2 = 7^2 + 24^2 = 49 + 576 = 625 = 25^2.$$

Thus

$$c = 25.$$

7. If $c = 17$ and $b = 8$, then

$$a^2 = 17^2 - 8^2 = 289 - 64 = 225 = 15^2.$$

Thus

$$a = 15.$$

9. If $a = \sqrt{2}$ and $b = \sqrt{2}$, then

$$c^2 = 2 + 2 = 4, \quad \text{or} \quad c = 2.$$

12. $a^2 + b^2 = (p^2 - q^2)^2 + (2pq)^2 = p^4 - 2p^2q^2 + q^4 + 4p^2q^2$
$= p^4 + 2p^2q^2 + q^4 = (p^2 + q^2)^2 = c^2.$

14. $(2n)^2 + (n^2 - 1)^2 = 4n^2 + n^4 - 2n^2 + 1 = n^4 + 2n^2 + 1 = (n^2 + 1)^2.$

17. $a^2 = (1 + x)^2 + y^2 = 1 + 2x + x^2 + y^2$
$b^2 = (1 - x)^2 + y^2 = 1 - 2x + x^2 + y^2$

Thus

$$a^2 + b^2 = 2 + 2(x^2 + y^2) = 2 + 2 = 4$$

1.18

1.

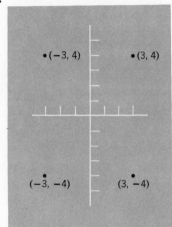

Solution to Exercise 1

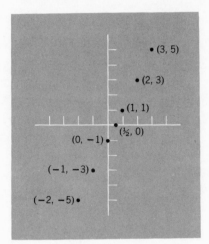

Solution to Exercise 3

5. If 3 is substituted for x and 4 for y,

$$x^2 + y^2 = 3^2 + 4^2 = 9 + 16 = 25.$$

Since the equation is satisfied, (3, 4) represents a point on the graph. Similarly, since $(-4)^2 + 3^2 = 16 + 9 = 25$, the point represented by $(-4, 3)$ is also on the graph.

7. In the seven bridges problem there are four regions, each accessible by an odd number of bridges. If a region can be reached by an odd number of paths, then not every path leading to the region can be paired with a path leading away. Thus the trip must either start or finish at any region accessible by an odd number of paths. Thus if a circuit can be made crossing each bridge just once, there must be either two odd junctions, one forming a starting point and the other the end, or no odd junctions, in which case the starting point and ending point coincide. In the given exercise, if any one bridge is removed we are left with two even and two odd junctions. As we have seen, this makes the trip possible.

9.

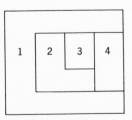

Solution to Exercise 9

1.23

1.

1 = 1	5 = 101	9 = 1001	13 = 1101	17 = 10001
2 = 10	6 = 110	10 = 1010	14 = 1110	18 = 10010
3 = 11	7 = 111	11 = 1011	15 = 1111	19 = 10011
4 = 100	8 = 1000	12 = 1100	16 = 10000	20 = 10100

3.

10 = 20	13 = 23	16 = 31	19 = 34
11 = 21	14 = 24	17 = 32	20 = 40
12 = 22	15 = 30	18 = 33	

5. $1432 =$

$1432 = $ ⅠⅠ∩∩∩??????

7.

$$(+)$$
$$\begin{array}{c|cc} & 0 & 1 \\ \hline 0 & 0 & 1 \\ 1 & 1 & 10 \end{array}$$

$$(\cdot)$$
$$\begin{array}{c|cc} & 0 & 1 \\ \hline 0 & 0 & 0 \\ 1 & 0 & 1 \end{array}$$

9. $10.101 = 2 + \dfrac{5}{8} = \dfrac{21}{8}$

11.
$$\begin{array}{r} \overset{//}{237} \\ 564 \\ \end{array}$$
$(\overline{1023})_8 = 8^3 + 2(8) + 3 = 512 + 16 + 3 = 531$

13.
$$\begin{array}{r} \overset{///}{101101} \\ 110110 \\ \end{array}$$
$(\overline{1100011})_2 = 2^6 + 2^5 + 2 + 1 = 64 + 32 + 2 + 1 = 99$

15.
$$\begin{array}{r} 1101 \\ 101 \\ \hline 1101 \\ \end{array}$$
$$\begin{array}{r} 1101 \\ \hline 1000001 \end{array} = 2^6 + 1 = 64 + 1 = 65$$

16. (a) LXXXIII   (c) XXXVIII

17. (a) LX   (c) MCXXII

1.28

1. Let $x = 5$. Then $x + 3x/5 = 5 + 3 = 8$. Since $40 = 5(8)$,

$$x = 5(5) = 25.$$

3. Let $x = 12$. Then $2x/3 - 5x/4 = 8 - 15 = -7$. Since $14 = -2(-7)$,

$$x = -2(12) = -24.$$

5. (a) $33 = 1 + 32$

1 *	37
2	74
4	148
8	296
16	592
32 *	1184
	$\overline{1221}$

(b) $29 = 1 + 4 + 8 + 16$

1 *	32
2	64
4 *	128
8 *	256
16 *	512
	$\overline{928}$

(c) $16 = 16$

1	43
2	86
4	172
8	344
16 *	688
	$\overline{688}$

(d) $71 = 1 + 2 + 4 + 64$

1 *	88
2 *	176
4 *	352
8	704
16	1408
32	2816
64 *	5632
	$\overline{6248}$

7. The set of all square roots of positive integers that are not perfect squares. The proof of the irrationality of $\sqrt{2}$ given in the text used only the fact that 2 was not a square. The same method works for 3, 5, 6, 7, or an integer that is not a square. Another set consists of all integral multiples of $\sqrt{2}$. If $n\sqrt{2}$ is rational, there are integers p and q such that $n\sqrt{2} = p/q$. But then $\sqrt{2} = p/qn$, or $\sqrt{2}$ is rational. Since this is false, $n\sqrt{2}$ is not rational for any integer n.

9. $\sqrt{102} = \sqrt{10^2 + 2} = 10 + 2/20 = 10.1$ approximately. From tables we find that $\sqrt{102} = 10.0995$ to four decimal places. The smallness of the error is a result of the nearness of 102 to a perfect square.

11. The first hypotenuse has length $\sqrt{2}$; the next is $\sqrt{2 + 1} = \sqrt{3}$; the next is $\sqrt{3 + 1} = \sqrt{4}$. The sequence of lengths is $\{\sqrt{2}, \sqrt{3}, \sqrt{4}, \sqrt{5}, \sqrt{6}, \ldots\}$. In other words, the construction method used in this problem permits us to construct a length corresponding to the square root of any natural number.

1.33

1. 6 is perfect. 12, 18, and 20 are abundant. The rest are deficient.

3. $945 = 1 \cdot 3 \cdot 3 \cdot 3 \cdot 5 \cdot 7$. If we form all combinations of these factors, we find: $1 + 3 + 5 + 7 + 9 + 15 + 21 + 27 + 35 + 45 + 63 + 105 + 135 + 189 + 315 = 975 > 945$. Hence 945 is abundant.

5. For $n = 2$, $2^{n-1}(2^n - 1) = 2(3) = 6$.
   For $n = 3$, $2^{n-1}(2^n - 1) = 4(7) = 28$.
   For $n = 5$, $2^{n-1}(2^n - 1) = 16(31) = 496$.
   For $n = 7$, $2^{n-1}(2^n - 1) = 64(127) = 8128$.

7. Two solutions are given by $x = -3$, $y = 4$, and by $x = 3$, $y = -3$. There are infinitely many solutions.

9. $29 = 16 + 9 + 4$

2.4

3. Plane geometry and the natural numbers are both logical systems based on observations and needs from the real world. The properties of the elements and operations of each system were deduced from a set of postulates, which were arrived at intuitively and which are accepted without proof.

5. Subtraction, division, and extraction of roots.

7. 24, 25, 26, 27, 28

9. 2 and 7

11. (a) $3(n - 1)$ (b) $n(n + 1)/2$

2.10

1. Let M be the set of natural numbers n for which the statement is true.

1. For $n = 1$, we have

$$1 = \frac{1(1 + 1)}{2} = 1.$$

Thus 1 belongs to M.

2. If any k belongs to M,

$$1 + 2 + \cdots + k = \frac{k(k + 1)}{2}.$$

For any true equation we can add the same thing to both sides. Let us add $k + 1$. Then

$$1 + 2 + \cdots + k + (k + 1) = \frac{k(k + 1)}{2} + (k + 1)$$

$$= (k + 1)\left(\frac{k}{2} + 1\right) = \frac{(k + 1)(k + 2)}{2}.$$

This tells us that $k + 1$ belongs to M. By the induction postulate, M contains all natural numbers, or the statement is true for *all* natural numbers.

3. Let M be the set of natural numbers for which the statement is true.

1. For $n = 1$,

$$1 = 2^1 - 1 = 1.$$

Thus 1 belongs to M.

2. If any k belongs to M, then

$$1 + 2 + \cdots + 2^{k-1} = 2^k - 1.$$

If this is true, we can add 2^k to both sides and obtain

$$1 + 2 + \cdots + 2^{k-1} + 2^k = 2^k - 1 + 2^k = 2 \cdot 2^k - 1 = 2^{k+1} - 1.$$

Since this states that $k + 1$ belongs to M, the given equation is true for all natural numbers.

4. (a) 1, 1, 2, 3, 5, 8, 13, 21, 34, 55
   (b) Since the first term of the sequence is defined, and since we have a method of extending a sequence of any length one more term, the entire sequence is well defined by the induction postulate.

5. If $S = 80$, $a = 2$, and $l = 54$, and $S = \dfrac{a - rl}{1 - r}$, then

$$80 = \frac{2 - 54r}{1 - r}, \quad \text{or} \quad 80 - 80r = 2 - 54r, \quad \text{or} \quad 26r = 78.$$

Hence,

$$r = 3.$$

Since $l = ar^{n-1}$,

$$54 = 2 \cdot 3^{n-1}, \quad \text{or} \quad 3^{n-1} = 27 = 3^3.$$

Hence,

$$n - 1 = 3, \quad \text{or} \quad n = 4.$$

7. (a) $3/2 = 2 - 1/2$ (b) $7/4 = 2 - 1/4$
   (c) $15/8 = 2 - 1/8$ (d) $31/16 = 2 - 1/16$
   (e) $63/32 = 2 - 1/32$ (f) $127/64 = 2 - 1/64$

9. (a) 1/4 yard   1/32 yard $1/2^{n-1}$ yard
   (b) For 9 jumps the distance from the pool is 1/64 yard, which is less than 1 inch.

11. $1! = 1$ $2! = 2$
    $3! = 6$ $4! = 24$
    $5! = 120$ $6! = 720$
    $7! = 5040$ $8! = 40{,}320$
    $9! = 362{,}780$ $10! = 3{,}627{,}800$

13. (a) $26^3 \cdot 10^3$ (b) $26 \cdot 25 \cdot 24 \cdot 10^3$ (c) $26 \cdot 25 \cdot 24 \cdot 10 \cdot 9 \cdot 8$

2.13

1. (a) A2   (c) C2   (e) M4   (g) M1   (i) If we write this as $5 + (2 + 4) =$
   $(5 + 2) + 4$, then A3.   (k) T   (m) E5   (o) E4

2. Suppose there is a natural number x such that $3x + 4 = 19$.

$$
\begin{array}{ll}
19 = 15 + 4 & \text{A1 (uniqueness)} \\
3x + 4 = 15 + 4 & \text{E4} \\
3x = 15 & \text{C1} \\
15 = 3 \cdot 5 & \text{M1 (uniqueness)} \\
3x = 3 \cdot 5 & \text{E4} \\
x = 5 & \text{C2}
\end{array}
$$

Thus, if there is a solution, it is 5. Since 5 satisfies the given equation, it is the desired solution.

5. (a)
$$
\begin{array}{ll}
(x - 2)(x - 3) = x(x - 3) - 2(x - 3) & \text{D} \\
= (x^2 - x \cdot 3) + (-2x - 2 \cdot -3) & \text{D} \\
= (x^2 - 3x) + (-2x + 6) & \text{M2 and Theorem 2} \\
= x^2 + (-3x - 2x) + 6 & \text{A3} \\
= x^2 + (-3 - 2)x + 6 & \text{D} \\
= x^2 - 5x + 6 & \text{A1}
\end{array}
$$

(b) For $x = 2$, $x - 2 = 0$, and for $x = 3$, $x - 3 = 0$. The desired conclusion follows from Theorem 1.

7. (a) $x = 1$. There are no more.

(b) $x = 3$. Any integer larger than 3.

9. Since $3 + 2 = 5$, $3 < 5$. If there were a natural number x for which $x + 5 = 3$, then $5 < 3$. By the trichotomy law this is false. Thus no such x exists.

2.16

1. Suppose there is an integer x such that $x + 6 = 2$. Then

$$
\begin{array}{ll}
(x + 6) + (-6) = 2 + (-6) & \text{E5} \\
x + [6 + (-6)] = 2 + (-6) & \text{A3} \\
x + 0 = 2 + (-6) & \text{A5} \\
x + 0 = 2 + [-2 + (-4)] & \text{A1} \\
x + 0 = [2 + (-2)] + (-4) & \text{A3} \\
x + 0 = 0 + (-4) & \text{A5} \\
x = -4 & \text{A4}
\end{array}
$$

Thus, if there is a solution, it is -4. Since -4 checks, it is the desired solution. The proof is much shorter if C1 is used.

$$
\begin{array}{ll}
x + 6 = -4 + 6 & \text{A1 (uniqueness)} \\
x = -4 & \text{C1}
\end{array}
$$

3. Suppose there is an x such that $3x - 4 = 2$. Then

$$
\begin{array}{ll}
(3x - 4) + 4 = 2 + 4 & \text{E5} \\
3x + (-4 + 4) = 6 & \text{A3 and A1} \\
3x + 0 = 3 \cdot 2 & \text{A5 and M1} \\
3x = 3 \cdot 2 & \text{A4} \\
x = 2 & \text{C2}
\end{array}
$$

Since 2 checks, it is the desired solution.

5. A1, A4

6. M4

9. Let M be the set of all natural numbers less than every number in S.

1. Then 1 belongs to M. If it did not, it would be the smallest number in S.
2. Suppose k belongs to M. Then all natural numbers from 1 to k belong to M, by the way M is defined. If $k + 1$ belongs to S, then it is the smallest element of S. Since S has no smallest element, $k + 1$ belongs to M. By the inductive postulate, M contains all natural numbers. Thus S is empty. But S is not empty by hypothesis. From this contradiction we conclude that S has a smallest element.

11. By A4,

$$x = 0 + x.$$

If $a + x = a$ for every a, then

$$0 + x = 0.$$

Hence

$$x = 0.$$

13. If x is a nonzero integer, then by T either x is positive or x is negative. All we need show is that if x is negative, x^2 is positive. However, if x is negative, then $-x$ is positive, and $x^2 = (-x)(-x) = (-x)^2$ by Theorem 2.

15. If $x^2 + 4 = 0$, then $x^2 < 0$, which contradicts what was proved in Exercise 13.

2.19

1. Suppose there is an x such that $2x - 3 = 7$. Then

$$
\begin{array}{ll}
2x - 3 = 10 - 3 & \text{A1 and def. of subtraction} \\
2x = 10 & \text{C1} \\
2x = 2 \cdot 5 & \text{M1} \\
x = 5 & \text{C2}
\end{array}
$$

Since 5 checks, it is the solution.

3. D

4. Suppose x and y are nonzero rational numbers such that $xy = 0$. Since $y \neq 0$, by M5 there is a rational number y^{-1} such that $yy^{-1} = 1$. Then

$$
\begin{array}{ll}
(xy)y^{-1} = 0 \cdot y^{-1} & \text{E5} \\
x(yy^{-1}) = 0 & \text{M3 and Theorem 1} \\
x \cdot 1 = 0 & \text{M5} \\
x = 0 & \text{M4}
\end{array}
$$

Thus, if $y \neq 0$, x must be 0. We cannot have both x and y zero.

6.
$$
\begin{array}{ll}
(x + y)(x - y) = x(x - y) + y(x - y) & \text{D and M2} \\
\quad = (x^2 - xy) + (yx - y^2) & \text{D} \\
\quad = (x^2 - xy) + (xy - y^2) & \text{M2} \\
\quad = x^2 + [-xy + (xy - y^2)] & \text{M3} \\
\quad = x^2 + [(-xy + xy) - y^2] & \text{M3} \\
\quad = x^2 + (0 - y^2) & \text{A5} \\
\quad = x^2 - y^2 & \text{A4}
\end{array}
$$

9. Multiply the fractions by 1 in the form of $\dfrac{12}{12}, \dfrac{6}{6}, \dfrac{4}{4}, \dfrac{3}{3}$, and $\dfrac{2}{2}$. Then

$$
1 + \frac{1}{2} + \frac{1}{3} + \frac{1}{4} + \frac{1}{6} = \frac{12}{12} + \frac{6}{12} + \frac{4}{12} + \frac{3}{12} + \frac{2}{12} \qquad \text{M4}
$$

$$
= (12 + 6 + 4 + 3 + 2)\left(\frac{1}{12}\right) \qquad \text{D}
$$

$$
= \frac{27}{12} \qquad\qquad\qquad \text{A1 and A3.}
$$

Or we can use Theorem 6.

$$
1 = \frac{12}{12} \qquad \text{M5}
$$

$$
\frac{1}{2} + \frac{1}{6} = \frac{8}{12} \qquad \text{Theorem 6}
$$

$$
\frac{1}{3} + \frac{1}{4} = \frac{7}{12} \qquad \text{Theorem 6}
$$

Thus the sum $= \dfrac{27}{12}$.

11. Suppose $ac = bc$ and $c \neq 0$. Then

$$
\begin{array}{ll}
(ac)c^{-1} = (bc)c^{-1} & \text{M5 and E5} \\
a(cc^{-1}) = b(cc^{-1}) & \text{M3} \\
a \cdot 1 = b \cdot 1 & \text{M5} \\
a = b & \text{M4}
\end{array}
$$

13. (a) If $r < s$, there is a positive rational c such that $s - r = c$. Then $st - rt = (s - r)t = ct > 0$ because $t > 0$. Thus

$$rt < st.$$

(b) As above, $st - rt = (s - r)t = ct < 0$ because $c > 0$ and $t < 0$. Thus

$$rt > st.$$

(c) If r and s are positive, so are r^{-1} and s^{-1}. Using part (a), multiply the three terms of $0 < r < s$ by $r^{-1}s^{-1}$ to get

$$0 < s^{-1} < r^{-1}.$$

15. (a) $2x^2 + 3x - 2 = (2x - 1)(x + 2) = 0$, or $x = 1/2$, $x = -2$.
   (b) $2x^2 + x - 3 = (2x + 3)(x - 1) = 0$, or $x = -3/2$, $x = 1$.

2.24

1. A2, A3, M2, M3, and D are inherited. A1 and M1 are satisfied because every entry in the tables of Section 2.19 is 0, 1, or 2. A4 is satisfied because the first row and column of the addition table are identical with the row and column headings. M4 is satisfied because the row and column labeled "1" are identical with the row and column headings. A5 is satisfied because there is one and only one 0 in each row and column of the addition table. M5 is satisfied because there is one and only one 1 in each nonzero row and column of the multiplication table.

4. (a)

(+)	0	1	2	3	4	5
0	0	1	2	3	4	5
1	1	2	3	4	5	0
2	2	3	4	5	0	1
3	3	4	5	0	1	2
4	4	5	0	1	2	3
5	5	0	1	2	3	4

(·)	0	1	2	3	4	5
0	0	0	0	0	0	0
1	0	1	2	3	4	5
2	0	2	4	0	2	4
3	0	3	0	3	0	3
4	0	4	2	0	4	2
5	0	5	4	3	2	1

(b) No. 2, 3, and 4 have no multiplicative inverse.
5. 4 and 6 are composite (are not prime), but 2, 3, and 5 are prime.
7. (a) 4, 3, 2, and 1   (b) 3, 2, and 4
10. (a) $-2 - 3i$ and $-4 + 5i$
   (b) $2/13 - (3/13)i$ and $4/41 + (5/41)i$

2.28

3. If $3 + \sqrt{2}$ is rational, then there are integers p and q such that $3 + \sqrt{2} = p/q$. Then

$$\sqrt{2} = \frac{(p - 3q)}{q}.$$

Since $(p - 3q)/q$ is rational and $\sqrt{2}$ has been proved to be irrational, we have a contradiction. Thus $3 + \sqrt{2}$ is irrational.

5. $3\sqrt{3}$

7. 16π

9.

$$\frac{n}{3n + 2} = \frac{1}{3} - \frac{2}{9n + 6}.$$

Thus $1/3$ is an upper bound. Let $\frac{1}{3} - m$ be any number smaller than $1/3$. Then

$$\frac{n}{3n + 2} > \frac{1}{3} - m \quad \text{if} \quad \frac{2}{9n + 6} < m.$$

This, in turn, is true if

$$\frac{2}{m} < 9n + 6, \quad \text{or} \quad n > \frac{(2 - 6m)}{9m}.$$

Thus no number less than $1/3$ is an upper bound.

11. (a) Since the real numbers form a field, we need prove only that the set satisfies A1, A4, A5, M1, M4, and M5.

A1: $(a + b\sqrt{2}) + (c + d\sqrt{2}) = (a + c) + (b + d)\sqrt{2}$

M1: $(a + b\sqrt{2})(c + d\sqrt{2}) = (ac + 2bd) + (bc + ad)\sqrt{2}$

A4: $0 = 0 + 0\sqrt{2}$, M4: $1 = 1 + 0\sqrt{2}$

M5: $\dfrac{1}{a + b\sqrt{2}} = \dfrac{a - b\sqrt{2}}{(a + b\sqrt{2})(a - b\sqrt{2})} = \dfrac{a}{a^2 - 2b^2} - \dfrac{b}{a^2 - 2b^2}\sqrt{2}$

In the last, the irrationality of $\sqrt{2}$ assures us that $\sqrt{2} \neq \dfrac{a}{b}$, or

$$2 \neq \frac{a^2}{b^2}, \quad \text{or} \quad a^2 - 2b^2 \neq 0.$$

(b) $\dfrac{5}{7} - \dfrac{3}{7}\sqrt{2}$

13. If b is any upper bound of S, then $x < b$ for every x in S. Then $-b < -x$, or $-b$ is a lower bound of the negative elements of S, and vice versa. If L is the least upper bound of S, the $L \leq b$, or $-b \leq -L$. Hence $-L$ is the greatest lower bound of the negatives of elements of S.

15. -3

17. The least upper bound is 3 and the greatest lower bound is 2/3. To prove the first, note that $(2n + 1)/(3n - 2) \le 3$ if and only if $2n + 1 \le 9n - 6$, or $7 \le 7n$. Since this is true for all n, 3 is an upper bound. Since $(2n + 1)/(3n - 2) = 3$ for $n = 1$, 3 is the least upper bound. For the second,

$$(2n + 1)/(3n - 2) = (2 + 1/n)/(3 - 2/n) > 2/3,$$

and the fraction can be made as close to 2/3 as desired by choosing n sufficiently large.

2.31

1. The area of the circle is 9π, and $\pi = 3.14159265\cdots$. We shall show that 3.142 is the desired approximation.

$$0 < 3.142 - \pi < 0.0005.$$

Thus

$$9(3.142) - 9\pi < .0045 < .005,$$

or the approximation is to within less than one half cent.

3. The length of the chain is $3\sqrt{2}$ feet $= 36\sqrt{2}$ inches, and

$$\sqrt{2} = 1.414214\cdots. \qquad 0 < \sqrt{2} - 1.4142 < 0.00002.$$

Thus

$$36\sqrt{2} - 36(1.4142) < 0.00072,$$

or the approximation is correct within a half cent.

6. The terms of the sequence are of the form

$$1 - \frac{1}{10^n} \quad \text{for} \quad n = 1, 2, \ldots.$$

Thus, since all terms are < 1, 1 is an upper bound. Let m be any positive number, no matter how small. There is some n such that $10^n > 1/m$, or $1/10^n < m$. Then

$$1 - 1/10^n > 1 - m,$$

or no number less than 1 is an upper bound.

7. There is *no* such number. If x were such a real number, what about $x/2$?

***9.** The total distance covered in successive numbers of jumps is given by

$$1 = 2 - 1, \qquad 1 + \frac{1}{2} = 2 - \frac{1}{2}, \qquad 1 + \frac{1}{2} + \frac{1}{4} = 2 - \frac{1}{4},$$

and, in general, by

$$2 - \frac{1}{2^n}.$$

Thus the least upper bound is clearly 2 yards.

11. $x_1 = \frac{9}{5}.$

$$x_2 = \frac{9/5 + 3/(9/5)}{2} = \frac{9/5 + 15/9}{2} = \frac{156}{90} = \frac{26}{15}.$$

$$x_3 = \frac{26/15 + 3/(26/15)}{2} = \frac{26/15 + 45/26}{2} = \frac{1351}{780} = 1.732051\cdots.$$

From tables, we find that $\sqrt{3} = 1.732051$ to six decimal places.

3.5

1. A set is clearly defined if it is always possible to tell whether a given element does or does not belong to the set.

2. (a) $A + B = \{\text{WESTRNAHIGO}\}$ (b) $B + D = \{\text{WASHINGTOCLE}\}$
   (c) $A + D = \{\text{WESTRNCOLG}\}$ (g) $A + A = \{\text{WESTRN}\} = A$

4. $C = \{\text{STAE}\}$. Subsets: $\varnothing$, $\{\text{S}\}$, $\{\text{T}\}$, $\{\text{A}\}$, $\{\text{E}\}$, $\{\text{ST}\}$, $\{\text{SA}\}$, $\{\text{SE}\}$, $\{\text{TA}\}$, $\{\text{TE}\}$, $\{\text{AE}\}$, $\{\text{STA}\}$, $\{\text{STE}\}$, $\{\text{SAE}\}$, $\{\text{TAE}\}$, $\{\text{STAE}\}$

6. If a set has n elements, it has 2^n distinct subsets. Let M be the set of natural numbers n for which this is true.

   1. Since a set with 1 element has 2 subsets, itself and the empty set, 1 belongs to M.
   2. If a set with k elements has 2^k subsets, consider a new set with one additional element. The subsets of the new set consist of all the subsets of the old one together with the subsets formed by adjoining the new element to each of the old subsets. Then the new set has twice as many subsets as the old, or a set of $k + 1$ elements has $2 \cdot 2^k = 2^{k+1}$ subsets. Hence, if k belongs to M, so does $k + 1$.

   By the induction postulate, the statement is true for all natural numbers.

9. $\varnothing$

11. Let $A = \{abcd\}$, $B = \{cdef\}$, $C = \{aef\}$. Then

$$A + B = \{abcdef\} = A + C, \quad \text{but} \quad B \neq C.$$

3.8

1. (a) $AB = \{\text{WSTN}\}$ (c) $AD = \{\text{E}\}$
   (e) $BD = \{\text{OG}\}$ (g) $AA = \{\text{WESTRN}\} = A$
   (i) $A(BC) = \{\text{ST}\}$ (k) $ABCD = \varnothing$

4. The elements in AB are in both A and B. In particular, it is always true that $AB \subset A$. Since it is always true that $A \subset A$, if $A \subset B$, $A \subset AB$. Thus if $A \subset B$, $AB = A$. On the other hand, if A is not a subset of B, there is some element of A that is not in B. In that case, AB cannot contain that element, or $AB \neq A$.

6. Let $A = \{a\}$, $B = \{b\}$, and $C = \{c\}$. Then $AB = \emptyset = AC$, but $B \neq C$.

7. XY

9. If the union of two sets is empty, each must be empty. Thus $AB = \emptyset$ and $CD = \emptyset$. From these equations we know that A and B are disjoint, as are C and D.

3.11

1. A

3. $\emptyset$, U, A, B, A', B', $A + B$, $A + B'$, $A' + B$, $A' + B'$, AB, AB', $A'B$, $A'B'$, $AB + A'B'$, $AB' + A'B$

5. $AC + ABC + AC' = A(C + C' + BC) = A(U + BC) = AU = A$

7. $ABC + A' + B' + C' = U$. If any element of U is not in ABC, it must be outside at least one of A, B, or C. That is, it must belong to A' or B' or C'. Hence every element of U is in the indicated set.

9. $(AB' + A'B)'(AB + A'B')' = (AB' + A'B + AB + A'B')' = U' = \emptyset$

11. $A'C + B'C + ABCD' = C(A' + B' + ABD') = C(A' + B' + AD')$

$$= C(A' + B' + D') = C(ABD)'$$

13. If $A = B$, then $A \subset B$, or $AB' = \emptyset$, and also $B \subset A$, or $BA' = \emptyset$. Thus

$$AB' + A'B = \emptyset.$$

On the other hand, if $AB' + A'B = \emptyset$, then

$$AB' = \emptyset, \quad \text{or} \quad A \subset B, \quad \text{and} \quad A'B \neq \emptyset, \quad \text{or} \quad B \subset A.$$

Hence,

$$A = B.$$

15. Draw a diagram in which the set of students who read French is labeled F, German G, and Spanish S. Work from the innermost set, FGS, out, inserting the number of students in each region of the diagram.

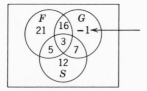

Solution to Exercise 15

According to the diagram, -1 students read German but not French or Spanish. The report is inconsistent.

16. 2^n

3.13

1. (a) A (b) B (c) $\varnothing$ (d) $\varnothing$

3. (a) No   (b) Yes   (c) $\varnothing$ (d) U

5.

Solutions to Exercise 5

7. 6

9.

Solutions to Exercise 9

10. $(AB)' = A' + B'$

3.17

2. (a) P2 (no 0), P3 ($+$ doesn't distribute over $\cdot$), and P4

(b) P3 ($+$ doesn't distribute over $\cdot$) and P4

(c) P2 (no 1), P3 ($+$ doesn't distribute over $\cdot$), and P4

(d) All are satisfied.

3. $b * a = b + a - ba = a + b - ab = a * b$. Hence, commutative.

$$a * (b * c) = a * (b + c - bc) = a + b + c - bc - ab - ac + abc$$

$$= (a + b - ab) + c - (a + b - ab)c = (a * b) * c.$$

Hence, associative.

5. $B * A = BA' + B'A = A'B + AB' = AB' + A'B = A * B$. Commutative.

$$A * (B * C) = A * (BC' + B'C) = A(BC' + B'C)' + A'(BC' + B'C)$$
$$= A(B' + C)(B + C') + A'BC' + A'B'C$$
$$= A(B'C' + CB) + A'BC' + A'B'C$$
$$= AB'C' + ABC + A'BC' + A'B'C.$$

$$(A * B) * C = (AB' + A'B)C' + (AB' + A'B)'C$$
$$= AB'C' + A'BC' + (AB + A'B')C$$
$$= AB'C' + A'BC' + ABC + A'B'C = A * (B * C). \text{ Associative.}$$

7. Yes, the entire proof can be reversed.

3.19

1.
$$\begin{array}{ll} 0 = aa' & \text{P4} \\ = a(a' + 0) & \text{P2} \\ = aa' + a0 & \text{P3} \\ = 0 + a0 & \text{P4} \\ = a0 & \text{P2} \end{array}$$

3. Proof that $a(a' + b) = ab$:

$$\begin{array}{ll} a(a' + b) = aa' + ab & \text{P3} \\ = 0 + ab & \text{P4} \\ = ab & \text{P2} \end{array}$$

Proof that $a'(a + b) = a'b$: Interchange a and a' in the first proof.

5. We have proved that $a' + b' = (ab)'$. Hence, $(a' + b')' = (ab)''$. Now interchange a and a' and b and b'. Then

$$(a + b)' = (a'b')'' = a'b'.$$

3.23

1.
$$\begin{array}{ll} (a + b)(a' + b) = (b + a)(b + a') & \text{P1} \\ = b + aa' & \text{P3} \\ = b + 0 & \text{P4} \\ = b & \text{P2} \end{array}$$

3.
$$\begin{array}{ll} ab + ab' + a'b + a'b' = a(b + b') + a'(b + b') & \text{P3} \\ = (a + a')(b + b') & \text{P3 and P1} \\ = 1 \cdot 1 = 1 & \text{P4 and P2} \end{array}$$

5.
$$\begin{array}{ll} (a + ab + abc)(a + b + c) = [a + a(b + bc)](a + b + c) & \text{P3} \\ = a(a + b + c) & \text{Th. 3} \\ = a & \text{Th. 3} \end{array}$$

7. $(ab + ab' + a'b')' = [a(b + b') + a'b']'$ P3
$= (a + a'b')'$ P4 and Th. 2
$= (a + b')'$ Th. 4
$= a'b$ Th. 9 and Th. 7

9. $(a + b' + c)(ab + a'c')' = [(a + c) + b'][(a + c)(a' + b')]$ P1 and Th. 9
$= (a' + b')\{(a + c)[(a + c) + b']\}$ Th. 5 and P1
$= (a' + b')(a + c)$ Th. 3
$= a'a + a'c + ab' + b'c$ P3 and P1
$= a'c + ab' + b'c$ P4 and P2
$= a'c + ab' + b'c(a + a')$ P4 and P2
$= a'c + ab' + ab'c + a'b'c$ P3 and P1
$= a'(c + b'c) + a(b' + b'c)$ P3
$= a'c + ab'$ Th. 3

10. $[(a' + b')' + a']' = (a' + b')a$ Th. 9
$= a(a' + b')$ P1
$= ab'$ Th. 4

12. If $a \leq b$ and $b \leq c$, then

$$a \leq c.$$

Since $a \leq c$ and $c \leq a$,

$$a = c.$$

3.26

1.

2.

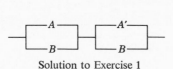

Solution to Exercise 1

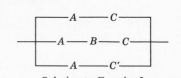

Solution to Exercise 2

5.

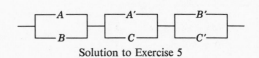

Solution to Exercise 5

7. $AB + AC + A'B + AC' = A(C + C') + B(A + A') = A + B$

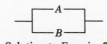

Solution to Exercise 7

9. $ABD + AB'D + ABD' + AB'D' + ABC + A'BC$

$= A(BD + B'D + BD' + B'D') + BC(A + A')$

$= A[B(D + D') + B'(D + D')] + BC = A(B + B') + BC = A + BC$

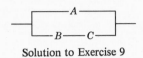

Solution to Exercise 9

11. The possible paths are indicated by

$$AD + ABC + BD + DC = A(D + BC) + D(B + C).$$

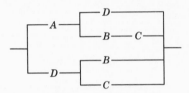

Solution to Exercise 11

3.29

1.

A	B	$A+B$	A'	$A'B$	$A + A'B$
0	0	0	1	0	0
0	1	1	1	1	1
1	0	1	0	0	1
1	1	<u>1</u>	0	0	<u>1</u>

3.

A	B	AB	A'	B'	$A'B'$	$A + A'B'$	$B(A + A'B')$
0	0	0	1	1	1	1	0
0	1	0	1	0	0	0	0
1	0	0	0	1	0	1	0
1	1	<u>1</u>	0	0	0	1	<u>1</u>

5.

A	B	AB	$(AB)'$	A'	B'	$A' + B'$
0	0	0	1	1	1	1
0	1	0	1	1	0	1
1	0	0	1	0	1	1
1	1	1	<u>0</u>	0	0	<u>0</u>

7.

A	B	C	AC	$AC + B$	C'	AB	BC'	BC	$AB + AC + BC' + BC$
0	0	0	0	0	1	0	0	0	0
0	0	1	0	0	0	0	0	0	0
0	1	0	0	1	1	0	1	0	1
0	1	1	0	1	0	0	0	1	1
1	0	0	0	0	1	0	0	0	0
1	0	1	1	1	0	0	0	0	1
1	1	0	0	1	1	1	1	0	1
1	1	1	1	1	0	1	0	1	1

9. $3! = 6$

11. $n!$

3.36

1. Let m be "Ice is cold." Let n be "Grass is green."
3. Let p be "$2 + 2 = 5$." Let q be "$2 \cdot 3 = 7$."
7. Theorem 3: $p + pq = p$. $2 + 2 = 5$, or both $2 + 2 = 5$ and $2 \cdot 3 = 7$ if and only if $2 + 2 = 5$.

   Theorem 4: $p + p'q = p + q$. $2 + 2 = 5$, or both $2 + 2 \neq 5$ and $2 \cdot 3 = 7$ if and only if $2 + 2 = 5$ or $2 \cdot 3 = 7$.

   Theorem 9: $(pq)' = p' + q'$. It is false that $2 + 2 = 5$ and $2 \cdot 3 = 7$ if and only if $2 + 2 \neq 5$ or $2 \cdot 3 \neq 7$.

9. Theorem 3: $q(q + n) = q$. $2 \cdot 3 = 7$ and either $2 \cdot 3 = 7$ or grass is green if and only if $2 \cdot 3 = 7$.

   Theorem 4: $q' + qn = q' + n$. $2 \cdot 3 \neq 7$ or both $2 \cdot 3 = 7$ and grass is green if and only if $2 \cdot 3 \neq 7$ or grass is green.

   Theorem 9: $(q + n)' = q'n'$. It is false that either $2 \cdot 3 = 7$ or grass is green if and only if $2 \cdot 3 \neq 7$ and grass is not green.

3.38

1. For all real x, $x^2 - 4x - 7 \neq 0$, or $x^2 - 4x - 7 = 0$ for no real x.
3. There is a real number x such that $x^2 + x + 1 = 0$.
5. The square of some rational number is 3.
7. The square of no odd integer is even.
9. At least one of our texts is inexpensive and not heavy.
11. p is false for all x.
13. There is an x for which p is true.

3.40

1. (a) If I study hard, I receive a good grade.
   (c) Either I don't study hard or I receive a good grade.
   (e) I study hard and receive a good grade if and only if I study hard.
3. $(yz)' \to x'$, or $(y' + z') \to x'$
5. $z' \to (xy)'$, or $z' \to (x' + y')$
7. (b) 0   (c) 1   (e) 1
9. $b = 1$

3.44

1.

x	y	$x \to y$	$x(x \to y)$	$x(x \to y) \to y$
0	0	1	0	1
0	1	1	0	1
1	0	0	0	1
1	1	1	1	1

3.

x	y	$x + y$	x'	$(x + y)x'$	$(x + y)x' \to y$
0	0	0	1	0	1
0	1	1	1	1	1
1	0	1	0	0	1
1	1	1	0	0	1

5. $xy \to y \equiv (xy)' + x \equiv x' + y' + x \equiv 1 + y' \equiv 1$
7. By modus ponens, $x(x \to y) \to y$. Thus, if x and $x \to y$ are both true, then y is true, and if y is true and $y \to z$ is true, then z is true.
8. Let b be "I ride a bus to work."
   Let d be "I drive to work."
   Let s be "My car starts."
   Let r be "It rains."
   Then, symbolically, we have
   (a) $b + d$, which is equivalent to $b' \to d$ or $d' \to b$
   (b) $r' \to s$, or $s' \to r$
   (c) $s' \to b$, or $b' \to s$
   (d) r'
   Thus $r' \to s$, but s does not logically imply anything else. This is as far as we can go. We can only conclude that my car started.

10. Let r be "The rain in Spain falls on the plain."
    Let s be "The wind is from the south."
    Then we are given $r' \to s'$, or $s \to r$.
    (a) It rains.
    (b) We can't say.
    (c) We can't say.
    (d) The wind was not from the south.
    (e) The rain in Spain falls in the plain whenever the wind is from the south.

4.4

1. The uniqueness of sums of residue classes makes this simple to prove. Let a, b, and c be any integers in residue classes r_1, r_2, and r_3, respectively. Since $a + (b + c) = (a + b) + c$ by the associative law for integers, it follows that $r_1 + (r_2 + r_3) = (r_1 + r_2) + r_3$.

3. By the definition given, $a \equiv b \pmod 0$ is meaningless, for division by 0 is not defined. However, an alternative definition is frequently given, that $a \equiv b \pmod m$ if there exists an integer k such that $a - b = km$. This definition is equivalent to that of the text for $m \neq 0$. For $m = 0$, however, the second definition is equivalent to equality.

5. $3 \equiv 15 \equiv 27 \equiv 39 \equiv -9 \equiv -21 \pmod{12}$

7. $16 \equiv 33 \equiv 50 \equiv 67 \equiv -1 \equiv -18 \pmod{17}$

9. If $13 \equiv 19 \pmod m$, then $19 - 13 = km$. This equation is satisfied for all k if m is a divisor of 6. Since $m > 1$, we can have $m = 2$, 3, or 6.

11. $(3n)^2 = 9n^2 = 3(3n^2) + 0$
    $(3n \pm 1)^2 = 9n^2 \pm 6n + 1 = 3(3n^2 \pm 2n) + 1$

13. If $x + 15 \equiv 2 \pmod 8$, then

$$x + 15 = 2 + 8k, \quad \text{or} \quad x = 8k - 13 = 8k - 16 + 3 = 8(k - 2) + 3.$$

Thus
$$x \equiv 3 \pmod 8.$$

15. $r_1 = $ 0,   1,   2,   3,   4,   5,   6
    $r_2 = $ 6,   5,   4,   3,   2,   1,   0

17. By trial of successive values, we find that $x = 5$ is a solution.

19. By trial, we find that three solutions are given by -7, 4, and 15.

4.7

1. Let a and b be any two integers in residue classes r_1 and r_2 respectively. Since $ab = ba$ in the set of integers, $r_1 r_2 = r_2 r_1$.

3. 2, 3, 5, 7, 11, 13, 17, 19, 23, 29

5.

(+)	0	1	2	3	4
0	0	1	2	3	4
1	1	2	3	4	0
2	2	3	4	0	1
3	3	4	0	1	2
4	4	0	1	2	3

(·)	0	1	2	3	4
0	0	0	0	0	0
1	0	1	2	3	4
2	0	2	4	1	3
3	0	3	1	4	2
4	0	4	3	2	1

7.

(·) (with 0 omitted)

	1	2	3	4	5	6	7	8	9	10	11
1	1	2	3	4	5	6	7	8	9	10	11
2	2	4	6	8	10	0	2	4	6	8	10
3	3	6	9	0	3	6	9	0	3	6	9
4	4	8	0	4	8	0	4	8	0	4	8
5	5	10	3	8	1	6	11	4	9	2	7
6	6	0	6	0	6	0	6	0	6	0	6
7	7	2	9	4	11	6	1	8	3	10	5
8	8	4	0	8	4	0	8	4	0	8	4
9	9	6	3	0	9	6	3	0	9	6	3
10	10	8	6	4	2	0	10	8	6	4	2
11	11	10	9	8	7	6	5	4	3	2	1

9. Yes. If $ax \equiv ay \pmod{p}$, then

$$ax = ay + kp, \quad \text{or} \quad a(x - y) = kp.$$

Since a is a divisor of kp, but p is prime, a is a divisor of k. That is, there is some n such that $k = na$. Thus

$$x - y = np, \quad \text{or} \quad x \equiv y \pmod{p}.$$

11. They cannot be ordered in such a way that the addition property is preserved. For instance, if $1 < 2$, then we should have $1 + 1 < 2 + 2$, but this is $2 < 1$.

4.11

1. (a) $72 = 2^3 \cdot 3^2$ (c) $1215 = 3^5 \cdot 5$ (e) $-1449 = -3^2 \cdot 7 \cdot 23$

2. (a) $(45, 63) = 9$ (c) $(102, 78) = 6$ (e) $(180, 108) = 36$

3. $(n, n + 1) = 1$

5. If $a|b$,

$$b = b_1 a.$$

If, further, $b|c$, then

$$c = c_1 b = c_1 b_1 a, \quad \text{or} \quad a|c.$$

7. $s = 3, t = -2$

9. $s = 12, t = -5$

11. (a) $x \equiv 6 \pmod 7$ (c) $x \equiv 6 \pmod{11}$ (e) $x \equiv 4 \pmod{11}$

12. (a) $x \equiv 3 \pmod 6$ (c) $x \equiv 4 \pmod 5$ (e) $x \equiv 3 \pmod 5$

4.13

1. $x \equiv 17 \pmod{29}$ **3.** $x \equiv 18 \pmod{37}$

5. $x \equiv 19 \pmod{41}$ **7.** $x \equiv 7 \pmod{18}$

9. $x \equiv 11 \pmod{19}$

11. $(1)m + (m - 1)(-1) = m - m + 1 = 1$. Thus $(m, -1) = 1$.

13. If $(a, m) = 1$, there exist s and t such that $sa + tm = 1$. Then

$$(-s)(-a) + tm = 1, \quad \text{or} \quad (-a, m) = 1.$$

14. If x is any integer such that $x^2 \equiv n \pmod{65}$, then $x^2 = n + 65k$. Then

$$(8x)^2 = 64x^2 = 64(n + 65k) = 64n + 65(64k)$$
$$= -n + 65(64k + n), \quad \text{or} \quad (8x)^2 \equiv -n \pmod{65}.$$

4.16

1. $x \equiv 38 \pmod{77}$ **3.** $x \equiv 1 \pmod{72}$ **5.** $x \equiv 14 \pmod{55}$

7. Reduce to $\begin{array}{l} 2x \equiv 6 \pmod 7 \\ 2x \equiv 3 \pmod 5 \end{array}$, and then to $\begin{array}{l} x \equiv 3 \pmod 7 \\ x \equiv 4 \pmod 5 \end{array}$. Hence, $x \equiv 24 \pmod{35}$.

9. Reduce to $\begin{array}{l} 3x \equiv 6 \pmod 7 \\ 2x \equiv 1 \pmod 3 \end{array}$, and then to $\begin{array}{l} x \equiv 2 \pmod 7 \\ x \equiv 2 \pmod 3 \end{array}$. Hence, $x \equiv 2 \pmod{21}$.

11. $x \equiv 2 \pmod 3$, $y \equiv 0 \pmod 3$

13. $x \equiv 0 \pmod 5$, $y \equiv 2 \pmod 5$

15. $x \equiv 7 \pmod{11}$, $y \equiv 5 \pmod{11}$

17. $x \equiv 8 \pmod{13}$, $y \equiv 0 \pmod{13}$

19. $x \equiv 3 \pmod 7$, $y \equiv 2 \pmod 7$, $z \equiv 3 \pmod 7$

21. If 3 times the second congruence is added to the first, the result is $0 \equiv 1 \pmod 7$.

4.18

2. HELP

3. EJWQ

6. SEND-HELP

5.5

1. When $x = 0$, $y = 3$, and when $y = 0$, $x = 4$. Thus $(0, 3)$ and $(4, 0)$ are points where the line crosses the axes. In general, if $x/a + y/b = 1$, then a is the x-intercept and b is the y-intercept.
3. $m = -1/2$
5. $m = 0$
7. $2x - 3y = -17$, $m = 2/3$
9. $x + y = 2$, $m = -1$
11. $2x - y = 1$
13. $2x - 3y = -5$
15. $7x + 3y = 23$

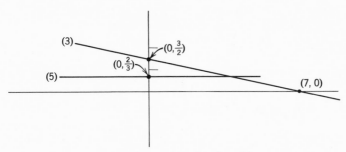

Solutions to Exercises 3 and 5

5.8

1. $2x - 3y = -5$
5. $2x - y = 1$
9. $x - 6y = 7$
13. $x = 2$

3. $6x + 4y = -32$
7. $3x + 2y = 12$
11. $x - 2y = -4$
15. $y = 3$.

17. (a) All have slope 2.
    (b) All have y intercept 2.
    (c) All are satisfied by $(3, 4)$.
    (d) All pass through the intersection of $2x + 3y - 5 = 0$ and $x - y + 7 = 0$.

5.12

1. $10x - 4y = -21$
5. $x^2 + y^2 = 25$

3. $(x + 3)^2 + (y - 5)^2 = 16$
7. Center: $(1, -2)$, $r = 4$

9. (a) $(x - 2)^2 + (y - 2)^2 = 4$
   (b) $(x - 2)^2 + (y - 2)^2 = 8$
11. $(x + 1)^2 + (y - 3)^2 = 25$.
13. Multiply out and subtract to get $3x - 2y - 3 = 0$.
15. (a) $12x - 16y + 200 = r^2$
    (b) $6x - 8y + 100 = 0$, the tangent line of Exercise 12.

5.15

1. $(y - 4)^2 = -12(x - 5)$ 3. $(x - 2)^2 = -4(y - 5)$
5. $(x + 1)^2 = (y + 1)$, vertex $(-1, -1)$

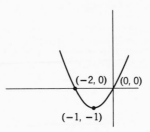

(−2, 0)   (0, 0)

(−1, −1)

Solution to Exercise 5

7. $(x + 1)^2 = (y + 2)/2$

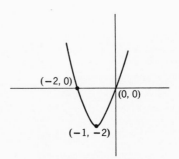

(−2, 0)   (0, 0)

(−1, −2)

Solution to Exercise 7

9. $y = 2x^2$
11. $x^2 + 4y = 0$
13. Let the origin be at the lowest point of the cable so that the ends have coordinates $(\pm 100, 50)$. Then the equation is $x^2 = 200y$.

15.

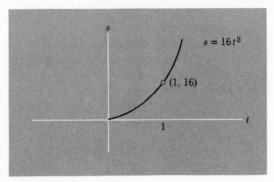

17. $(y - k)^2 = -4p(x - h)$
19. $(x - h)^2 = -4p(y - k)$

5.19

1. $a = 5, b = 4, c = 3$
   Center $(0, 0)$
   Foci $(\pm 3, 0)$
   Vertices $(\pm 5, 0)$
   $e = 3/5$

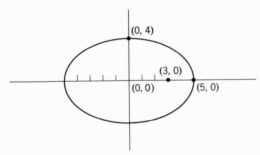

Solution to Exercise 1

3. $x^2 + \dfrac{y^2}{2} = 1, a = \sqrt{2}, b = 1, c = 1$

   Center $(0, 0)$
   Foci $(0, \pm 1)$
   Vertices $(0, \pm\sqrt{2})$
   $e = 1/\sqrt{2}$

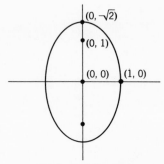

Solution to Exercise 3

5. Center $(2, 3)$
   Foci $(2 \pm 3, 3)$
   Vertices $(2 \pm 5, 3)$
   $e = 3/5$

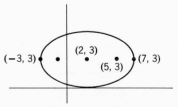

Solution to Exercise 5

7. Center $(6, -1)$
   Foci $(6, -1 \pm \sqrt{2})$
   Vertices $(6, -1 \pm 2)$
   $e = \sqrt{2}/2$

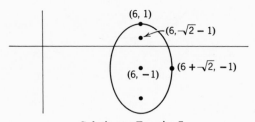

Solution to Exercise 7

9. $\dfrac{(x + 1)^2}{25} + \dfrac{(y - 2)^2}{9} = 1$

   Center $(-1, 2)$
   Foci $(-1 \pm 4, 2)$

Vertices $(-1 \pm 5, 2)$
$e = 4/5$

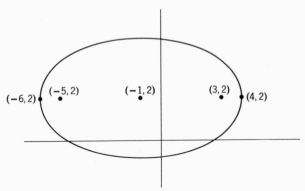

Solution to Exercise 9

11. $x^2/25 + (y - 1)^2 = 1$
    Center $(0, 1)$
    Foci $(\pm 2\sqrt{6}, 1)$
    Vertices $(\pm 5, 1)$
    $e = 2\sqrt{6}/5$

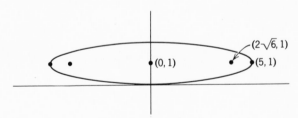

Solution to Exercise 11

13. Center $(0, 0)$, $a = 6$, $b = 4$, $\dfrac{x^2}{36} + \dfrac{y^2}{16} = 1$.

15. Center $(2, 3)$, $a = 5$, $\dfrac{c}{a} = \dfrac{4}{5}$, $c = 4$, $b = 3$, $\dfrac{(x - 2)^2}{25} + \dfrac{(y - 3)^2}{9} = 1$.

5.23

1. Center $(0, 0)$
   Foci $(\pm\sqrt{2}, 0)$
   Vertices $(\pm 1, 0)$
   Asymptotes $y = \pm x$

384

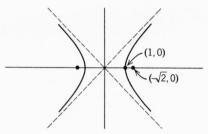

Solution to Exercise 1

3. Center (0, 0)
   Foci (± 5, 0)
   Vertices (± 3, 0)
   Asymptotes $y = \pm \dfrac{4x}{3}$

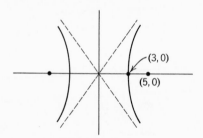

Solution to Exercise 3

5. Center (0, 0)
   Foci (0, ± 13)
   Vertices (0, ± 12)
   Asymptotes $y = \pm \dfrac{5x}{12}$

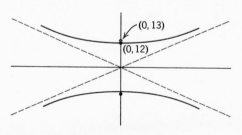

Solution to Exercise 5

7. Center $(2, 3)$

Foci $(2 \pm 5, 3)$

Vertices $(2 \pm 4, 3)$

Asymptotes $y - 3 = \pm \dfrac{3(x - 2)}{4}$

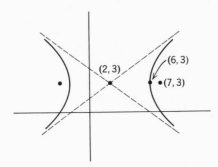

Solution to Exercise 7

9. Center $(-1, 6)$

Foci $(-1, 6 \pm 3)$

Vertices $(-1, 6 \pm 1)$

Asymptotes $y - 6 = \pm(x + 1)/\sqrt{2}$

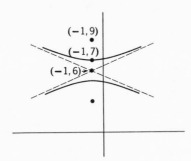

Solution to Exercise 9

11. Center $(5, -1)$

Foci $(5 \pm 6, -1)$

Vertices $(5 \pm 4, -1)$

Asymptotes $y + 1 = \pm\sqrt{5}(x - 5)/2$

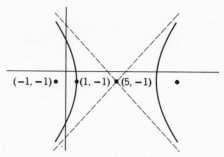

Solution to Exercise 11

13. Center $(-3, 1)$

Foci $(-3, 1 \pm \sqrt{6})$

Vertices $(-3, 1 \pm \sqrt{3})$

Asymptotes $y - 1 = \pm(x + 3)$

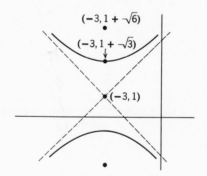

Solution to Exercise 13

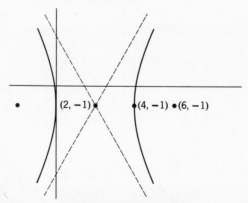

Solution to Exercise 15

15. $\dfrac{(x-2)^2}{4} - \dfrac{(y+1)^2}{12} = 1$

    Center $(2, -1)$

    Foci $(2 \pm 4, -1)$

    Vertices $(2 \pm 2, -1)$

    Asymptotes $y + 1 = \pm\sqrt{3}(x - 2)$

17.

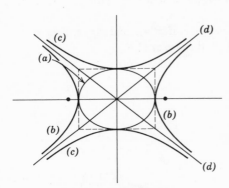

Solution to Exercise 17

19. Hyperbola: When the square is completed, if the constant on the right is 0, the graph is two intersecting lines. Algebraically, this happens when $E = \dfrac{C^2}{4A} + \dfrac{D^2}{4B}$.

    Ellipse: In this case the graph of the ellipse is merely a point.

5.26

1. $(x + 1)^2 + (y - 2)^2 = 10$
3. $S = \sqrt{(a - h)^2 + (b - k)^2} - r^2$
5. The altitude through (a, b) has equation $x = a$.

    The altitude through $(c, 0)$ has equation $ax + by = ac$.

    The altitude through $(0, 0)$ has equation $(a - c)x + by = 0$.

    The common solution to the first two is $x = a$, $y = a(c - a)/b$, which satisfies the third.

6.3

1. Domain and range: real numbers. $(0, 2)$, $(1, 3)$; $(0, 0)$, $(1, 1)$
3. Domain: real numbers; range: real numbers ≥ 4. $(0, 4)$, $(1, 5)$; $(0, 0)$, $(1, 1)$
5. Domain and range: real numbers from -5 to 5. $(3, 4)$, $(5, 0)$; $(0, 0)$, $(1, 1)$
7. Domain and range: real numbers. $(0, 1)$, $(1, 0)$; $(0, 0)$, $(1, 1)$

9. Domain and range: real numbers. $(0, 0)$, $(1, 1)$; $(5, 1)$, $(10, 2)$

11. Domain: real numbers; range: -5. $(1, -5)$, $(2, -5)$; $(0, 0)$, $(1, 1)$

13. Domain and range: positive integers. $(2, 3)$, $(5, 7)$; $(2, 4)$, $(9, 12)$

15. Domain and range: real numbers. $(1, 3)$, $(17.5, 15.5)$; $(0, 0)$, $(1, 1)$

17. Domain and range: subsets of U. $(\emptyset, A)$ for any A, (A, B) for any disjoint A and B; if A and B are nonempty, (A, A) and $(B, B) \notin R$.

19. (a) By E1 of Chapter 2, $x = x$. Thus $(x, x) \in R$.
    (b) By E2 of Chapter 2, if $x = y$, then $y = x$. Thus, if $(x, y) \in R$, then $(y, x) \in R$.
    (c) By E3 of Chapter 2, if $x = y$ and $y = z$, then $x = z$. Thus, if $(x, y) \in R$ and $(y, z) \in R$, then $(x, z) \in R$.

6.9

1. 1, 2, 4, and 7

3. $f = \{(x, y) : y = (x + 1)(x - 1)\}$

5. $f = \{(x, y) : y = -x\}$

7. $g^{-1} = \{(x, y) : y = (x - 7)/3\}$

9. $f^{-1} = \{(r, s) : s = \dfrac{\sqrt[3]{r + 1}}{2}\}$

11. $h^{-1} = \{(x, y) : 3x - 2y + 5 = 0\}$

13. none

15. none

17. (a) $f(0) = 2$ (c) $f(2) = 4$ (e) $f(x^2) = x^2 + 2$
    (g) $f(x + h) - f(x) = x + h + 2 - x - 2 = h$
    (i) $\dfrac{f(x) - f(t)}{x - t} = \dfrac{x + 2 - t - 2}{x - t} = 1$

19. $h = \{(x, y) : y = x^2 + 2\}$

21. (a) $f(g(2)) = 3$ (c) $f(f(2)) = 38$ (e) $f(g(t)) = (t + 2)^2$
    (g) $f(x + 3) = (x + 3)^2 + 2$ (i) $f(g(x + h)) = (3(x + h) - 5)^2 + 2$

6.13

1.

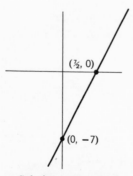

$(\tfrac{7}{2}, 0)$

$(0, -7)$

Solution to Exercise 1

3.

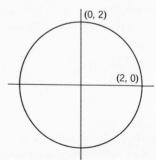

$(0, 2)$

$(2, 0)$

Solution to Exercise 3

5.

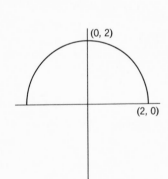

Solution to Exercise 5

7.

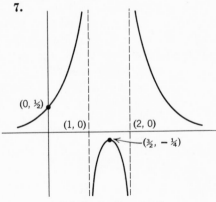

Solution to Exercise 7

9.

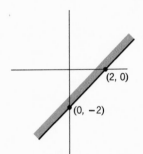

Solution to Exercise 9

11.

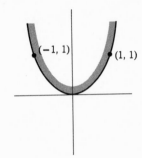

Solution to Exercise 11

13.

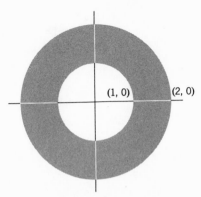

Solution to Exercise 13

15.

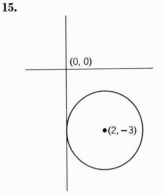

Solution to Exercise 15

17. $y < (x + 2)/2, y > 2x - 2, y > x + 1$

19. $y \leq x + 1, y \geq x - 1, y \leq -x + 1, y \geq -x - 1$

6.19

1. (a) 2   (c) 1   (e) 1   (g) −21

3.

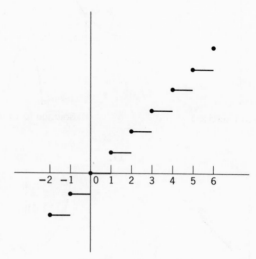

Solution to Exercise 3

5.

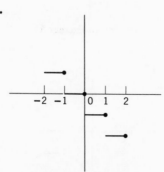

Solution to Exercise 5

7.

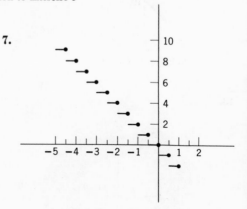

Solution to Exercise 7

9.

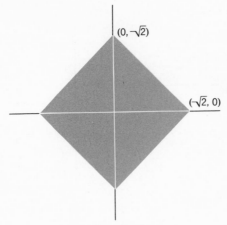

Solution to Exercise 9

11.

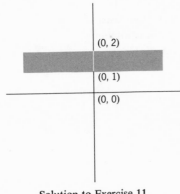

Solution to Exercise 11

13.

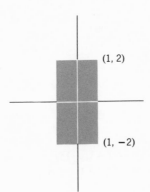

Solution to Exercise 13

15.

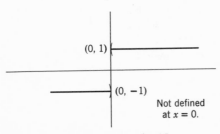

Solution to Exercise 15

17.

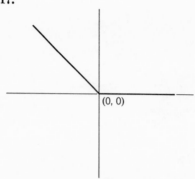

(0, 0)

Solution to Exercise 17

19.

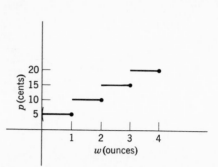

Solution to Exercise 19

7.3

1. 1, continuous
5. −21, continuous
9. 1000, continuous
13. 0, continuous
17. 5, continuous
21. m

3. −63, continuous
7. −63/8, continuous
11. No limit exists.
15. No limit exists.
19. 3, not continuous

23. $\dfrac{1}{2\sqrt{x}}$

7.6

1. $4x + 12, (-3, -15)$
5. $10x + 3, (-0.3, -7.45)$
9. $\dfrac{2}{3} - 4x, \left(\dfrac{1}{6}, \dfrac{1}{18}\right)$

3. $-2x, (0, 0)$

7. $\dfrac{1 - 2x}{3}, \left(\dfrac{1}{2}, \dfrac{3}{4}\right)$

11. $3x^2$

13. $4y^3$
15. $A'(x) = p/2 - 2x$. If $A'(x) = 0$, $x = p/4 = p/2 - x$. Since $A(x)$ is positive for $0 < x < p/2$, $A(x) = 0$ at the endpoints, and $A(x)$ is continuous for $0 \leq x \leq p/2$, the maximum is at $x = p/2$.
17. Tangent: $y = -7$, Normal: $x = 1$
19. Tangent: $x + 4y = 4$, Normal: $4x - y = 15/2$

7.10

1. $6x + 6$
5. $60x^2 - 72x + 12$

3. $5x^4 - 12x^3 + 6x^2 - 12x + 10$

7. $1 - 2x + 6x^2 - 12x^3 + 20x^4 - 30x^5$

9. $6x^5 - 24x^2$

11. $(x^3 - 4)(2x) + (x^2 + 1)(3x^2) = 5x^4 + 3x^2 - 8x$

13. $(2x^2 + 3x - 1)(2x + 1) + (x^2 + x + 1)(4x + 3) = 8x^3 + 15x^2 + 8x + 2$

15. $D_x(x^5 - 1) = 5x^4$ 17. $2x + 3 + 5/x^2 - 12/x^3$

19. $\dfrac{(x^2 - x + 1)(3x^2) - (x^3 + 1)(2x - 1)}{(x^2 - x + 1)^2} = \dfrac{x^4 - 2x^3 + 3x^2 - 2x + 1}{(x^2 - x + 1)^2} = 1$

21. Any constant   23. $x^2 + 5x +$ any constant

25. $\dfrac{x^{n+1}}{n + 1} +$ any constant

7.17

1. $y' = 2x + 4$. Minimum at $(-2, -14)$. Decreasing for $x < -2$; increasing for $x > -2$.

3. $y' = (5 - 2x)/2$. Maximum at $(5/2, 37/8)$. Increasing for $x < 5/2$; decreasing for $x > 5/2$.

5. $y' = 5$. No maximum or minimum. Increasing for all x.

7. $y' = 6x^2 + 6x - 6$. Maximum for $x = (-1 - \sqrt{5})/2$; minimum for $x = (-1 + \sqrt{5})/2$. Increasing for $x < (-1 - \sqrt{5})/2$ or $x > (-1 + \sqrt{5})/2$. Decreasing between these values.

9. $y' = 5x^4 - 5$. Maximum at $(-1, 7)$; minimum at $(1, -1)$.

11. $4''$ deep, $8''$ wide

13. Radius $= 3$, height $= 6$

7.19

1. (a) 16 ft   (b) 8 ft/sec   (c) 2 ft/sec^2

3. (a) $t = 1$ and 2   (b) $a(1) = -6, a(2) = 6$ (c) 4, when $t = 2$
   (d) 5, when $t = 1$ (e) 85, when $t = 5$

5. $v(t) = t^2 +$ any constant. If $v(0) = 6$, $v(t) = t^2 + 6$.

7.22

1. $y = 2x + c$ 3. $y = \dfrac{3x^2}{3} - 5x + c$

5. $y = x^3 - 3x^2 + 2x + c$ 7. $y = 2x^6 - \dfrac{7x^4}{4} + 5x^2 + c$

9. $y = x^2 + 2x + c$ 11. $y = 2x - 9$

13. $y = 4 - \dfrac{x}{2}$

15. (a) $v = 40 - 32t,$
$\quad\quad s = 200 + 40t - 16t^2$
(b) 225 ft.   (c) 5 seconds

17. $f(x) = 2x^3 - 2x^2 + 8x - 12$

19. (a) $x^{1/2}$ or $\sqrt{x}$ (b) x^{-1} or $1/x$

7.24

1. $\dfrac{26}{3}$

3. $\dfrac{27}{2}$

5. $\dfrac{16}{3}$

7. 8

9. $\displaystyle\int_0^4 x^{1/2}\, dx = \left.\dfrac{2x^{3/2}}{3}\right|_0^4 = 16/3$

7.29

1. 10

3. $\dfrac{16}{3}$

5. $\dfrac{64}{5}$

7. 8130

9. $\dfrac{508}{15}$

11. $\displaystyle\int_a^b f(x)\, dx = \int_a^b F'(x)\, dx = F(x)\Big|_a^b = F(b) - F(a)$

13. $\displaystyle\int_0^4 (4x - x^2)\, dx = 32/3$

15. $\displaystyle\int_0^1 (x^2 - x^3)\, dx = 1/12$

17. 0

19. $(x^2 + 3x - 2)\big|_1^2 = 6$

8.7

1. $2, -3, -12, 2h - 3k, 2x - 3y + 8, -x, 5x, 2b + 3a, 2b + 3a - x, 2a - 3b$
3. $13, 11, 11, 14, 1$
5. (a) $(4\ \ 6)$ (c) $(5\ \ -1\ \ 13)$ (e) $(4\ \ -2\ \ 7/3)$ (g) $(a + 3\ \ b\ \ c\ \ d + 2)$
    (i) $(x - 1\ \ -2\ \ 2x - 3\ \ 4x - 4)$
7. $(-6\ \ 10\ \ -8)$
9. $(0\ \ 17)$
11. $(22/5\ \ -1\ \ 3/5)$

8.11

3. $(\mathbf{a} + \mathbf{b}) + \mathbf{c} = (5\ \ 5\ \ -1) + (-3\ \ -2\ \ 1) = (2\ \ 3\ \ 0)$
    $\mathbf{a} + (\mathbf{b} + \mathbf{c}) = (2\ \ 1\ \ -3) + (0\ \ 2\ \ 3) = (2\ \ 3\ \ 0)$

5. $-\mathbf{a} = (-2 \quad -1 \quad 3)$, $-\mathbf{b} = (-3 \quad -4 \quad -2)$, $-\mathbf{c} = (3 \quad 2 \quad -1)$

7. $(0 \quad -5 \quad -13)$

9. $(-12 \quad -13 \quad -9)$

11. (a) $\begin{pmatrix} 2 \\ -3 \end{pmatrix}$ (b) $\begin{pmatrix} 1 \\ 4 \end{pmatrix}$ (c) $\begin{pmatrix} 3 \\ 1 \end{pmatrix}$ (d) $\begin{pmatrix} -1 \\ -26 \end{pmatrix}$ (e) $\begin{pmatrix} 6 \\ -20 \end{pmatrix}$

13. (a) $\begin{pmatrix} 1 \\ -2 \\ 1 \end{pmatrix}$ (b) $\begin{pmatrix} 2 \\ 1 \\ 3 \end{pmatrix}$ (c) $\begin{pmatrix} 3 \\ 2 \\ 1 \end{pmatrix}$ (d) $\begin{pmatrix} -1 \\ -3 \\ -2 \end{pmatrix}$ (e) $\begin{pmatrix} -1 \\ -5 \\ -6 \end{pmatrix}$

15. (a) $(3/5 \quad 6/5)$ (b) $(-6/5 \quad 3/5)$ (c) $(6 \quad 0)$ (d) $(39/5 \quad -42/5)$
    (e) $(19/5 \quad 3/5)$

17. $\begin{pmatrix} 5 & 8 \\ 7 & 10 \end{pmatrix}$

19. $\begin{pmatrix} -1 & -4 & -7 \\ 1 & -2 & -5 \\ 3 & 0 & -3 \end{pmatrix}$

8.15

1. $\begin{pmatrix} 4 & 2 \\ 27 & -19 \end{pmatrix}$

3. $\begin{pmatrix} -1 & 6 \\ 24 & -18 \end{pmatrix}$

5. $\begin{pmatrix} 10 & -5 \\ 5 & 10 \end{pmatrix}$

7. $\begin{pmatrix} 10 & -5 \\ 5 & 10 \end{pmatrix}$

9. $\begin{pmatrix} ac - bd & ad + bc \\ -ad - bc & ac - bd \end{pmatrix}$

11. $\begin{pmatrix} 2 & 3 \\ 1 & -2 \end{pmatrix} \begin{pmatrix} x \\ y \end{pmatrix} = \begin{pmatrix} 7 \\ 3 \end{pmatrix}$

13. $\begin{pmatrix} 7 & -7 \\ 2 & 3 \end{pmatrix} \begin{pmatrix} x \\ y \end{pmatrix} = \begin{pmatrix} 10 \\ 2 \end{pmatrix}$

15. $\begin{pmatrix} 1 & 0 \\ 0 & 1 \end{pmatrix} \begin{pmatrix} x \\ y \end{pmatrix} = \begin{pmatrix} 3 \\ 5 \end{pmatrix}$

17. $x + 2y = 2$
    $5x + 3y = -3$

19. $3x - 5y = 6$
    $x + 2y = -6$

21. $x = 2$
    $y = 3$

8.21

1. (a) 1 (b) -1 (c) 22 (d) $x^2 + y^2$ (e) $h^2 - k^2$

3. (a) $\begin{pmatrix} 8 & -3 \\ -5 & 2 \end{pmatrix}$ (b) $\begin{pmatrix} 4 & -5 \\ 7 & -9 \end{pmatrix}$ (c) $\begin{pmatrix} 7/32 & 2/22 \\ 3/22 & 4/22 \end{pmatrix}$

(d) $\begin{pmatrix} \dfrac{x}{x^2 + y^2} & \dfrac{-y}{x^2 + y^2} \\ \dfrac{y}{x^2 + y^2} & \dfrac{x}{x^2 + y^2} \end{pmatrix}$ (e) $\begin{pmatrix} \dfrac{h}{h^2 - k^2} & \dfrac{-k}{h^2 - k^2} \\ \dfrac{-k}{h^2 - k^2} & \dfrac{h}{h^2 - k^2} \end{pmatrix}$

5. (a) $\begin{pmatrix} x \\ y \end{pmatrix} = \begin{pmatrix} 8 & -3 \\ -5 & 2 \end{pmatrix} \begin{pmatrix} 9 \\ -7 \end{pmatrix} = \begin{pmatrix} 93 \\ -59 \end{pmatrix}$

(b) $\begin{pmatrix} x \\ y \end{pmatrix} = \begin{pmatrix} 4 & -5 \\ 7 & -9 \end{pmatrix} \begin{pmatrix} 31 \\ 12 \end{pmatrix} = \begin{pmatrix} 64 \\ 109 \end{pmatrix}$

(c) $\begin{pmatrix} x \\ y \end{pmatrix} = \begin{pmatrix} 7/22 & 2/22 \\ 3/22 & 4/22 \end{pmatrix} \begin{pmatrix} 44 \\ -66 \end{pmatrix} = \begin{pmatrix} 8 \\ -6 \end{pmatrix}$

(d) $\begin{pmatrix} x \\ y \end{pmatrix} = \begin{pmatrix} 3/25 & -4/25 \\ 4/25 & 3/25 \end{pmatrix} \begin{pmatrix} 50 \\ -25 \end{pmatrix} = \begin{pmatrix} 10 \\ 5 \end{pmatrix}$

(e) $\begin{pmatrix} x \\ y \end{pmatrix} = \begin{pmatrix} 5/9 & 4/9 \\ 4/9 & 5/9 \end{pmatrix} \begin{pmatrix} -27 \\ 18 \end{pmatrix} = \begin{pmatrix} -7 \\ -2 \end{pmatrix}$

7. $\left| \begin{pmatrix} a & b \\ c & d \end{pmatrix} \begin{pmatrix} u & v \\ x & y \end{pmatrix} \right| = \begin{vmatrix} au + bx & av + by \\ cu + dx & cv + dy \end{vmatrix}$

$= (au + bx)(cv + dy) - (cu + dx)(av + by)$

$= acuv + aduy + bcvx + bdxy - acuv - bcuy - advx - bdxy$

$= ad(uy - vx) - bc(uy - vx)$

$= (ad - bc)(uy - vx) = \begin{vmatrix} a & b \\ c & d \end{vmatrix} \cdot \begin{vmatrix} u & v \\ x & y \end{vmatrix}$

9. $\begin{vmatrix} a & b \\ 0 & 0 \end{vmatrix} = a \cdot 0 - b \cdot 0 = 0, \begin{vmatrix} a & 0 \\ b & 0 \end{vmatrix} = a \cdot 0 - b \cdot 0 = 0$

11. $\begin{pmatrix} 2 & 3 \\ 4 & 6 \end{pmatrix}$

8.28

1. $A + B = (a_{ij}) + (b_{ij}) = (a_{ij} + b_{ij}) = (b_{ij} + a_{ij}) = (b_{ij}) + (a_{ij}) = B + A$

3. $A + 0_n = (a_{ij} + 0) = (a_{ij}) = A$

5. $A(B + C) = \begin{pmatrix} 2 & 3 \\ -1 & 5 \end{pmatrix} \begin{pmatrix} -2 & 3 \\ 4 & 5 \end{pmatrix} = \begin{pmatrix} 8 & 21 \\ 22 & 22 \end{pmatrix}$

$AB + AC = \begin{pmatrix} 2 & 3 \\ -1 & 5 \end{pmatrix} \begin{pmatrix} 2 & 1 \\ 3 & 2 \end{pmatrix} + \begin{pmatrix} 2 & 3 \\ -1 & 5 \end{pmatrix} \begin{pmatrix} -4 & 2 \\ 1 & 3 \end{pmatrix}$

$= \begin{pmatrix} 13 & 8 \\ 13 & 9 \end{pmatrix} + \begin{pmatrix} -5 & 13 \\ 9 & 13 \end{pmatrix} = \begin{pmatrix} 8 & 21 \\ 22 & 22 \end{pmatrix}$

7. No; multiplication is not commutative.

9. Since $\begin{pmatrix} x & y \\ -y & x \end{pmatrix} + \begin{pmatrix} a & b \\ -b & a \end{pmatrix} = \begin{pmatrix} x + a & y + b \\ -(y + b) & x + a \end{pmatrix} \in S$, S is closed under addition. Since

$$\begin{pmatrix} x & y \\ -y & x \end{pmatrix} \begin{pmatrix} a & b \\ -b & a \end{pmatrix} = \begin{pmatrix} ax - by & bx + ay \\ -(bx + ay) & ax - by \end{pmatrix} \in S,$$

S is closed under multiplication. Let $x = y = 0$. Then $0_2 \in S$. Let $x = 1, y = 0$. Then $I_2 \in S$. Since

$$\begin{pmatrix} a & b \\ -b & a \end{pmatrix} \begin{pmatrix} x & y \\ -y & x \end{pmatrix} = \begin{pmatrix} ax - by & bx + ay \\ -(bx + ay) & ax - by \end{pmatrix} = \begin{pmatrix} x & y \\ -y & x \end{pmatrix} \begin{pmatrix} a & b \\ -b & a \end{pmatrix},$$

multiplication is commutative in S. Finally, since

$$\begin{pmatrix} x & y \\ -y & x \end{pmatrix} \begin{pmatrix} x/(x^2 + y^2) & -y/(x^2 + y^2) \\ y/(x^2 + y^2) & x/(x^2 + y^2) \end{pmatrix} = I_2 \quad \text{for} \quad x^2 + y^2 \neq 0,$$

every nonzero element of S has a multiplicative inverse in S.

11. (a) R, C, U (b) R, C, U, F (c) R, C, U, F (d) R, C, U (e) R, U

8.31

1. $\begin{pmatrix} 2 & -3 & 16 \\ 3 & 4 & 7 \end{pmatrix} \rightarrow \begin{pmatrix} 1 & -3/2 & 8 \\ 3 & 4 & 7 \end{pmatrix} \rightarrow \begin{pmatrix} 1 & -3/2 & 8 \\ 0 & 17/2 & -17 \end{pmatrix} \rightarrow \begin{pmatrix} 1 & -3/2 & 8 \\ 0 & 1 & -2 \end{pmatrix}$

$\rightarrow \begin{pmatrix} 1 & 0 & 5 \\ 0 & 1 & -2 \end{pmatrix}, \begin{array}{l} x = 5 \\ y = -2 \end{array}$

3. $\begin{pmatrix} 2 & 5 & 7 \\ 3 & -2 & 3 \end{pmatrix} \rightarrow \begin{pmatrix} 1 & 5/2 & 7/2 \\ 3 & -2 & 3 \end{pmatrix} \rightarrow \begin{pmatrix} 1 & 5/2 & 7/2 \\ 0 & -19/2 & -15/2 \end{pmatrix}$

$\rightarrow \begin{pmatrix} 1 & 5/2 & 7/2 \\ 0 & 1 & 15/19 \end{pmatrix} \rightarrow \begin{pmatrix} 1 & 0 & 29/19 \\ 0 & 1 & 15/19 \end{pmatrix}, \begin{array}{l} x = 29/19 \\ y = 15/19 \end{array}$

5. $\begin{pmatrix} 2 & 1 & -1 & -1 \\ 3 & -2 & 1 & 7 \\ -1 & -1 & 2 & 4 \end{pmatrix} \rightarrow \begin{pmatrix} 2 & 1 & -1 & -1 \\ 7 & 0 & -1 & 5 \\ 1 & 0 & 1 & 3 \end{pmatrix} \rightarrow \begin{pmatrix} 3 & 1 & 0 & 2 \\ 8 & 0 & 0 & 8 \\ 1 & 0 & 1 & 3 \end{pmatrix}$

$\rightarrow \begin{pmatrix} 3 & 1 & 0 & 2 \\ 1 & 0 & 0 & 1 \\ 1 & 0 & 1 & 3 \end{pmatrix} \rightarrow \begin{pmatrix} 0 & 1 & 0 & -1 \\ 1 & 0 & 0 & 1 \\ 0 & 0 & 1 & 2 \end{pmatrix}, \begin{array}{l} x = 1 \\ y = -1 \\ z = 2 \end{array}$

7. $\begin{pmatrix} 2 & -1 & 1 & 3 \\ 1 & -1 & 2 & 4 \\ 0 & 1 & -1 & 2 \end{pmatrix} \rightarrow \begin{pmatrix} 2 & 0 & 0 & 5 \\ 1 & 0 & 1 & 6 \\ 0 & 1 & -1 & 2 \end{pmatrix} \rightarrow \begin{pmatrix} 1 & 0 & 0 & 5/2 \\ 1 & 0 & 1 & 6 \\ 0 & 1 & -1 & 2 \end{pmatrix}$

$\rightarrow \begin{pmatrix} 1 & 0 & 0 & 5/2 \\ 0 & 0 & 1 & 7/2 \\ 0 & 1 & -1 & 2 \end{pmatrix} \rightarrow \begin{pmatrix} 1 & 0 & 0 & 5/2 \\ 0 & 0 & 1 & 7/2 \\ 0 & 1 & 0 & 11/2 \end{pmatrix}, \begin{array}{l} x = 5/2 \\ y = 11/2 \\ z = 7/2 \end{array}$

9. $\begin{pmatrix} 1 & 1 & -1 & 4 \\ 2 & -1 & 1 & 1 \\ 4 & 1 & -1 & 5 \end{pmatrix} \rightarrow \begin{pmatrix} 1 & 1 & -1 & 4 \\ 3 & 0 & 0 & 5 \\ 3 & 0 & 0 & 1 \end{pmatrix} \rightarrow \begin{pmatrix} 1 & 1 & -1 & 4 \\ 0 & 0 & 0 & 4 \\ 3 & 0 & 0 & 1 \end{pmatrix}$, or $0 = 4$.

11. $\begin{pmatrix} 1 & 2 & -3 & -7 \\ 2 & -1 & 1 & 5 \end{pmatrix} \rightarrow \begin{pmatrix} 1 & 2 & -3 & -7 \\ 0 & -5 & 7 & 19 \end{pmatrix} \rightarrow \begin{pmatrix} 1 & 2 & -3 & -7 \\ 0 & 1 & -7/5 & -19/5 \end{pmatrix}$

$\rightarrow \begin{pmatrix} 1 & 0 & -1/5 & 3/5 \\ 0 & 1 & -7/5 & -19/5 \end{pmatrix}$, or

$\begin{array}{l} x = \frac{1}{5}z + \frac{3}{5} \\ y = \frac{7}{5}z - \frac{19}{5} \end{array}$ Solutions are: $\begin{array}{l} x = \frac{3}{5},\ y = -\frac{19}{5},\ z = 0 \\ x = 1,\ y = -1,\ z = 2 \\ x = 0,\ y = -8,\ z = -3 \end{array}$

8.34

1. $\begin{pmatrix} 1 & 0 & \vdots & 2 & -3 \\ 0 & 1 & \vdots & 3 & 4 \end{pmatrix} \rightarrow \begin{pmatrix} 1/2 & 0 & \vdots & 1 & -3/2 \\ 0 & 1/3 & \vdots & 1 & 4/3 \end{pmatrix} \rightarrow \begin{pmatrix} 1/2 & 0 & \vdots & 1 & -3/2 \\ -1/2 & 1/3 & \vdots & 0 & 17/6 \end{pmatrix} \rightarrow$

$\begin{pmatrix} 1/2 & 0 & \vdots & 1 & -3/2 \\ -3/17 & 2/17 & \vdots & 0 & 1 \end{pmatrix} \rightarrow \begin{pmatrix} 4/17 & 3/17 & \vdots & 1 & 0 \\ -3/17 & 2/17 & \vdots & 0 & 1 \end{pmatrix}$

3. $\begin{pmatrix} 1 & 0 & \vdots & 2 & 5 \\ 0 & 1 & \vdots & 3 & -2 \end{pmatrix} \rightarrow \begin{pmatrix} 1/2 & 0 & \vdots & 1 & 5/2 \\ 0 & 1/3 & \vdots & 1 & -2/3 \end{pmatrix} \rightarrow \begin{pmatrix} 1/2 & 0 & \vdots & 1 & 5/2 \\ -1/2 & 1/3 & \vdots & 0 & -19/6 \end{pmatrix} \rightarrow$

$\begin{pmatrix} 1/2 & 0 & \vdots & 1 & 5/2 \\ 3/19 & -2/19 & \vdots & 0 & 1 \end{pmatrix} \rightarrow \begin{pmatrix} 2/19 & 5/19 & \vdots & 1 & 0 \\ 3/19 & -2/19 & \vdots & 0 & 1 \end{pmatrix}$

5. $\begin{pmatrix} 1 & 0 & \vdots & 0 & 3 \\ 0 & 1 & \vdots & -2 & 1 \end{pmatrix} \to \begin{pmatrix} 1/3 & 0 & \vdots & 0 & 1 \\ 0 & 1 & \vdots & -2 & 1 \end{pmatrix} \to \begin{pmatrix} 1/3 & 0 & \vdots & 0 & 1 \\ -1/3 & 1 & \vdots & -2 & 0 \end{pmatrix} \to$

$\begin{pmatrix} 1/3 & 0 & \vdots & 0 & 1 \\ 1/6 & -1/2 & \vdots & 1 & 0 \end{pmatrix} \to \begin{pmatrix} 1/6 & -1/2 & \vdots & 1 & 0 \\ 1/3 & 0 & \vdots & 0 & 1 \end{pmatrix}$

7. $\begin{pmatrix} 1 & 0 & 0 & \vdots & 1 & 1 & -1 \\ 0 & 1 & 0 & \vdots & 1 & -1 & 1 \\ 0 & 0 & 1 & \vdots & 1 & 0 & 1 \end{pmatrix} \to \begin{pmatrix} 1 & 0 & -1 & \vdots & 0 & 1 & -2 \\ 0 & 1 & -1 & \vdots & 0 & -1 & 0 \\ 0 & 0 & 1 & \vdots & 1 & 0 & 1 \end{pmatrix} \to$

$\begin{pmatrix} 1 & 1 & -2 & \vdots & 0 & 0 & -2 \\ 0 & 1 & -1 & \vdots & 0 & -1 & 0 \\ 0 & 0 & 1 & \vdots & 1 & 0 & 1 \end{pmatrix} \to \begin{pmatrix} -1/2 & -1/2 & 1 & \vdots & 0 & 0 & 1 \\ 0 & -1 & 1 & \vdots & 0 & 1 & 0 \\ 0 & 0 & 1 & \vdots & 1 & 0 & 1 \end{pmatrix} \to$

$\begin{pmatrix} -1/2 & -1/2 & 1 & \vdots & 0 & 0 & 1 \\ 0 & -1 & 1 & \vdots & 0 & 1 & 0 \\ 1/2 & 1/2 & 0 & \vdots & 1 & 0 & 0 \end{pmatrix} \to \begin{pmatrix} 1/2 & 1/2 & 0 & \vdots & 1 & 0 & 0 \\ 0 & -1 & 1 & \vdots & 0 & 1 & 0 \\ -1/2 & -1/2 & 1 & \vdots & 0 & 0 & 1 \end{pmatrix}$

9. $\begin{pmatrix} 1 & 0 & 0 & \vdots & 1 & 1 & 0 \\ 0 & 1 & 0 & \vdots & 1 & 0 & 1 \\ 0 & 0 & 1 & \vdots & 0 & 1 & 1 \end{pmatrix} \to \begin{pmatrix} 1 & 0 & 0 & \vdots & 1 & 1 & 0 \\ -1 & 1 & 0 & \vdots & 0 & -1 & 1 \\ 0 & 0 & 1 & \vdots & 0 & 1 & 1 \end{pmatrix} \to$

$\begin{pmatrix} 1 & 0 & -1 & \vdots & 1 & 0 & -1 \\ -1 & 1 & 1 & \vdots & 0 & 0 & 2 \\ 0 & 0 & 1 & \vdots & 0 & 1 & 1 \end{pmatrix} \to \begin{pmatrix} 1 & 0 & -1 & \vdots & 1 & 0 & -1 \\ -1/2 & 1/2 & 1/2 & \vdots & 0 & 0 & 1 \\ 0 & 0 & 1 & \vdots & 0 & 1 & 1 \end{pmatrix} \to$

$\begin{pmatrix} 1/2 & 1/2 & -1/2 & \vdots & 1 & 0 & 0 \\ -1/2 & 1/2 & 1/2 & \vdots & 0 & 0 & 1 \\ 1/2 & -1/2 & 1/2 & \vdots & 0 & 1 & 0 \end{pmatrix} \to \begin{pmatrix} 1/2 & 1/2 & -1/2 & \vdots & 1 & 0 & 0 \\ 1/2 & -1/2 & 1/2 & \vdots & 0 & 1 & 0 \\ -1/2 & 1/2 & 1/2 & \vdots & 0 & 0 & 1 \end{pmatrix}$

11. $\begin{pmatrix} 1 & 0 & 0 & \vdots & 1 & 1 & -1 \\ 0 & 1 & 0 & \vdots & 2 & -1 & 1 \\ 0 & 0 & 1 & \vdots & 4 & 1 & -1 \end{pmatrix} \to \begin{pmatrix} 1 & 0 & 0 & \vdots & 1 & 1 & -1 \\ 1 & 1 & 0 & \vdots & 3 & 0 & 0 \\ -1 & 0 & 1 & \vdots & 3 & 0 & 0 \end{pmatrix} \to$

$\begin{pmatrix} 1 & 0 & 0 & \vdots & 1 & 1 & -1 \\ 1 & 1 & 0 & \vdots & 3 & 0 & 0 \\ -2 & -1 & 1 & \vdots & 0 & 0 & 0 \end{pmatrix}$

8.37

1. -11 **3.** 64

5. 0 **7.** 0

9. $-3x - 2y + 18$

11. First and third columns are alike.

13. The second column is -4 times the third.

15. The third row is the sum of the first two.

17. $|AB| = \begin{vmatrix} 16 & 16 \\ 10 & 31 \end{vmatrix} = 336, \quad |A| \cdot |B| = 14 \cdot 24 = 336$

19. $|AB| = \begin{vmatrix} -4 & 4 & -1 \\ 8 & 8 & 10 \\ 8 & 8 & 11 \end{vmatrix} = -64, \quad |A| \cdot |B| = 64(-1) = -64$

8.39

1. $K = \dfrac{1}{2}\begin{vmatrix} 1 & 3 & 1 \\ 7 & 2 & 1 \\ 5 & 6 & 1 \end{vmatrix} = \dfrac{1}{2}\begin{vmatrix} 1 & 3 & 1 \\ 6 & -1 & 0 \\ 4 & 3 & 0 \end{vmatrix} = \dfrac{1}{2}\begin{vmatrix} 6 & -1 \\ 4 & 3 \end{vmatrix} = 11$

3. $K = \dfrac{1}{2}\begin{vmatrix} 1 & 4 & 1 \\ -5 & -3 & 1 \\ 5 & -1 & 1 \end{vmatrix} = \dfrac{1}{2}\begin{vmatrix} 1 & 4 & 1 \\ -6 & -7 & 0 \\ 4 & -5 & 0 \end{vmatrix} = \dfrac{1}{2}\begin{vmatrix} -6 & -7 \\ 4 & -5 \end{vmatrix} = 29$

5. $K = \dfrac{1}{2}\left(\begin{vmatrix} -1 & 1 & 1 \\ -2 & -4 & 1 \\ 2 & -3 & 1 \end{vmatrix} + \begin{vmatrix} -1 & 1 & 1 \\ 2 & -3 & 1 \\ 3 & 4 & 1 \end{vmatrix}\right)$

$= \dfrac{1}{2}\left(\begin{vmatrix} -1 & 1 & 1 \\ -1 & -5 & 0 \\ 3 & -4 & 0 \end{vmatrix} + \begin{vmatrix} -1 & 1 & 1 \\ 3 & -4 & 0 \\ 4 & 3 & 0 \end{vmatrix}\right)$

$= \dfrac{1}{2}\left(\begin{vmatrix} -1 & -5 \\ 3 & -4 \end{vmatrix} + \begin{vmatrix} 3 & -4 \\ 4 & 3 \end{vmatrix}\right) = \dfrac{1}{2}(19 + 25) = 22$

7. $\dfrac{1}{2}\begin{vmatrix} x & y & 1 \\ 1 & 2 & 1 \\ -3 & 1 & 1 \end{vmatrix} = \pm 8$

9. (a) $x = \dfrac{\begin{vmatrix} 3 & -1 \\ 5 & 2 \end{vmatrix}}{\begin{vmatrix} 2 & -1 \\ 3 & 2 \end{vmatrix}} = \dfrac{11}{7},\ y = \dfrac{\begin{vmatrix} 2 & 3 \\ 3 & 5 \end{vmatrix}}{\begin{vmatrix} 2 & -1 \\ 3 & 2 \end{vmatrix}} = \dfrac{1}{7}$

(c) $x = \dfrac{\begin{vmatrix} 5 & 1 \\ 7 & 3 \end{vmatrix}}{\begin{vmatrix} 2 & 1 \\ 2 & 3 \end{vmatrix}} = \dfrac{8}{4} = 2,\ y = \dfrac{\begin{vmatrix} 2 & 5 \\ 2 & 7 \end{vmatrix}}{\begin{vmatrix} 2 & 1 \\ 2 & 3 \end{vmatrix}} = \dfrac{4}{4} = 1$

(e) $x = \dfrac{\begin{vmatrix} 1074 & -353 \\ -863 & 153 \end{vmatrix}}{\begin{vmatrix} 162 & -353 \\ 212 & 153 \end{vmatrix}} = -\dfrac{140317}{99622},\ y = \dfrac{\begin{vmatrix} 162 & 1074 \\ 212 & -863 \end{vmatrix}}{\begin{vmatrix} 162 & -353 \\ 212 & 153 \end{vmatrix}} = -\dfrac{367494}{99622}$

9.5

1.

	Binary	Decimal		Binary	Decimal
$2^0 =$	1	1	$2^6 =$	1000000	64
$2^1 =$	10	2	$2^7 =$	10000000	128
$2^2 =$	100	4	$2^8 =$	100000000	256
$2^3 =$	1000	8	$2^9 =$	1000000000	512
$2^4 =$	10000	16	$2^{10} =$	10000000000	1024
$2^5 =$	100000	32			

3. 10
7. 45
11. 3/4 = 0.75
15. 5/32 = 0.15625
19. 11001
23. 111111111
27. .0101

5. 31
9. 31
13. 5/8 = 0.625
17. 7/8 = 0.875
21. 111111
25. .001

9.8

1. 1000011
7. 100000
13. 1
19. 1.1001

3. 111110
9. 101.0011
15. 11011

5. 101010
11. 10111
17. 100010

9.12

1. 11110011
7. 1.111111

3. 1111111
9. 1.010011

5. 1010011
11. 0010100
   0001101
   0000111

13. 0100001
   0101101
   1110100
19. 1.001000
   1.001100
   0.010100
25. 1.011011 1.011011
   1.110011 0.001101
   1.001110 1.001110

15. 1101001
   0110000
   0011001
21. 0101101 0101101
   1001100 0110100
   1111001 1111001

17. 0.001101
   0.010100
   1.111001
23. 1001110 1001110
   0010111 1101001
   1100101 1100101

9.14

1.
F	E
0.101011	00110

3.
F	E
1.001110	00100

5.
F	E
0.110101	00011

7.
F	E
0.101010	00010

9.
F	E
0.100000	00001

11. Multiply the fractional portions and add the exponents. If a normalized result is desired, it may be necessary to renormalize after multiplying.

9.18

1. (a) 0   (b) 0   (c) Stays 0.
3. (a) 1   (b) 0   (c) Stays in its original state.
5. (a) 0   (b) 1   (c) Alternates 0 and 1.
7. $A + B'$ 9. $A'B$
11. AB, $A'B'$, and $AB + A'B'$ 13. $A' + B$, $A(A' + B) = AB$
15. $A + B'$, $A' + B$, and $(A + B')(A' + B)$

9.22

1. $_1p_1 = P_1'P_2P_3$, $_1p_2 = P_2'P_3$, $_1p_3 = P_3'$
   $_0p_1 = P_1P_2P_3$, $_0p_2 = P_2P_3$, $_0p_3 = P_3$
3. $_1t_{31} = P_1P_2P_3P_4P_5'$
   $_0t_{31} = T_{31}$

5. (a) $_1f_1 = F_3'$, $_0f_1 = F_3$

F_1	F_2	F_3
0	0	0
1	0	0
1	1	0
1	1	1
0	1	1
0	0	1
0	0	0

$_1f_2 = F_1$, $_0f_2 = F_1'$
$_1f_3 = F_2$, $_0f_3 = F_2'$

7.

P_1	P_2	P_3
1	1	1
1	1	0
1	0	1
1	0	0
0	1	1
0	1	0
0	0	1
0	0	0

$_1p_1 = P_1'P_2'P_3'$
$_0p_1 = P_1P_2'P_3'$
$_1p_2 = P_2'P_3'$
$_0p_2 = P_2P_3'$
$_1p_3 = P_3'$
$_0p_3 = P_3$

9.27

1. It must be bistable, capable of retaining one of two states until receiving a signal to change.

3. $5; 2^4 < 26 < 2^5$

5. $7; 2^6 < 88 < 2^7$

7.

Location	Operation	Address
1	Fetch	101
2	Subtract	100
3	BAN	10
4	Fetch	100
5	Store	90
6	Fetch	101
7	Store	100
8	Fetch	90
9	Store	101
10	Halt	

Index